The
8088
Project Book

Robert Grossblatt

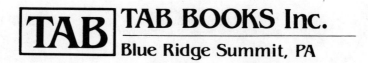

TAB BOOKS Inc.

Blue Ridge Summit, PA

For my parents and my wife

FIRST EDITION
FIRST PRINTING

Copyright © 1989 by TAB BOOKS Inc.
Printed in the United States of America

Reproduction or publication of the content in any manner, without express permission of the publisher, is prohibited. The publisher takes no responsibility for the use of any of the materials or methods described in this book, or for the products thereof.

Library of Congress Cataloging in Publication Data

Grossblatt, Robert.
The 8088 project book / by Robert Grossblatt.
p.   cm.
Includes index.
ISBN 0-8306-0271-2   ISBN 0-8306-3171-2 (pbk.)
1. Electronic circuit design—Amateurs' manuals. 2. Intel 8088
(Microprocessor)—Amateurs' manuals.   I. Title. II. Title: Eight
thousand eighty-eight project book.
TK7867.G73   1989
621.395—dc 19   89-4283
                                                                 CIP

TAB BOOKS Inc. offers software for
sale. For information and a catalog,
please contact TAB Software Department,
Blue Ridge Summit, PA 17294-0850.

Questions regarding the content of this book
should be addressed to:

Reader Inquiry Branch
TAB BOOKS Inc.
Blue Ridge Summit, PA 17294-0214

Edited by David M. Gauthier

Contents

Acknowledgments

Nobody works in a vacuum, and nowhere is that more evident than in the production of a book like this. While no one was willing to do any of the work for me, (and I asked), lots of people were willing to help make the job easier.

A complete list would be just as long as this book, but I can't let things pass without giving a bit of thanks where thanks is due. In no particular order, I'd like to extend my heartfelt thanks to:

1. The people at Autodesk for producing AutoCAD. Some of the artwork couldn't have been produced without it.

2. The people at ORCAD for producing SDT. I shudder to think what it would have been like to produce schematics without it.

3. The Okidata company for lending me a printer. It generated beautiful artwork and printed out lots of versions of lots of words.

I've left out a bunch of people but they know who they are and, more importantly, so do I.

Introduction

The last ten years or so have seen enormous changes in electronic design. Once upon a time you could use a ruler to measure a circuit's sophistication—the more square inches of silicon, the more sophisticated the circuit. Because complex circuits are really a collection of smaller ones, the size of the board was generally a good indicator of how big a job it was designed to perform. It was also a good indicator of how much of its operation you could hope to understand. Man wasn't made to deal with systems featuring parts like IC-3000 and whose schematics were bound in volumes more than an inch thick.

The larger the boards became, the more the individual designer became a specialist; square wave oscillators were designed on one side of the room and sine waves on the other. Only a few people had the responsibility of dealing with the operation of the entire circuit, and even they couldn't tell you why R-3495 was 500 ohms instead of 50k ohms—that was the specialist's job.

This development had a significant effect on the hobbyist. The difference between the output of a design team and the work that could be produced by an individual was enormous. After all, there's only so much you can do on Saturday afternoons. It takes a lot of man-years of work to get to the point where you label a part with a number like IC-3000. As the us-against-them gap got bigger and bigger, it seemed the hobbyist was doomed to a life of producing light dimmers and function generators. Then one day everything changed.

Enter the microprocessor.

When microprocessor chips began to show up on the market at reasonable prices, the us-against-them gap started to shrink. You could sit at your bench and design circuits using the same techniques and (for the most part) the same hardware used by large design teams. The microprocessor is the great equalizer. But, like a lot of other things, you have to put in a lot of work before it can do work for you.

There are tremendous advantages to microprocessor-based design. One design can do lots of different things: part counts reach an all time low, PC board layouts are much simpler, circuits can react to changing conditions . . . the list is endless.

So, you may well ask, how do I get started? What do I have to do to take advantage of all these neat things? Good questions.

There are many microprocessors on the market and each of them has its own advantages, disadvantages, and things to watch out for. Which one you use, naturally, will depend on what kind of design you have in mind. The general techniques involved in putting together a microprocessor-based design, however, are the same for all of them.

By the time you finish this book, you'll have enough knowledge under your belt to build circuits around microprocessors in general and the 8088 in particular. Even though all of our discussions will be geared around the 8088, they're easily transportable to just about any other microprocessor on the market. Although there might be differences in the bus width, addressing range, instruction set, and so on, every microprocessor has to address external memory, be driven by clocks, handle interrupts, and deal with I/O. When you get right down to it, there are more similarities than differences.

If you're familiar with the basic techniques of microprocessor-based design, you'll have no trouble shifting from one to another.

Designing hardware around a microprocessor is very similar to a gates-only design. You'll find yourself dealing with the same sort of decoders, counters, and logical glue used in a standard circuit. The only real hardware differences you'll notice are that you'll need a lot less silicon to get a particular job done, and timing could be more crucial. But none of these will cause any extensive brain damage. What will drive you up the wall is a different area altogether. Of course I'm talking about the great god SOFTWARE.

Microprocessors are wonderful time savers. They can do all sorts of terrific things, but there's a catch. You have to tell them what to do; you have to write software. Programming a CPU is a whole science in itself. It takes a whole new way of thinking and a new numbering system as well. There's also no way around it. The inescapable truth is this:

> **IF YOU WANT TO USE THE HARDWARE
> YOU HAVE TO USE THE SOFTWARE**

If you have some experience in digital circuit design and know a bit about programming—even BASIC programming—you'll feel right at home as you work your way through these pages. But if you think that CMOS is a Russian satellite or a JUMP is just an Olympic event, you'll have a hard time understanding the material covered in this book. Everything is covered step by step but I'm going to assume you've already burnt your hands with a soldering iron a few times, and as far as software is concerned, I'm not going to pull any punches with the numbering system. The name of the game is hex.

So, for all you who haven't been scared off, let's roll up our collective sleeves and start looking at the 8088.

1

The 8088: A First Look

THE HALLMARK OF A MICROPROCESSOR—WHAT MAKES IT DIFFERENT FROM ANY OTHER sort of IC—is that a standard IC does what it's designed to do while a microprocessor does what it's told to do.

WHAT IS A MICROPROCESSOR, ANYWAY?

The best way to understand exactly how a microprocessor works is to think of it as a collection of separate IC's in one package. If you were to slice one open, you'd find things like flip-flops, memory, counters, gates, and all the other standard elements available as individual IC's. All of these sections are necessary for a microprocessor to work, but they're not what makes a microprocessor unique. If you assembled all these separate elements exactly as they're arranged in a microprocessor, you might get an interesting circuit, but you wouldn't have a microprocessor.

The real heart and soul of a CPU are two sections that don't have any counterpart anywhere else—the *Arithmetic Logic Unit* (ALU) and the *Instruction Decoder*. There have been a lot of changes in CPU design since Intel introduced the 4004, the first microprocessor, in 1971. Microprocessors have become faster, bigger, smarter, and more versatile, but no matter which one you pick, the reason they're able to do what they do is the ALU and the Instruction Decoder.

The ALU is the CPU's engine. It knows how to access the chip's internal storage registers, move data from one to another, do both mathematical and logical operations, and so on. Now, if you have some experience with microprocessors, you might think that these are precisely the sorts of operations you build into programs. Well, they are and they aren't—how's that for being logical?

The ALU only does primitive operations. When you write a program for a microprocessor, even the simplest instruction is actually made up of a series of primitives. As an example, let's consider what has to be done to add one to the value stored in one of the CPU's registers. The instruction you give would be something as simple as "Increment the register" but the actual operation carried out by the microprocessor is much more complicated. In order to carry it out, the following series of events has to happen:

1. The register has to be accessed.
2. The stored value has to be read.
3. The value has to be incremented by one.
4. The new value has to be stored in the register.

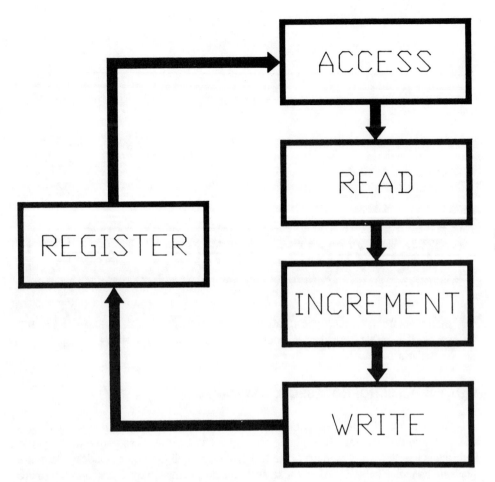

Fig. 1-1. Graphic representation of an INCREMENT instruction.

When the instruction is more complex it can be broken into many more primitive steps. If these primitive operations were the only way you could talk to a microprocessor, programmers would be really hard pressed to come up with things like spreadsheets, word processors, and games. Fortunately, we don't have to talk directly to the ALU, that's the Instruction Decoder's job.

The Instruction Decoder is an *interpreter*. It can recognize a predefined collection of commands and translate them into a series of primitive operations that can be understood by the ALU. If we go back to our previous example, the Instruction Decoder would take the "Increment" command, break it up into primitives, and then have the ALU carry out the primitives one by one. An "Increment" command to the microprocessor would cause the Instruction Decoder to tell the ALU to:

1. Access the register.
2. Read the value.
3. Add one to it.
4. Store the value.

It doesn't take much to see that the Instruction Decoder makes it much easier to use the microprocessor. Notice that I didn't say it was easy, only easier. In order to get the microprocessor to do a particular job, you have to be familiar with the repertoire of the Instruction Decoder—known more familiarly as the microprocessor's *"Instruction Set"*.

Each CPU has its own unique instruction set and, if you want to talk to it, you've got to learn to speak its language. As you can see, while microprocessors may be very powerful tools, they're pretty hardheaded as well. You can tell a microprocessor to do

just about anything you want as long as you pay attention to the one thing it tells you—
namely:

DO IT MY WAY OR DON'T DO IT AT ALL

The bottom line is simple. Basing a circuit design around a CPU can save all sorts of
time, energy, and aggravation when you follow all the rules. But break just one of the
rules—even accidentally—and you'll discover a new meaning for the word "grief".

The secret to a successful design is a good understanding of the hardware, a thor-
ough grounding in the software, and a systematic approach to the problem. Trying to
put together a microprocessor-based circuit without these three requirements is the best
way I know to reserve space in the rubber room where you can spend all your design
time bouncing off the walls.

GETTING TO KNOW THE HARDWARE

So why use the 8088? That's a good question considering that there are lots of other microprocessors to choose from.

The answer is very simple.

There are CPU's that are more powerful, more versatile, or more intelligent. You
also don't have to travel too far to find a CPU that's faster or even easier to use. What
you won't find, however, is a CPU of equivalent power that also meets the two
overridingly important requirements of the tinkerer's market—namely price and
availability. It's all well and good to talk about some CPU that can address multiple
gigabytes of memory or execute instructions at a rate just below the speed of light but
if you can't get them in onesies for less than ten bucks apiece they're not worth playing
around with. Remember the eighth Law of Life and Design:

IF YOU CAN'T AFFORD TO BLOW IT UP
YOU CAN'T AFFORD TO USE IT

Write that down in "End of the World" type and nail it on the wall over your bench.

The 8088 was one of the pioneer members of the third generation microprocessor
club—a direct descendant of the 4004, the world's first CPU and the grandson of the
8080, the heart of the earliest home computers.

Being a third generation microprocessor means the 8088 packs a real wallop. VLSI,
(*Very Large Scale Integration*), techniques have given the chip a lot of muscle—the ability
to manipulate sixteen bit data, directly address a megabyte of memory, a hefty operating
speed, and a versatile sixteen-bit instruction set. Even though the chip is more than
ten years old, it's still a terrific choice for use in driving circuits designed to do a particular
job.

The 8088 is a kind of wolf in sheep's clothing since it looks like an eight-bit chip
to the hardware but a sixteen-bit chip to the software. In actual fact, it's completely
software compatible with the 8086, its real sixteen-bit big brother. A lot of people point
to the eight-bit data bus as a disadvantage but, if the truth be known, this is really one
of the CPU's most attractive features. It means you can use standard eight-bit support
chips, (both cheap and available, remember?), and PC board layouts are simpler. How
does Intel manage to pack 16 bits of processing power into what hardware sees as an
eight-bit chip? The only way to see this is to pin one down and take it apart.

When we start putting our hardware together, you'll notice that the 8088 feels warm when it runs. By the time you finish this book and you understand how much it can do, you'll probably wonder why it doesn't hum as well. The CPU spends all its time—absolutely every moment its powered up—doing stuff. Not only that, but even if you tell it to do nothing whatsoever, its idea of doing nothing is to keep doing something—executing No Operation instructions over and over. We've just covered our first official lesson . . .

MICROPROCESSORS ARE WORKAHOLICS

Give them voltage and a clock and that's that—they punch in to work and they don't punch out.

Every microprocessor ever made, including the 8088, goes about its business by reading your instructions and then executing them. Even though there are differences between CPUs, they all deal with your instructions in the same way—by breaking them down into a logical series of steps. This is the second official lesson that you should commit to memory.

MICROPROCESSORS ALWAYS DO THINGS IN A LOGICAL WAY

It may not always seem that way, but it's true.

When you give the 8088 an instruction, it breaks it down into a list of primitive operations, and then does them one at a time. This is the essential truth of a CPU. It treats everything it has to do as a series of sequentially ordered steps and, short of turning it off, there's absolutely nothing you can do to change it.

Accept it.

The CPU's lifeblood—its heartbeat—is the *system clock*. All the steps it performs for every instruction it executes are broken down into a specific number of clock pulses. The real measure of a microprocessor's efficiency, and one of the main factors determining how fast it's going to run, is how many clock cycles it takes to do a complete instruction from beginning to end. In life, someone once said, timing is everything.

The most basic CPU timing parameter, known as the *"T Cycle"*, is equal to one complete cycle of the system clock. If you're running the 8088 at 5 MHz, one T Cycle is going to last 200 nanoseconds. The time it takes the 8088 to execute a particular instruction is always measured in T Cycles, or more commonly, "clocks".The CPU takes four of these clock cycles and combines them into a *"Machine Cycle"*—this is the time it needs to transfer data between itself and an external memory or I/O location.

Keeping this in mind, you may be surprised to hear that the 8088 can take as long as 150 clocks to execute some instructions and as few as 2 clocks for others. This becomes even stranger when you see that how long an instruction takes to execute has nothing to do with the number of bytes of code needed to write the instruction. As a matter of fact, some two byte instructions take 2 clocks while other two byte instructions take 150 clocks.

So what's the answer?

Believe it or not, I've already given you the answer. Part of the reason is that the 8088 divides each instruction into a sequence of primitive operations and some instructions are broken down into more parts than others. The other part is that a microprocessor can only handle one address and one piece of data during each machine cycle.

It's also important to remember that while the 8088 is a sixteen bit microprocessor inside its silicon walls, its data bus is only eight bits wide. When you tell the 8088 to handle a sixteen-bit word, its bus can only deal with eight bits at a time. As a result, if you transfer a 16-bit quantity from memory to a register, it will take two machine cycles to get the job done. And don't forget that adding more machine cycles means adding more clocks to the time it takes the 8088 to execute the instruction. The bottom line here is that it will always take longer to do an external operation on a sixteen-bit word than on an eight-bit byte. This is even true when you're talking about the same instruction.

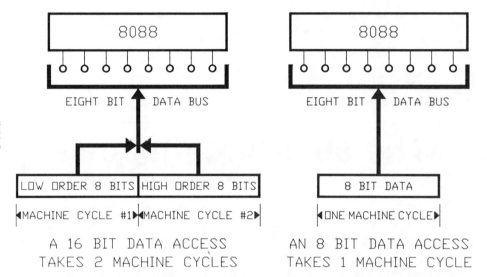

Fig. 1-2. A sixteen-bit data access takes twice as long as an eight-bit access because of the width of the 8088's external data bus.

If you tell the 8088 to decrement one of its registers, it will actually get the job done in less than one machine cycle because the only trip it has to make to the outside world is to go and get the instruction. Decrementing the register takes place inside the CPU. Tell the CPU to decrement a memory location, however, and the whole situation becomes very different. The 8088 needs one cycle to read the number stored in memory, two cycles to do the arithmetic, and a fourth one to write the new value back into memory.

If you really get into the nuts and bolts of the 8088's internal timing, you'll see that while the CPU needs a complete machine cycle to do one data transfer on the bus, it's more accurate to count the number of clock cycles. The 8088's unique internal design allows it to execute more than one instruction during one machine cycle. In the example we just saw, decrementing a register takes only two clock cycles, so the 8088 can execute two of them during the time taken for one machine cycle (four clock cycles). Pretty amazing stuff. How is it possible?

The answer to this riddle and the secrets behind all the other mysteries of the 8088 are buried in the silicon. So pack a box lunch, put on a pair of travelling shoes, and let's take a hike through the CPU to see what we can find.

2

The 8088 Architecture

IT'S MISLEADING TO THINK OF THE 8088, OR ANY MICROPROCESSOR FOR THAT MATTER, AS A single IC. Even though it's housed under one roof in a single piece of plastic, the CPU is actually a collection of separate IC's under one roof. If you were able to slice one open and look at its component parts, you'd find a'lot of familiar bits and pieces staring at you. The CPU is a complex circuit composed of old standbys like ROM, RAM, adders, decoders, and counters. To say nothing of the thousands of gates needed to glue everything together and make the chip work.

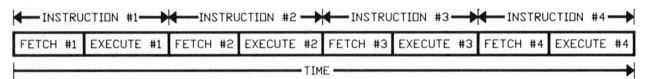

Fig. 2-1. Standard CPU sequential instruction processing.

No matter what kind of microprocessor you talk about, it spends a major part of its working day doing two basic things over and over again—fetching instructions and then executing them. Since the traditional microprocessor could only do one thing at a time, if it was busy fetching an instruction it couldn't execute one. This has always been a major bottleneck affecting performance. Whenever the CPU finished executing one instruction, it had to wait for the next one to be gotten from system memory. This waiting represented a lot of lost and potentially usable processor time. Enter the 8088.

One of the features introduced with the 8088, (and all of Intel's 16-bit microprocessors), is the idea of the instruction queue. This unique feature is a regular part of most mainframes, but had never appeared in a single chip CPU until it was designed into the 8088.

The 8088 has been divided in half—one part, (called the *Bus Interface Unit* or BIU), takes care of talking to the external world on all the system busses and control lines while the other, (the *Execution Unit* or EU), handles internal CPU stuff. Since these two sections are completely independent of each other, the 8088 can do two things at the same time. Really.

The two parts of the 8088 function independently and talk to each other over the internal CPU busses. At the same time the Execution Unit is busy carrying out instructions, the Bus Interface Unit gets the next program instruction and puts it in the queue, also called the *pipeline*. When the Execution Unit finishes with an instruction, it doesn't have to wait for the next one to be fetched since it's already available in the

6

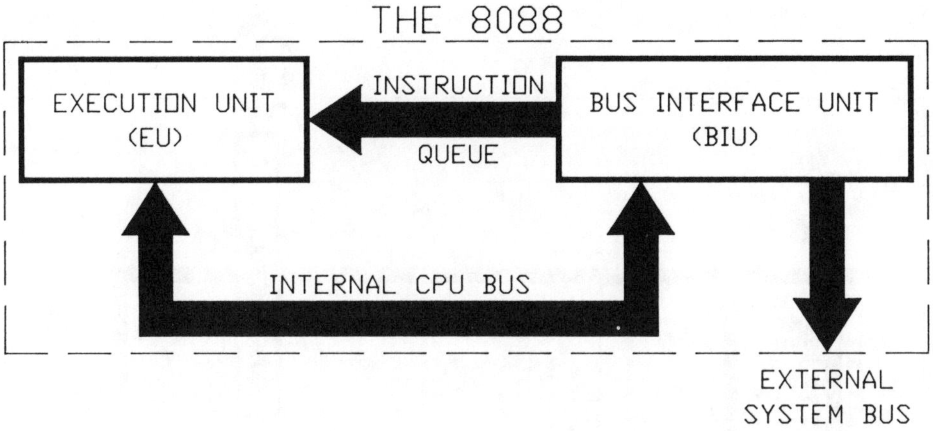

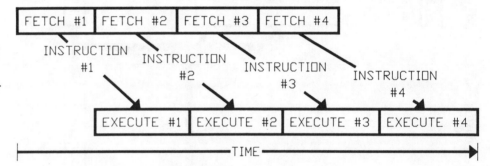

THE 8088

EXECUTION UNIT
(EU)

INSTRUCTION
QUEUE

BUS INTERFACE UNIT
(BIU)

INTERNAL CPU BUS

EXTERNAL
SYSTEM BUS

Fig. 2-2. The 8088 instruction queue.

pipeline. Parallel fetch and execution operations translate into a significant increase in CPU throughput without the need to up the clock rate.

The Execution Unit is completely isolated inside the 8088 and is totally dependent on the Bus Interface Unit for communicating with the real world. It decodes instructions, manipulates data, and uses the BIU to transfer data back and forth to system memory, I/O, and other external devices. The instructions it follows are delivered by the BIU and are, as you've probably already guessed, the program stored in external memory.

FETCH #1 FETCH #2 FETCH #3 FETCH #4

INSTRUCTION #1   INSTRUCTION #2   INSTRUCTION #3   INSTRUCTION #4

Fig. 2-3. 8088 parallel processing.

EXECUTE #1 EXECUTE #2 EXECUTE #3 EXECUTE #4

TIME

When you talk about the arrangement of the internal elements of the CPU, you're really talking about its *"architecture"*—the kind of structure shown in the block diagram of Fig. 2-4. As you can see, the 8088 really is divided in half. The BIU and EU each take care of their own jobs and pass information back and forth over the internal busses shown in the diagram.

If you're familiar with earlier eight-bit microprocessors, you should recognize some of the registers in the diagram. Before we get into the details of the 8088's private parts, let's spend a bit of time looking at the registers. Some of them are carryovers from the eight-bit days and some of them are unique to the sixteen-bit world.

Understanding the register setup in the 8088 isn't just a matter of satisfying your curiosity either. Unless you have a good handle on what they are and how they work, you'll have no luck coming to grips with the 8088's unusual addressing scheme. Remember that a one meg memory map means the CPU has to have a way of generating a twenty-bit address. That can be accomplished several ways and, as we'll see, Intel chose a less than obvious method of getting the job done.

All the 8088 registers are shown in Fig. 2-5. To give you a good idea of just how much more flexibility is provided in this sixteen-bit CPU, I've highlighted all the registers that are also found in the 8085, Intel's last eight-bit microprocessor. At first glance things can be a bit confusing. After all, there are nine 16-bit registers, four 8/16-bit registers, and one 16-bit status (or flag) register. The most convenient way to get a handle on all the registers is to break them up into the four groups shown in the drawing.

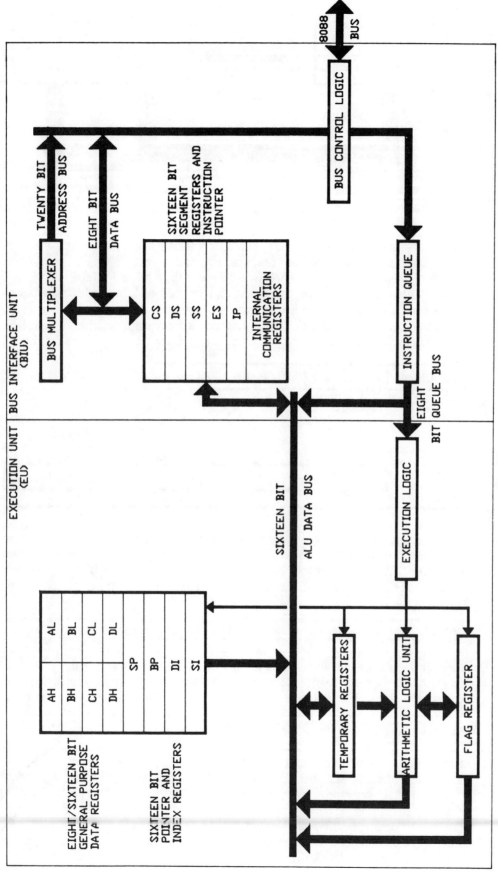

Fig. 2-4. 8088 block diagram.

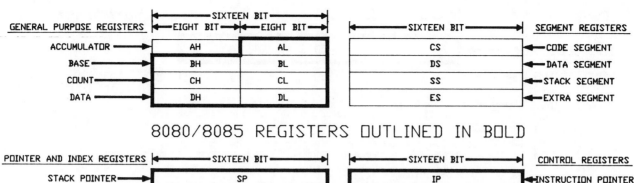

Fig. 2-5. The 8088 registers—the original 8080/8085 registers are outlined in bold.

GENERAL PURPOSE DATA REGISTERS

The *"Data Registers"* that are handled by the Execution Unit are like the ones you'll find in most microprocessors. As a matter of fact, the only major change here is that the 8088's *Accumulator* has been widened to sixteen bits. These registers can be treated as either two eight-bit registers or one single sixteen-bit register. As in the 8085, these data registers are used for general arithmetic or logical operations. When we get to the 8088 instruction set, we'll see that some of these registers are specially designed to be used for particular purposes such as counting or indexing, but this is more a function of the instruction set than a characteristic of the particular register.

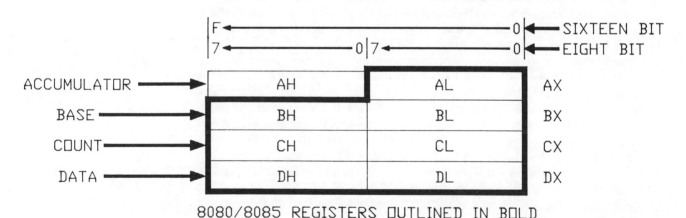

Fig. 2-6. The data registers—the original 8080/8085 registers are outlined in bold.

THE POINTER AND INDEX REGISTERS

The Execution Unit also has control over four *"Pointer* and *Index Registers"*. Although these can also be treated as general purpose registers, they're really designed to do very specific jobs. The SP (*Stack Pointer*) and BP (*Base Pointer*) registers are used mainly for taking care of the 8088's stack. Some microprocessors, such as the 6502, fix their single stack at a definite memory location. The 8088, however, can handle an unlimited number of stacks. Each one can be up to 64K in size and located anywhere in the 8088's one meg address space. The only restrictions that apply to the stacks are

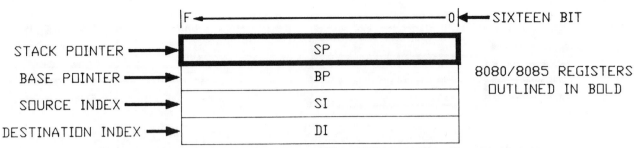

Fig. 2-7. The pointer and index registers—the original 8080/8085 registers are outlined in bold.

their 64K size limit and they must start at an address boundary that is an even multiple of 16 bytes.

The 8088 builds a 16-bit wide stack and uses the SP register to point to it's top. The stack is referred to as *"Top Down"* because it builds down in memory from a base address. Pushing two bytes on the stack will automatically decrement the value in the SP register as well as storing the two bytes at the new "Top" of the stack. If you're popping something off the stack, the 8088 will transfer the data and increment the SP register. If this seems confusing, and it is sort of brain bending to consider that the top of the stack is lower down in memory, take your time and work through the stack operation shown graphically in Fig. 2-8. Make sure you get this straight in your head since, unfortunately,

YOU AIN'T SEEN NOTHIN' YET

The BP (*Base Pointer*) register is like a second stack pointer. It can be used for any general purpose but it was intended to be something like the piece of paper you put between two pages to mark a particular place in a book. Since the 8088 is capable of building a very large stack, Intel thought it would be a good idea to include a pointer whose value wouldn't automatically change whenever a stack operation was executed. In actual fact, if you think about it, it's a terrific idea.

Consider this.

Popping data off the stack doesn't zap it from stack memory. The string of bytes put on the stack stay in exactly the same place you put them—the only thing that changes is the number stored in the stack register. Now, let's say that you're about to pop a byte off the stack that your program plans on using frequently. The standard way of handling this would be to reserve a location in memory and stash the value there. This is really rather wasteful now that we know the byte will still be in stack memory. It's more economical to transfer the Stack Pointer to the Base Pointer before we pop the stack. If we pop the stack after doing this, the SP register will, as we've seen, be incremented, but the original value of the Stack Pointer will be stored safely away in the Base Pointer.

The two last members of this group are the SI (*Source Index*) and DI (*Destination Index*) registers. As with the other registers, both of these can be used for general storage but their real strength shows up when they're used in the 8088's powerful string handling functions. Since both of these registers are capable of automatic incrementing and decrementing, they really shine when you use some of the 8088's unique table lookup features. When you plan on an application that has to depend on huge data structures, (certain math operations, maintaining tables of data, etc.), the instructions you'll be using will make heavy use of these two registers.

THE CONTROL REGISTERS

The 8088's two *control registers* are pretty much the same as the ones that have existed since the (now) prehistoric days of the old 8008. The IP (*Instruction Pointer*)

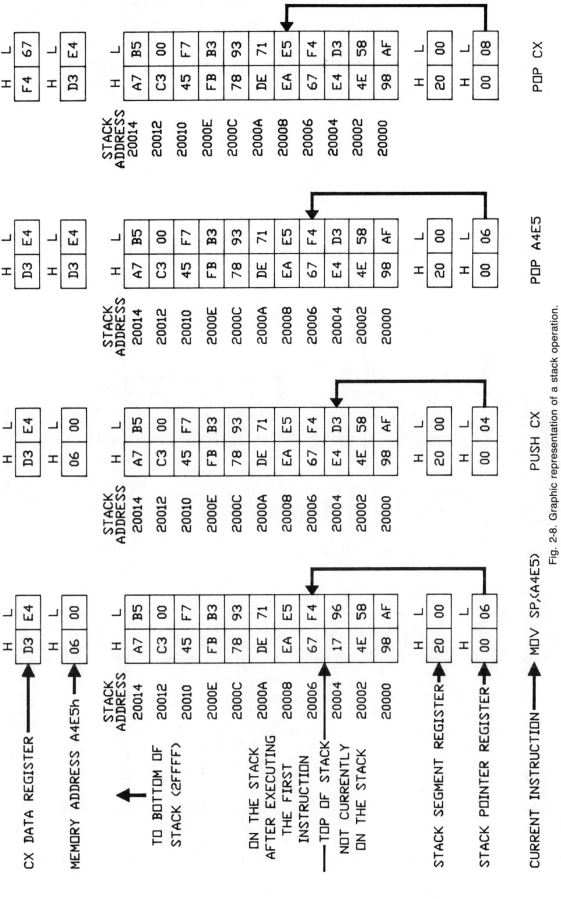

Fig. 2-8. Graphic representation of a stack operation.

11

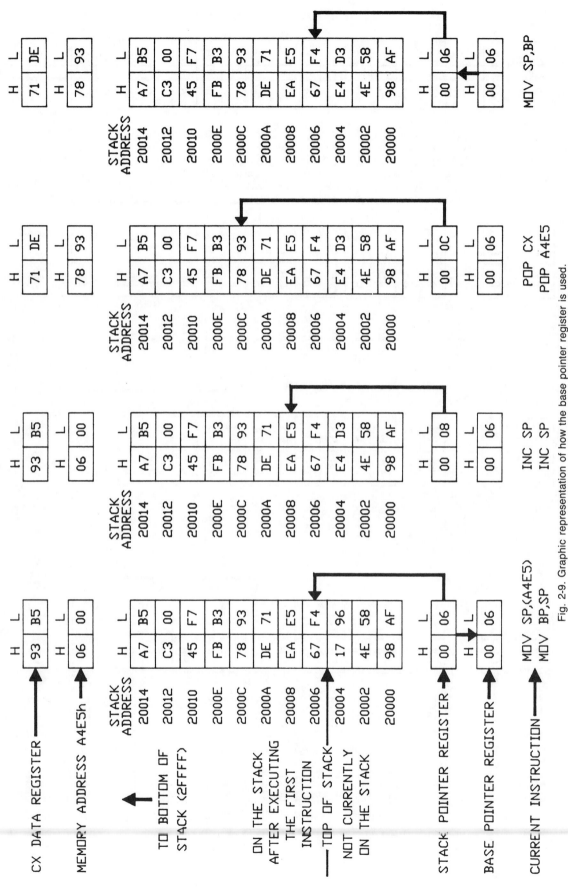

Fig. 2-9. Graphic representation of how the base pointer register is used.

12

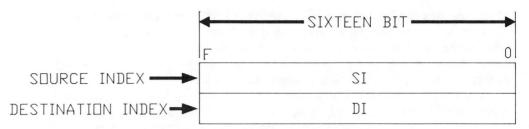

Fig. 2-10. The 8088 string registers.

is the register that used to be called the "Program Counter" back in the old eight-bit days and its job hasn't changed very much since then. The only thing it has to do is keep track of the next program instruction in line to be executed.

There's one important difference.

Because of the 8088's unique instruction queue, there are usually three instructions that are of immediate concern, namely;

1. The instruction the Execution Unit is currently carrying out.
2. The instruction currently stored in the instruction queue.
3. The instruction to be fetched by the Bus Interface Unit.

8080/8085 REGISTERS OUTLINED IN BOLD

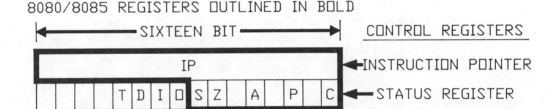

FLAG DEFINITIONS

S — SIGN FLAG   C — CARRY FLAG
O — OVERFLOW FLAG   P — PARITY FLAG
D — DIRECTION FLAG   A — AUXILIARY CARRY FLAG
T — TRAP FLAG   Z — ZERO FLAG
I — INTERRUPT ENABLE FLAG

Fig. 2-11. The 8088 control registers—the original 8080/8085 registers are outlined in bold.

In a traditional microprocessor the program counter would point to the memory address of the next instruction to execute while in the 8088, because of the instruction queue, the IP register will be pointing to the next instruction to be fetched.

The *Status* (or Flags) *register* is sixteen bits wide but only nine of the bits are used. I suppose that Intel had some ideas for new flags but the chip has been essentially unchanged since it was first rolled off the silicon assembly line ten years ago. Now that the 8088 has gone from being the new kid on the block to an established silicon superstar, the chances are mighty slim that Intel, or anyone second sourcing the chip, is going to stick something new on the substrate. Redoing the architecture also means adding to the 8088's instruction set and that's not something you can toss off between breakfast and lunch. As if all that isn't enough, Intel has made a lot of serious money off the 8088. The all-important rule is

YOU DON'T SCREW AROUND WITH SUCCESS

and that one was first thought up when all people did with flags was salute them.

As we've seen so often before in looking at the 8088, a good part of the contents of this register is a direct carryover from the old eight-bit world. Five of the flags built into the 8088 are exactly the same ones Intel has been using since the days of the 8008 and they also occupy the same bit positions in the register.

The *Carry Flag*, (Bit 0), indicates if the result of an arithmetic operation has caused the high order bit, (8 or 16 bit word), to be changed. Since this flag only reflects a carry on the high order byte, it's used by the operations that do multibyte arithmetic.

The *Parity Flag*, (Bit 2), will be set to a "1" if an operation has produced an even number of high (1) bits. The most common use for this flag is to check the integrity of received data after it's been transferred from one place to another. A lot of systems, such as the IBM-PC, make heavy use of this flag for detecting, and then reporting, memory errors. What IBM owner hasn't, at one time or another, seen the infamous "Parity Error at" message?

You can use this kind of error checking in the software you write for your own circuit but keep in mind that a parity check is no real guarantee of data integrity—as a matter of fact, you'd really have to stretch your brain to find anything more primitive. Just look at the odds of catching an error with a parity check.

To take a simple example, let's see what kind of insurance we can get from a parity check when we're dealing with a four-bit digit.

1. One possible value has none of the bits set high.
2. Four possible values have only one of the bits set high.
3. Six possible values have only two of the bits set high.
4. Four possible values have only three of the bits set high.
5. One possible value has all of the bits set high.

Since there are only sixteen possible values, everything's great if we're transferring a "0" or an "F", but the odds of having a parity check catch an error with the other 14 digits are only 62.5% in the worst case and 75% in the best case!

So much for parity checking.

The *Auxiliary Carry Flag*, (Bit 4), is very similar to the carry flag. It can be tested to see if an arithmetic operation resulted in a carry between the two nibbles of an eight-bit byte. If the flag is set, there has been a carry from the low order nibble to the high order nibble, and if it's clear, the reverse has taken place. The most popular use for this flag is in doing decimal arithmetic.

The *Zero Flag*, (Bit 6), is straightforward. It will be set if the result of an operation is zero. This is the flag used for most compare operations such as testing for the press of a particular key on the keyboard, detecting the end of a counting loop, and so on.

The *Sign Flag*, (Bit 7), can be tested to see whether the result of an operation has been positive or negative. In the frequently backwards world of microprocessors, if the sign flag has been set to a "1", (high), the result is negative, and if it's been cleared to a "0", (low), the result is positive.

Some CPU manufacturers try to make things a bit more intuitive by referring to this flag as the "Negative Flag", but it can still be confusing. This seemingly cockeyed state of affairs results from the use of "2's complement signed binary" as the standard CPU way of representing negative numbers. I agree that it's a weird way to do business, but you can't blame Intel for that. The remaining four flags are unique to the 8088.

The *Overflow Flag*, (Bit 8), will let you know if an operation has caused the loss of the most significant digit. This can be a very important consideration when you're doing arithmetic and it can be trapped by including the IOF (*Interrupt On Overflow*) instruction in the early part of your program. If an overflow occurs after you've issued this instruction, the 8088 will generate an interrupt and run the related interrupt handling routine whose starting address you've stored in the interrupt table.

The *Interrupt Enable Flag*, (Bit 9), does exactly what you think it does. If it's set, the 8088 will respond to external interrupts and if it's cleared, the 8088 will ignore them.

It's important to remember that the 8088 will always recognize NMI, regardless of how this flag is set.

The *Direction Flag*, (Bit 10), determines which way strings will be processed. If the flag is set, all of the 8088 string handling instructions will autodecrement, which means that strings will be handled from right to left. Clearing the flag will cause strings to be handled from left to right (autoincrement).

The *Trap Flag*, (Bit 11), is Intel's gift to programmers and you'll probably take advantage of it when you start writing software. When this flag is set, the 8088 single steps through instructions. The CPU generates an internal interrupt after each instruction which means you can run diagnostic routines between instructions. These can include conditional tests, memory dumps, or anything else you want. All you have to do to use this feature of the 8088, is store the starting address in the interrupt table.

If you've had some experience with microprocessor circuit design, you already know what a colossal headache software development can be. It's hard enough to work the kinks out of code written to run on an existing computer system and there you have the benefits of a (theoretically) debugged operating system and a host of utilities. Writing software for your own hardware means you're out there on your lonesome—no utilities, no debuggers, no nothing. I'm saying this now because I want to make sure all of you understand that the trap flag is really a terrific thing.

But you'll find that out for yourselves.

THE SEGMENT REGISTERS

If you're a sharp reader and have been digesting the occasionally undigestible stuff we've been talking about so far, there should be one BIG question in your mind. Since the 8088 registers are only sixteen bits wide, how in the name of something or other can you generate twenty-bit addresses?

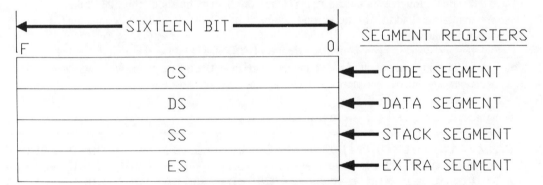

Fig. 2-12. The 8088 segment registers.

During the design of their 16-bit CPU's, Intel had to, (no pun intended), address the same problem. There are two ways to deal with this. You could

1. Make the data and control registers at least 20 bits wide.
2. Combine two 16-bit registers to handle a 20-bit address.

For better or worse, Intel decided on the second choice. The first one is viable as well—Motorola used this in the 68000—but there are advantages to the second one that were of particular interest to Intel.

Ever since the days of the old 8008, Intel has made it a point to maintain upward compatibility from one generation of microprocessors to the next. This makes the new CPU's much more attractive to the people who use them—system designers. Being able to use all the improved features of a new microprocessor without having to learn a whole new instruction set or design rules saves all kinds of time, energy, and brain damage.

Intel's decision to go with solution number one was very heavily influenced by the enormous popularity of the 8080. Don't forget that CP/M was designed around the 8080 so there was a huge amount of software built from and ready to run on a compatible 8088 instruction set.

Intel's answer to handling the 20-bit addresses needed by their new sixteen-bit microprocessor while still keeping the register set compatible with the older CPU's was to add an additional set of new registers designed exclusively for formulating addresses.

These became the four sixteen-bit *Segment Registers*.

The 8088 breaks its 1 meg memory space into four separate 64K chunks—one for each of the segment registers. Why four different registers? Because it makes the 8088 extremely flexible. But let's see how the 20-bit addresses are constructed before we look at each of the segment registers in detail.

A 20-bit address is formed by combining the 16-bit number stored in a segment register with another 16-bit number called the offset. The two numbers are added together but, as you probably realize, there's more to the story than this, since the last time I checked, the most you can get from adding two 16-bit numbers is a 17 bit, not a 20 bit number. The best way to see this is to actually add the largest possible 16-bit number—FFFFh—to itself.

```
This     FFFF      1111 1111 1111 1111
Plus     FFFF      1111 1111 1111 1111
      _____

Equals   1FFFE   1 1111 1111 1111 1110
```

The result, as you would expect, is a 17-bit number. It's obvious that the 8088 is doing something else besides simple addition.

When the 8088 decides to create a 20-bit address, it adds both of these numbers together alright, but first it takes the number in the segment register, shifts it four bits to the left (adding four zeros on the right). Once the shift is finished, the 8088 takes this new number and adds it to the second number (the offset). Sound a bit confusing? Let's do it all manually.

Suppose we want to access memory location C80BDh. The first thing we have to do is put C800h in the segment register and use 00BDh as the offset. Once we've done this, we can turn the BIU in the 8088 loose to calculate the address.

```
Segment register contains   C800           1100 1000 0000 0000
      _____

Shift it left 4 bits   --> C8000    1100 1000 0000 0000 0000
Get the offset value   -->  00BD           0000 0000 1011 1101
Add together and get   --> C80BD    1100 1000 0000 1011 1101
```

The result is the twenty-bit address we were looking for. But this isn't the end of the story.

We've already seen that the 8088 deals with its one meg address space in 64K chunks. What's really happening is that the segment register is defining the base point (0000h) of a 64K block while the offset number indicates the address within the block. The 8088 can only deal with 64K of memory at a time, but that 64K is just a small window on the entire one meg address space. When you want to use a particular location, you first tell the 8088 what location to regard as 0000h by loading it in the segment register. After you've stored this starting location, you can access any address that's between it and 64K (FFFFh) above it by giving the BIU, (where all of the address calculations are done), the offset address.

If you've got this straight in your mind, it should occur to you that since the segment registers are 16 bits wide, they can hold any value from 0000h to FFFFh (or 65535 for you people with ten fingers). That means you can have 65536 different base addresses.

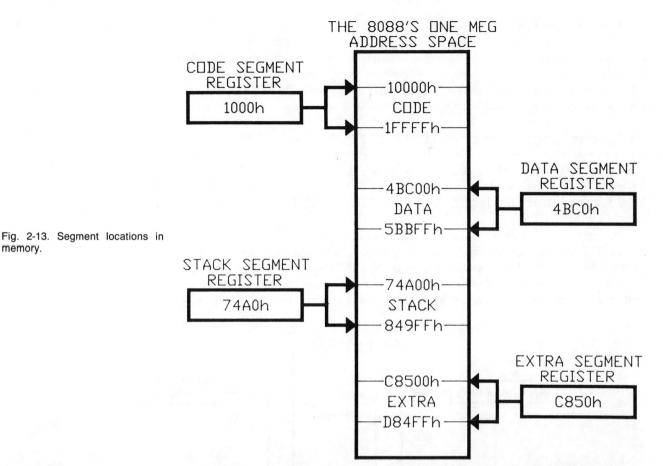

THE 8088'S ONE MEG
ADDRESS SPACE

CODE SEGMENT
REGISTER

1000h

10000h
CODE
1FFFFh

DATA SEGMENT
REGISTER

4BC0h

4BC00h
DATA
5BBFFh

Fig. 2-13. Segment locations in memory.

STACK SEGMENT
REGISTER

74A0h

74A00h
STACK
849FFh

EXTRA SEGMENT
REGISTER

C850h

C8500h
EXTRA
D84FFh

Since the offset is also 16 bits wide, it can hold any one of 65536 different addresses as well. It would seem therefore, that by combining these two registers, you can specify any one of 65536 times 65536, or up to 4,294,967,296 separate locations—an address space some 4000 times larger than the 8088's one meg universe.

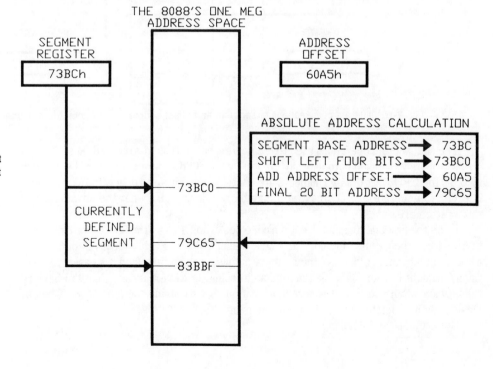

THE 8088'S ONE MEG
ADDRESS SPACE

SEGMENT
REGISTER

73BCh

ADDRESS
OFFSET

60A5h

ABSOLUTE ADDRESS CALCULATION

SEGMENT BASE ADDRESS ➡ 73BC
SHIFT LEFT FOUR BITS ➡ 73BC0
ADD ADDRESS OFFSET ➡ 60A5
FINAL 20 BIT ADDRESS ➡ 79C65

73BC0

CURRENTLY
DEFINED
SEGMENT

79C65

83BBF

Fig. 2-14. Building a twenty-bit address from two sixteen-bit addresses.

17

So what's going on?

The answer is that we're taking one real physical address and breaking it up into two logical addresses. We reached address C80BDh by combining C800h and 00BDh but we could get to C80BDh by using lots of other number combinations. For example, if the segment register was loaded with C7FFh and we used 00CDh as the offset, the 8088 would generate the same address.

```
Segment register contains   C7FF           1100 0111 1111 1111
─────────────────────────────────────────────────────────────
Shift it left 4 bits   -->  C7FF0     1100 0111 1111 1111 0000
Get register value     -->   00CD          0000 0000 1100 1101
Add together and get   -->  C80BD     1100 1000 0000 1011 1101
```

Try this yourself with other combinations until you're sure you understand how it works. The segment registers, and the idea of segmented addressing are unique features of the 8088 and both of them are basic parts of the CPU's operation. If you don't get a handle on them now, you'll have a hard time later on. Trying to come to grips with software without understanding the hardware is a sure road to the funny farm.

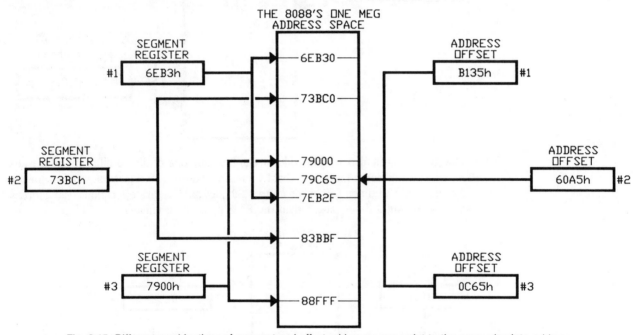

Fig. 2-15. Different combinations of segment and offset addresses can point to the same absolute address.

The shift and add operations used to create a 20-bit address from two 16-bit addresses are, fortunately, handled automatically for you by the 8088. Your only part in the process is to tell the CPU what the two numbers are. But since you have to deal with two numbers in order to generate one address, you may be wondering just what the advantages of this system are.

I'll be the first one to admit that it's nice to deal with CPU's, (the 68000, for example), that address their entire memory in a neat linear fashion. Each address is defined by a unique combination of bytes—the memory map is more intuitive and it's easier to keep things straight in your mind. Segmented addressing, however, means that you have to think twice when you want to address a location that's outside the current 64K block. Dealing with code, therefore, is a bit confusing.

But only at the beginning.

If your program can live inside a single 64K segment—and let's be fair, 64K is a lot of code—the only contact you'll have with the segment registers is to load them with an appropriate value at the outset of your program. The classic case of "set it and forget it". The fact that the 8088 is going through all sorts of hassles to calculate the correct addresses is its problem, not yours.

The really big plus you get from Intel's segmented addressing scheme is that it's a snap to write relocatable code. As a matter of fact, it takes extra work on your part to create code that has to live in a unique memory location! Not only that, but dealing with memory in segments makes it easy to write re-entrant code, handle large data tables, and all sorts of other goodies as well.

All this terrific stuff is possible because users, (that's us), only deal with addresses that are relative to the values stored in the segment registers—the 8088 has the headache of translating them into absolute memory locations. Using a segment register will seem a bit weird at first, but once you get used to it you'll think of it as the most natural thing in the world.

The 8088, like any other microprocessor, has three main uses for external memory—holding programs, storing data, and maintaining the stack. Since each of these areas has to be handled differently, Intel gave each of them a separate segment register. This gives you a lot of control over the memory map. Your code lives in one place, your data in another, and the stack in a third. The fourth segment register—officially known as the *"Extra Segment Register"*—can be used to point to another data location, a second stack, or whatever you want.

Most 8088 applications use the segment registers in a very linear fashion. The *"Code Segment Register"* points to the beginning of the program address space, the *"Stack Segment Register"* contains the base location of the current stack, the *"Data Segment Register"* has the address of one data area, and the *"Extra Segment Register"* has the starting address of another. In general, segment registers keep everything nicely organized and, as we'll see, this is a big help in creating software. What's really happening here is that the 8088 is forcing you to think of memory in a modular sort of way and that's a good thing since all successful software has to have these three key ingredients:

STRUCTURE, STRUCTURE AND STRUCTURE

There's no way in the world that you're going to be able to make the 8088 do anything if you don't treat the project in a systematic and organized manner.

You can design around the 8088 without being on intimate terms with all the details of its internal architecture but the more you know about it, the better your design will be. How easily you can get from place to place inside the 8088 depends on how familiar you are with all the silicon sidestreets and shortcuts. A description of the 8088's architecture is really a list of the tools available to make the 8088 do whatever you have in mind. And you can't get the job done if you don't know how to use the tools.

There's a big difference between knowing what the tools are and knowing how to use them. This brings us face to face with what makes the process of designing around microprocessors so totally different from building with discreet components.

The first time you power up a gates only circuit, it does what it was designed to do (or so you hope). Getting the hardware wired up in a microprocessor-based circuit is only part of the job. You can power it up but we all know that it's not going to do anything—it may start smoking and smell funny, but that's another story. Making the 8088 do the job you want means manipulating the tools—you have to tell it what to do.

And that, as we all know, means software.

But before we get there, we still have some hardware to look at. Now that we've gone through the 8088's internal arrangement, let's examine the CPU lines we have to work with. After all, the only way we can talk to the CPU is by using the signals it makes available on the pins.

3

The 8088 Pinouts

IF YOU'RE NEW TO SIXTEEN-BIT STUFF, THE FIRST THING THAT SHOULD CROSS YOUR MIND is how in the world do you get a 1 meg address space into a standard 40-pin dip? An off the cuff answer would be that you do it with mirrors and if you carefully examine the pinouts of the 8088, you'll see that's not far from the truth since several of the pins do double duty. Remember that being able to directly talk to a megabyte of memory means the 8088 needs 20 address outputs, A0 through A19. When you add that to the 8 data pins, power, ground, and the miscellaneous control signals, you're going to rapidly run out of available pins.

As you can see from Fig. 3-1, Intel's solution to this problem is to let two signals time share the same physical pin. The 8088 pins can be grouped into three basic categories.

1. Address and Data
2. Power and Timing
3. Control

As we take a look at each group of pins, you'll begin to understand the differences and similarities between this microprocessor and all of its eight-bit ancestors.

ADDRESS PINS

When you talk about the address outputs, you also have to talk about the data pins since the data is time multiplexed on the lower eight address pins, A0 through A7. Pin sharing is nothing new. If you're familiar with the Z-80, for example, you'll probably remember that the refresh counter for dynamic memory appears on the lower part of the address bus while the CPU is busy elsewhere doing instruction decoding. Even Intel's own 8085 combined the address and data lines.

Now, time sharing pins is a good way to pack more features into a chip—we'll see that it makes the 8088 extremely powerful. But remember the third Law of Life and Design:

THERE'S NO SUCH THING AS A FREE LUNCH

The price you pay for 8088's enhanced functions is an increase in the size of the headache you'll get when you design around it. You need decoders and latches to grab

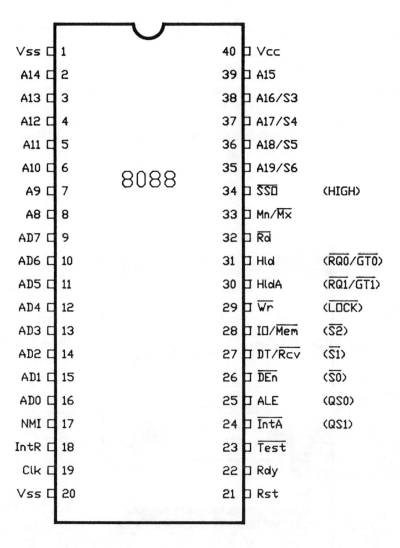

Vss	1		40	Vcc	
A14	2		39	A15	
A13	3		38	A16/S3	
A12	4		37	A17/S4	
A11	5		36	A18/S5	
A10	6		35	A19/S6	
A9	7	8088	34	$\overline{SSO}$	(HIGH)
A8	8		33	Mn/$\overline{Mx}$	
AD7	9		32	$\overline{Rd}$	
AD6	10		31	Hld	($\overline{RQ0}/\overline{GT0}$)
AD5	11		30	HldA	($\overline{RQ1}/\overline{GT1}$)
AD4	12		29	$\overline{Wr}$	($\overline{LOCK}$)
AD3	13		28	IO/$\overline{Mem}$	($\overline{S2}$)
AD2	14		27	DT/$\overline{Rcv}$	($\overline{S1}$)
AD1	15		26	$\overline{DEn}$	($\overline{S0}$)
AD0	16		25	ALE	(QS0)
NMI	17		24	$\overline{IntA}$	(QS1)
IntR	18		23	$\overline{Test}$	
Clk	19		22	Rdy	
Vss	20		21	Rst	

Fig. 3-1. The 8088 pinouts.

the appropriate information from the chip at the right time. Besides having to be careful about the system timing, it also means you have to plan on some extra silicon overhead when you're laying out your circuit. All the miscellaneous logic we have to add to demultiplex the signals is stuff that really belongs inside the CPU itself.

It's anyone's guess as to why Intel went this route. They had done the same thing with the 8085, (their super-duper 8080), and it had gotten a somewhat less than enthusiastic response from most of the industry. Of course, by the time they finally got around to introducing it, Zilog's Z-80 had already been around for three years and was the overwhelming chip of choice for 8080 type applications.

The 8088 (and 8086) are really sixteen-bit versions of the eight-bit 8085—as we get into the 8088 we'll see that even the internal architecture is similar. As a matter of fact, software written for the 8085 can be modified to run on the 8088 with an absolute minimum of brain damage.

For whatever it's worth, there's no doubt in my mind that if IBM hadn't decided to use Intel stuff for their PC's, Intel wouldn't be as big a company as they are now. It takes more than just a good microprocessor to make a silicon superstar—it has to be used in a major application. But we're getting way ahead of ourselves.

The address pins on the 8088 are functionally divided into three groups—AD0 through AD7, A8 through A15, and A16 through A19. The reason for breaking them up like this is that not all of them carry the address all the time. Just about the only two things they have in common are that their portion of the address is valid during the beginning of each instruction cycle and the lines float when some other device takes control of the bus. We'll take a closer look at this when we talk about the control signals.

The first group, AD0 through AD7, is the most versatile. During the first part of an instruction cycle, (we'll get into timing in a bit), the 8088 puts the least significant part of the address, (the lower eight bits), on these pins. As soon as the CPU gets to the second part of the instruction cycle, it removes the address from these lines and floats them (tristated) to get them ready for their next job. When the 8088 reaches the third part of its instruction cycle, it uses these pins as the data lines. Since data has to be able to go two ways, these pins become bidirectional during this stage of the instruction cycle.

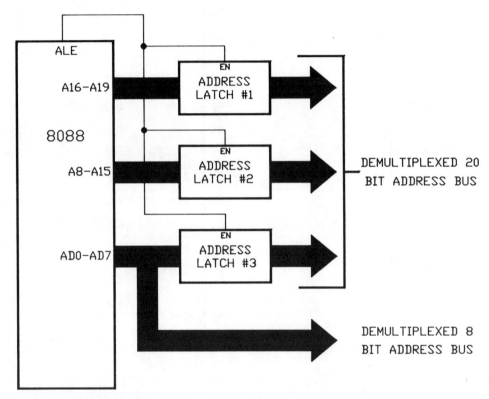

Fig. 3-2. Demultiplexing, or separating, the address and data busses.

The second group of address pins, A8 through A15, are a set of plain vanilla address pins and the portion of the complete address they carry stays valid for the entire instruction cycle.

The final address pins, A16 through A19, are what make the 8088 a sixteen-bit CPU since they're the addresses from 10000h, (that's a decimal 65,536), to FFFFFh, (or decimal 1,048,575). These lines carry valid address data at the same time as the first group of address lines, (the beginning of each instruction cycle), and then carry status signals which indicate the address segment currently in use, (S3 and S4), the state of

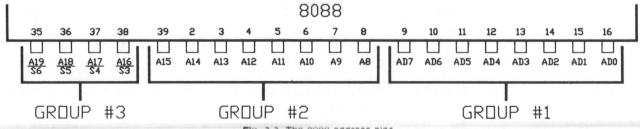

Fig. 3-3. The 8088 address pins.

the interrupt enable flag, (S5), and a flag to indicate that the 8088 has control of the bus, (S6).

POWER AND TIMING PINS

The 8088 operates off a single five-volt supply and the standard HMOS version of the chip can draw as much as 350 mA. If you don't have a supply that can handle that, there are CMOS versions of the 8088 that only need about 10 mA per MHz of operating speed. The HMOS and CMOS versions of the chip are functionally identical and the only one able to tell which one you're using is your local electric company. Obviously, if you plan on doing a lot of battery operated stuff, CMOS is the way to go.

There are two ground pins on the 8088, pin #1 and pin #20. The voltage for Vcc should be 5 volts +/-10% and it's a good idea to decouple the VCC pin with a small bypass capacitor (about .1μF). It is really, REALLY important to remember that these two ground pins are NOT electrically connected in the chip! Making the assumption that they're tied together, (and letting one float), will guarantee flakey operation at best and foul smelling smoke at worst. This is generally the sort of mistake you only make once. Fortunately, as we've already seen, 8088's are cheap enough to keep this from being a complete disaster.

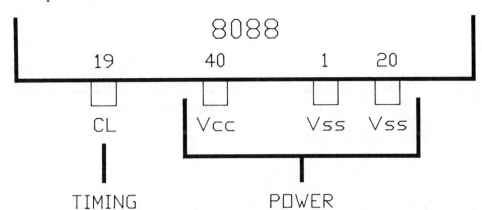

Fig. 3-4. The 8088 power and timing pins.

The 8088 has nice and simple clock requirements. Once upon a time in Intel's history, (with the 8080), they insisted on having the CPU supplied with two non-overlapping clocks. Luckily for all of us, that requirement disappeared with the 8085 and all of the Intel CPU's that followed, including the 8088, only needed a single clock. It has to be asymmetrical, (33% duty cycle), with steep rise and fall times, (no more than 10 nanoseconds).

The basic system clock is fed to the CLK input and The 8088 is fairly tolerant about waveforms. Just about any oscillator that meets the speed and duty cycle requirements of the data sheets can be used—but there's a better way. Intel makes the 8284—a chip that generates clock pulses perfectly tailored to the 8088. And as if that isn't enough, it also provides fully synchronized startup and manual reset as well.

Since the 8088 registers are made from dynamic memory cells, they have to be constantly refreshed. This means the minimum clock speed for any 8088 is 2 MHz but the maximum rate depends on the version of the chip you're using. This can be either 5 MHz (an 8088), 8 MHz (an 8088-2), or 10 MHz (8088-1). You pay more for faster parts but even the super-speedy model is sold by most of the major mail order houses for under fifteen bucks.

CONTROL PINS

The control signals of the 8088 are where we start to see the big differences between this chip and its eight-bit ancestors. How many control signals you have available

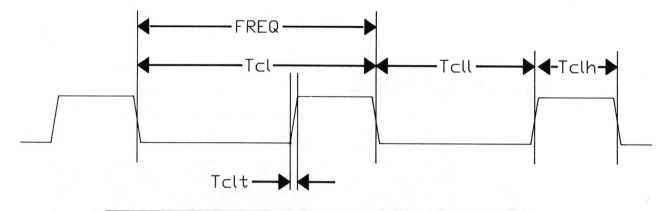

NAME	DEFINITION	MAX	MIN	UNIT	CHIP
Tcl	CLOCK CYCLE PERIOD	500	200	ns	8088
		500	125	ns	8088-2
		500	100	ns	8088-1
FREQ	CLOCK FREQUENCY	5.00	2.00	MHz	8088
		8.00	2.00	MHz	8088-2
		10.00	2.00	MHz	8088-1
Tcll	CLOCK LOW TIME	.5Tcl	.67Tcl	ns	ALL
Tclh	CLOCK HIGH TIME	.5Tcl	.33Tcl	ns	ALL
Tclt	RISE OR FALL TIME	10		ns	ALL

Fig. 3-5. The 8088's clock requirements.

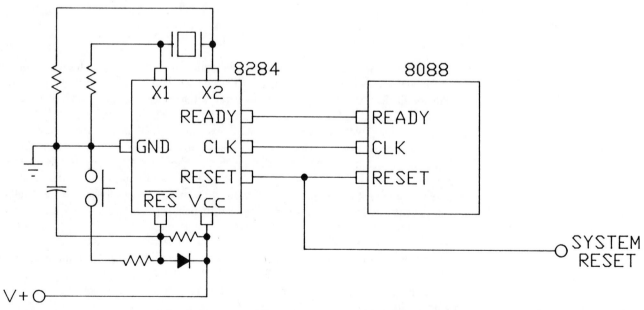

Fig. 3-6. Using an 8284 to generate the basic 8088 system clock.

depends on whether you operate the 8088 in the "Minimum" or "Maximum" mode. You choose one or the other by tying pin #33 either high, (Minimum mode), or low, (Maximum mode). While configuring the chip to run in the Maximum mode gives you a much more complete set of control signals, it takes another chip, an 8288 bus controller, to make it happen. Before we get into the differences between these two modes, let's take a look at the control signals that are the same for both.

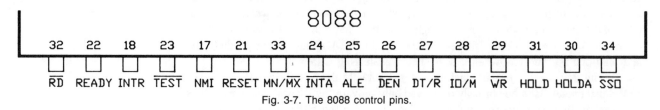

Fig. 3-7. The 8088 control pins.

The $\overline{RD}$ line is similar to the equivalent line found on all other microprocessors. It's an active low output that indicates the 8088 wants to read data either from memory or an I/O port. Since the data bus is multiplexed with the bottom part of the address bus, you might expect a timing hassle in determining when the bus is ready for data.

Fortunately, Intel took care of this by guaranteeing that $\overline{RD}$ will remain high until the address is removed from the bus. We already saw that AD0 through AD7 first carry the address, then float, and then function as the data bus. The $\overline{RD}$ line doesn't become active until the bus floats. As a result, when $\overline{RD}$ is active, the only bits you'll see on the bus are data. Problem solved.

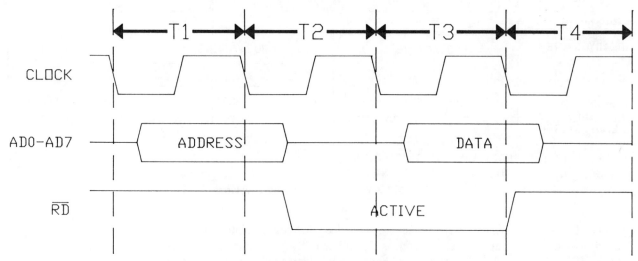

Fig. 3-8. The 8088's READ timing waveforms.

The READY input is the signal used by either memory or I/O to let the 8088 know when the requested data operation is finished. When the data transfer is completed, the external device can let the 8088 know it's done by putting a high on the READY line. Remember that the 8088, like any microprocessor, allows a finite amount of time for each instruction and that holds true for operations involving an external device as well. How much time is allowed is a function of the CPU's clock speed and the particular instruction that's being executed.

The most common use for the READY line is to slow the 8088 down when it's dealing with external devices that can't handle data at CPU speed.

Let's suppose we're using an I/O device that can't transfer data fast enough to meet the 8088's required timing. By putting a low on the READY line after the start of the T2 clock cycle, the CPU will extend the machine cycle and wait until the READY line is brought high again to indicate that the transfer is completed. The 8088 extends the instruction cycle by adding what are officially known as "Wait States" between the T3 and T4 cycles. Every time a wait state is added however, you'll see a significant degradation in the CPU's performance since the addition of only one wait state will lengthen the instruction time by as much as 25%.

If you're designing a system that uses lots of slow I/O, it can be quite a job to make sure your I/O hits the CPU's READY line at the right time all the time. A good way around this is to think of your circuit as normally not ready—in other words, you want the 8088 to wait for your I/O every single time they have to talk to each other. You can do this by having the external devices hold the CPU READY line normally high (active) and only pull the line low when it's finished transferring data.

Circuit designs that use I/O fast enough to deal with the bus at full CPU speed can consider themselves to be normally ready and only activate the READY line during those times when they need more time on the data bus than the CPU normally allows.

When we actually start designing 8088 circuitry, we'll see what has to be done to minimize the amount of wait states. In general, though, doing this means carefully picking the right number for the CPU clock and balancing it against the kind of devices you plan on hanging on the bus.

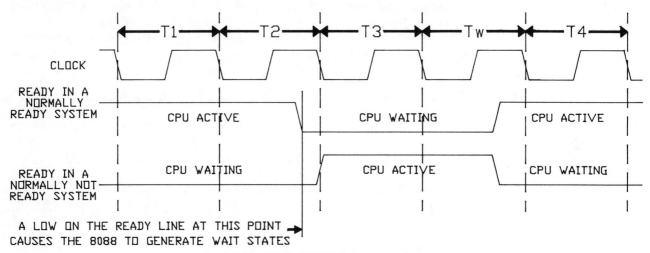

Fig. 3-9. The 8088's READY timing waveforms.

The INTR pin, the *Interrupt Request* input, is the door that gets you into the 8088's powerful external interrupt servicing routines. This is one of the most exciting features of the CPU and what makes it ideal for small board, stand-alone applications. The 8088 can handle 256 vectored, prioritized levels of interrupt and it looks at INTR at the end of each instruction cycle. If the CPU sees that the line has been made active (brought high) by an external device it will jump (or vector) to the subroutine whose address has been stored in memory in a lookup table.

The location of the lookup table is fixed (00000h - 003FFh) but the contents are entirely up to you. Building the interrupt vector table is one of the first things that should be done by the system firmware. We'll see that while it's certainly possible to design around the 8088 without using interrupts at all, it's a pretty silly thing to do since they provide an unbelievable amount of flexibility for even a small board system.

The INTA (*Interrupt Acknowledge*) line is an output that becomes active (low) when an external device makes an interrupt request by putting a high on the INTR pin. Whenever the 8088 receives this request, it waits until the current instruction cycle is ended and then puts out a low pulse on the INTA line for two consecutive cycles. Intel refers to these, logically enough, as "interrupt acknowledge" cycles. The first one is to let the device generating the interrupt know that the interrupt is being serviced. During

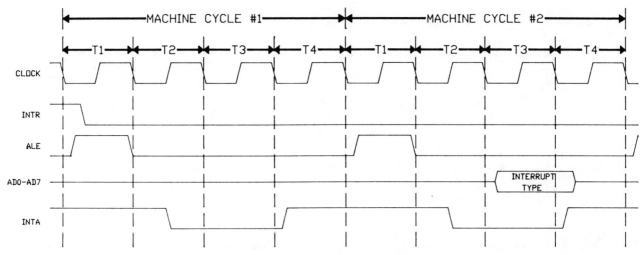

Fig. 3-10. The 8088's Interrupt timing waveforms.

the second cycle, the CPU expects the external device to have put the interrupt level (0 to 255) on the data bus. The 8088 then takes this code, finds the appropriate entry in the interrupt vector lookup table, and executes the code it finds there.

The $\overline{\text{TEST}}$ input is a way of stopping the 8088 until it's started up again by some external event. If you issue a "Wait" instruction, the 8088 will go into cruisamatic until the $\overline{\text{TEST}}$ input is brought low. As soon as the low is detected, the 8088 will zip back into drive and go on its merry way executing instructions. Think of this as manually triggering a scope—it's pretty much the same thing.

Fig. 3-11. The structure of the 8088's interrupt vector table.

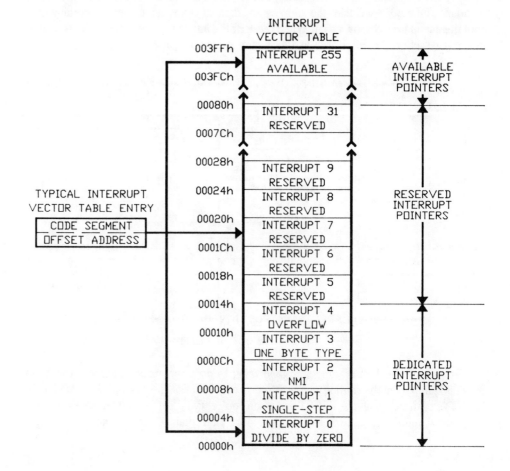

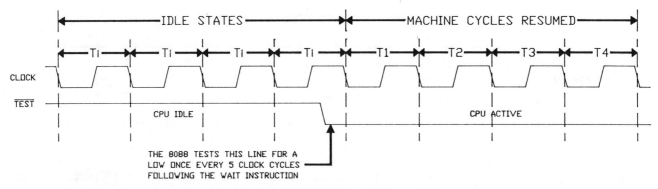

Fig. 3-12. The 8088's TEST input timing waveforms.

The *NMI* line is the *Non-Maskable Interrupt*—otherwise known as the "Disaster Line". It's called this because, since there's no way for it to be disabled by software, most systems use it to indicate that some sort of catastrophic event is going to happen. This might be something like an imminent loss of power, a memory error, or any other type of "end of the world" event.

To make the input even more responsive, the NMI input is edge, rather than level, triggered. This means the 8088 will react during the low to high transition of the NMI line instead of waiting for it to reach a high. Once the line has been activated, the 8088 will finish executing the current instruction and then jump to the NMI handling routine whose starting address has been stored in the appropriate place in the lookup table.

The *RESET* pin is an active high signal that stops the 8088 dead in its tracks. There's a bit of a failsafe on this line since the RESET signal has to stay high for at least four clock cycles before it will be taken seriously by the CPU. Once this time requirement is satisfied, the 8088 will float the address and data lines and do absolutely nothing else until the line is brought low again. When the RESET line is released, the CPU will jump to the instruction you've stored at the power-up location of FFFF0h.

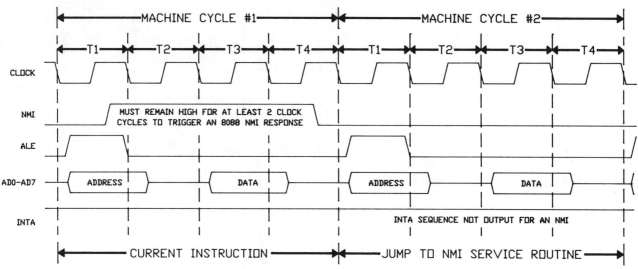

Fig. 3-13. The 8088's NMI timing waveforms.

Triggering the RESET line is a good thing to do at powerup since you can have the 8088 jump to all the routines needed to properly initialize the system. It's also handy to be able to manually hit the RESET line when you're trying out new code, since software in the development stage produces crashes more often than results. Or so they tell me.

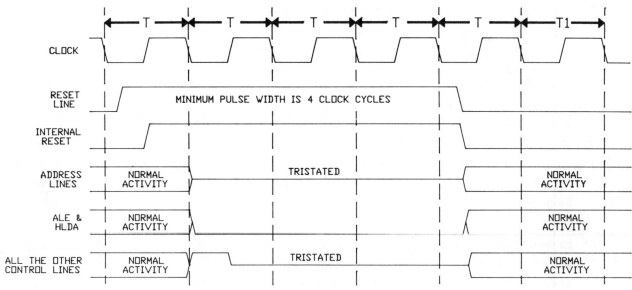

Fig. 3-14. The 8088's Reset timing waveforms.

The MN/$\overline{\text{MX}}$ pin is used to set the microprocessor in either the MINIMUM or MAXIMUM mode. Strapping this pin one way or the other will redefine the functions the 8088 assigns to a few of the control pins. In general, configuring the 8088 to run in the $\overline{\text{MAXIMUM}}$ mode, (MN/$\overline{\text{MX}}$ tied low), is a good idea if you want to design a system that has several microprocessors accessing the address and data busses. When the 8088 is in $\overline{\text{MAXIMUM}}$ mode, it has to be used with the 8288 Bus Controller. The redefined 8088 pins, (shown in parentheses), drive the 8288, which decodes them into an expanded set of control signals. As a result, you get twenty control lines in $\overline{\text{MAXIMUM}}$ mode as opposed to thirteen in MINIMUM mode. Intel did things this way for the same reason they multiplexed the address and data lines—there are only so many signals you can make available with a 40-pin dip.

Single board systems, like the one we're going to put together later on, can get along very well with the control signals provided by running the 8088 in MINIMUM mode (MN/$\overline{\text{MX}}$ tied high). Once we've gone through the design of the MINIMUM system, you'll have no trouble designing a system that runs in $\overline{\text{MAXIMUM}}$ mode.

Don't fall into the trap of thinking that you're shortchanging yourself by running a MINIMUM mode system. Most of the MINIMUM mode circuit designs don't even need all the control signals provided directly by the CPU alone. As a matter of fact, you'll see that the 8088's native control signals are more than adequate to control even a fully IBM-XT compatible system. No kidding.

The control lines that are altered by the MN/$\overline{\text{MX}}$ setting show up on pin #24 through pin #31 and pin #34. If you have some experience in microprocessor-based design, you'll recognize most of the MINIMUM mode control signals.

The ALE (*Address Latch Enable*) output is the way you separate the low order address and data. Since these signals are multiplexed on the same pins, you need an external signal to let you know what kind of information is currently on the pins. When ALE becomes active, (goes high), the 8088 is telling you that the entire 20-bit address is on the bus. It's possible to design systems that don't have to separate the address and data lines, but any designer who has his head screwed on tight, will use ALE to latch the address in external buffers. Besides eliminating potential brain damage in the design, a lot of external devices want the address to be available for the entire instruction cycle. Besides, latches are cheap.

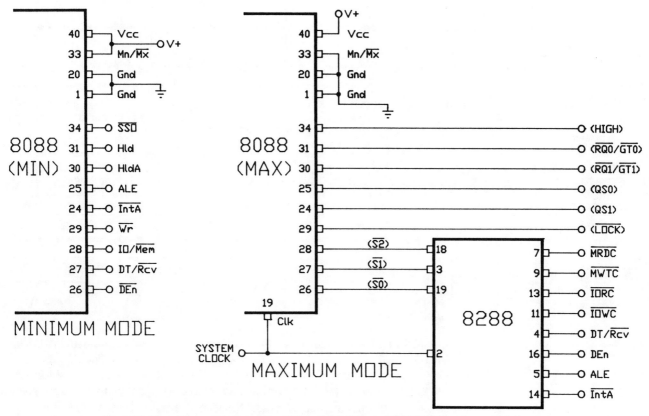

Fig. 3-15. The difference between the 8088's MINIMUM and MAXIMUM mode control signals.

The $\overline{\text{DEN}}$ (*Data Enable*) output is an active low signal that's most often used to control the enabling of external data buffers. When the line is active, the 8088 is telling the rest of the system that the data bus is available for use. By letting $\overline{\text{DEN}}$ control access to the data bus, you're guaranteed not to have any timing hassles, at least not any caused by bus contention. And since the seventh Law of Life and Design is:

> **AVOIDING HASSLES IS A GOOD THING**

it makes a lot of sense to let the 8088 do as much of the work as possible.

The DT/$\overline{\text{R}}$ (*Data Transmit/Receive*) line is a companion to the $\overline{\text{DEN}}$ line. When $\overline{\text{DEN}}$ lets the buffers know that the 8088 isn't using the data bus, DT/$\overline{\text{R}}$ tells them whether

The IO/$\overline{\text{M}}$ (*Input-Output/Memory*) output tells the system what kind of data transfer the 8088 wants to do. This line goes high to indicate that the CPU is talking to an I/O port and low when the CPU wants to deal with system memory.

The $\overline{\text{WR}}$ (*Write*) line is an active low signal used by the 8088 to signal the system that a write operation is taking place. You might be thinking that we have a bit of redundancy here since the $\overline{\text{RD}}$ and $\overline{\text{WR}}$ outputs seem to be doing much the same job as DT/$\overline{\text{R}}$. Well, to be political about it, I'll keep as many friends as possible by saying yes and no.

When we start talking about system timing, you'll see that DT/$\overline{\text{R}}$ becomes active a bit earlier in the instruction cycle than either $\overline{\text{RD}}$ or $\overline{\text{WR}}$. This can be a handy thing to know if you're using a storage device that needs some advance notice when it's going to be accessed by the CPU. This would cover parts that have longer access times or require some precharge time when you want to talk to them.

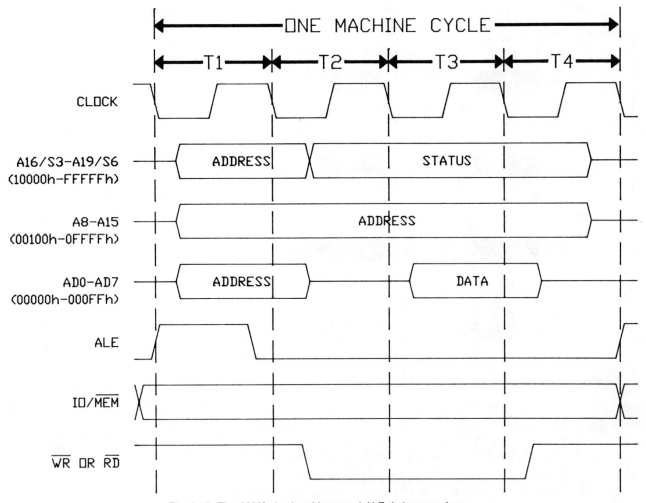

Fig. 3-16. The 8088's basic address and ALE timing waveforms.

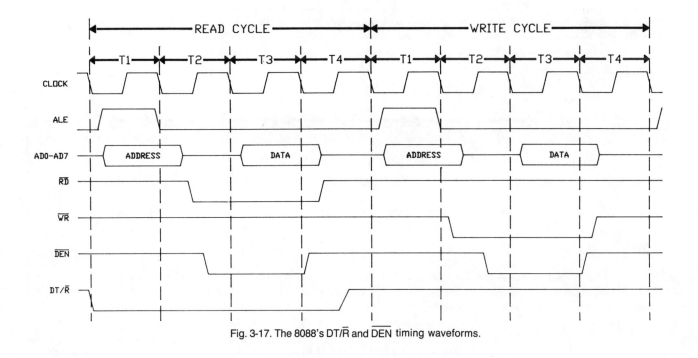

Fig. 3-17. The 8088's DT/R̄ and D̄ĒN̄ timing waveforms.

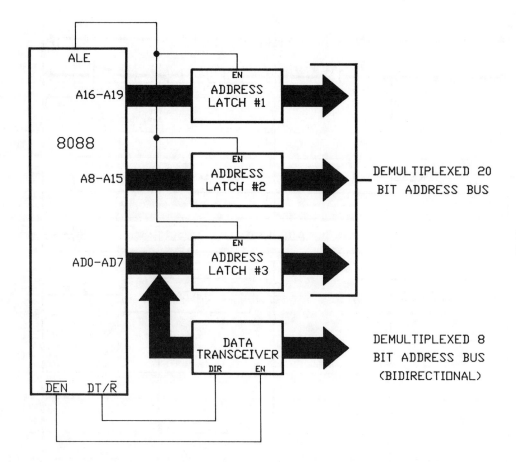

Fig. 3-18. Using DT/$\overline{\text{R}}$ and $\overline{\text{DEN}}$ to control data flow direction.

the CPU is expecting them to send (DT/$\overline{\text{R}}$ low) or receive (DT/$\overline{\text{R}}$ high) data. Both of these outputs were designed to work with Intel's 8286 or 8287 data transceivers, but they can be used with any transceiver whose outputs can be floated such as one of the standard 7424X parts (either TTL or CMOS).

Some 8088 based systems make heavy use of DT/$\overline{\text{R}}$ as well as $\overline{\text{RD}}$ and $\overline{\text{WR}}$ while other systems don't use DT/$\overline{\text{R}}$ at all. Going one way or the other has absolutely nothing to do with the complexity of the system or the size of the job it has to do. The only real deciding factor is how you go about the design. Microprocessors are versatile tools and there's always more than one way to get the job done. It's time for the eleventh Law of Life and Design:

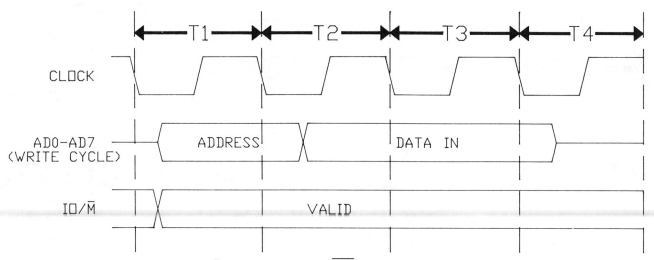

Fig. 3-19. The 8088's IO/$\overline{\text{MEM}}$ timing waveforms.

IF YOU ONLY SEE ONE SOLUTION,
YOU DON'T UNDERSTAND THE PROBLEM

So keep your mind open when you're doing circuit design. If you get stuck somewhere go for a walk, use a different color pen, or as an absolute last resort, eat a Twinkie.

The HOLD line is an input that's used by an external device that wants to get control of the system busses and control lines. When a high is put on this line, the 8088 will float both its control and bus lines and then let the external device know that it can use the bus. The CPU will stay in this state until it sees a low on the HOLD line again.

HOLD is useful for multiprocessor systems since it's a perfect signal for avoiding bus contention. The most common use for HOLD is doing *DMA*, (Direct Memory Access). DMA is a powerful way to get things done without having to involve the 8088—a lot of operations can be done much faster if you keep the microprocessor from putting its two cents in. One of the best examples of this sort of thing is dynamic RAM refresh. If you let the 8088 handle it, the processor's built in overhead, (due to the instruction fetch and decode times), will really stretch out the operation.

This is a bad thing for two main reasons. On one hand, dynamic RAM refresh is a very time sensitive operation—should your routine take too long, you might as well not bother doing it since all your data will get trashed anyway. On the other hand, if you do manage to write some slick routine that gets the job done in time, you'll be running the routine so often that the rest of your program will appear to be running at a snail's pace.

The HLDA (*Hold Acknowledge*) line is the output used by the 8088 to let external devices know that it has removed itself from the bus and has floated all the lines. If you're using a device like Intel's 8237 DMA Controller, (a good choice, by the way), it will connect directly to the 8088 control lines and properly handle the HOLD and HOLDA signals.

The $\overline{\text{SSO}}$ (*Status Signal Output*) will give you an up to the minute report of what the 8088 is currently doing on the bus (if anything at all). The information can be gotten by decoding $\overline{\text{SSO}}$ along with IO/$\overline{\text{M}}$ and DT/$\overline{\text{R}}$ as shown in the following table.

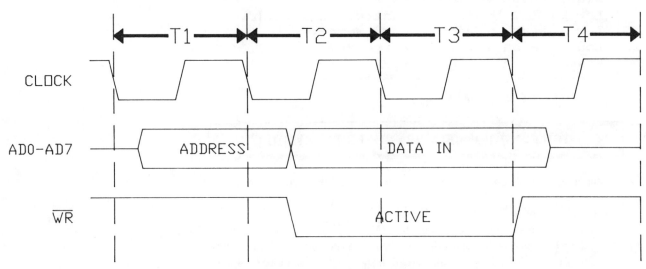

Fig. 3-20. The 8088's Write timing waveforms.

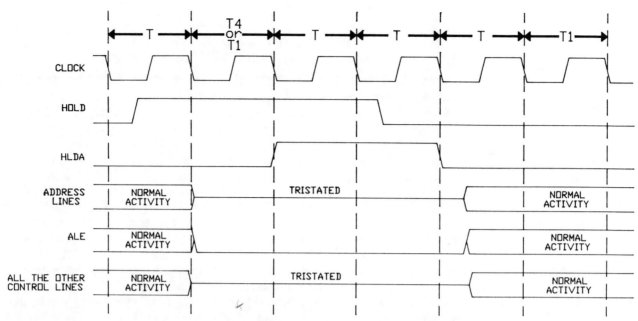

Fig. 3-21. The 8088's HOLD and HOLDA timing waveforms.

It's not necessary to remember all this stuff, it's only important to keep in mind that this sort of information is available when you have a need for it. In general, a microprocessor is a very complex piece of silicon and the only way to get all the details straight in your mind is to absorb it by experience.

IO/M	DT/R	SSO	Bus Activity
High	Low	Low	Interrupt Acknowledge
High	Low	High	Read I/O Port
High	High	Low	Write I/O Port
High	High	High	Halt
Low	Low	Low	Instruction Fetch
Low	Low	High	Read Memory
Low	High	Low	Write Memory
Low	High	High	No Activity

Table 3-1. Decoding $\overline{SSO}$, IO/$\overline{M}$, and DT/$\overline{R}$ to Monitor the Activity of the 8088.

The fifteenth Law of Life and Design:

YOU CAN'T POSSIBLY REMEMBER EVERYTHING

Brain real estate is just too valuable to waste by storing details you can always find in a book.

Grey cells are no substitute for a data sheet.

I'm not going to go into super detail about $\overline{MAXIMUM}$ mode control lines since operating the 8088 this way means another chip has to be added (an 8288 Bus Controller), system timing becomes a bit tighter, and circuit design tends to be more complex. Once we've got a basic handle on MINIMUM mode operation, it will be much easier to ease your way into $\overline{MAXIMUM}$ mode.

There are other considerations as well.

Since $\overline{MAXIMUM}$ mode is really aimed at multiprocessor applications where several CPU's need access to the system busses, this situation doesn't really arise in single board designs. And if you do plan on putting together a system that requires the extended control lines available in $\overline{\text{MAXIMUM}}$ mode, your chances of success are better with a good understanding of MINIMUM mode operation.

You can check on the status of the instruction queue by decoding QS0 (*Queue Status 0*) and QS1 (*Queue Status 1*). The information you get is shown in Table 3-20.

Table 3-2. Decoding QSQ and QS1 in MAXIMUM Mode to Monitor the State of the 8088 Queue.

QS0	QS1	Queue Activity
Low	Low	No Operation
Low	High	First Opcode Byte
High	Low	Empty the Queue
High	High	Next Opcode Byte

The S0, S1, and S2 (*Status 0*, *Status 1*, and *Status 2*) outputs are used by the 8288 Bus Controller to generate all the memory and I/O control signals. Decoding these lines when the 8088 is in $\overline{\text{MAXIMUM}}$ mode will give you exactly the same information provided by decoding $\overline{\text{SSO}}$, IO/$\overline{\text{M}}$, and DT/$\overline{\text{R}}$ in MINIMUM mode.

The $\overline{\text{LOCK}}$ signal is an active low output that the 8088 uses to let other processors on the bus know that it would be a bad idea to take control of the bus right at the moment. Whenever a $\overline{\text{LOCK}}$ command is issued, the lock output goes low for the duration of the next instruction cycle. Other CPU's that share the bus should keep an electronic eye on this line and leave the bus alone while the line is active.

The RQ/GT0 (*Request/Grant 0*) and RQ/GT1 (*Request/Grant 1*) lines are bidirectional lines similar to the MINIMUM mode HOLD and HOLDA signals. Since these lines are bidirectional in the $\overline{\text{MAXIMUM}}$ mode, both the HOLD and HOLDA functions are available on one line. This lets the 8088 share the bus with two external processors (instead of only one in the MINIMUM mode). The lines are prioritized and there are strict timing requirements that have to be met if they're used. In MINIMUM mode, the timing requirements for HOLD and HOLDA are a bit more relaxed and, in general, the use of these lines is much more straightforward.

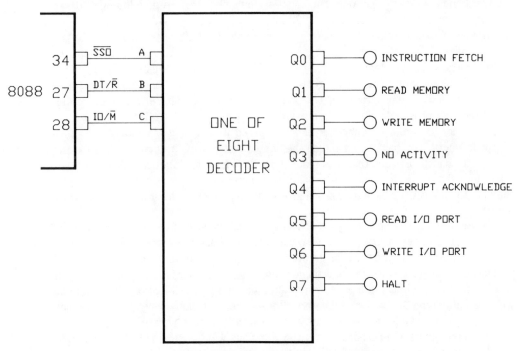

Fig. 3-22. Hardware setup to monitor 8088 activity.

4

Software: The 8088 Instruction Set

SOFTWARE—SOMEONE ONCE SAID THAT THE ONLY GOOD THING ABOUT IT IS THAT IT won't break if it falls on the floor. Hardware people have a hard time with it because they can't put a meter on it but there's no way to avoid it when you're doing microprocessor-based designs.

If you're coming to the 8088 with experience in CPU circuits, you won't have any trouble adapting to the 8088. If, on the other hand, this is your first trip to microprocessor land, you're in for quite a few surprises—and a lot of work.

Developing the software for an 8088 based system is at least as much, if not more, work than putting together the hardware. This seemingly strange state of affairs comes about because the 8088, and every other microprocessor ever made, has a lot of capabilities but not a lot of brains. It knows how—you have to tell it what. And the operative verb in that sentence is "tell".

Writing software means telling the CPU what operations to perform as well as specifying the order of execution. And no matter how powerful the microprocessor is, it understands one, and only one, language—its own. In order to develop 8088 based hardware, you'll have to talk to the 8088 in its native language—machine code.

Before we start to look at the 8088's instruction set, let's take some time to talk about programming in general. Since your success in dealing with the 8088 depends entirely on how well you learn to communicate with it, you'll be at a distinct disadvantage if you go into this with the idea that creating software for your own single board systems is the same as writing programs on a computer. There are big differences. Believe me.

If the only programming experience you have is in BASIC, you'll find that writing machine code is tedious—someone once compared it to building a mountain with a teaspoon—since you have to handle all the details that BASIC ordinarily takes care of for you. This includes such things as reading the keyboard, arithmetic, and all the other operations that a high level language makes transparent to the programmer. Just about the only thing a BASIC background will give you is a general understanding of program flow.

When we start building our system, you'll see that we also have to deal with certain mechanical difficulties in writing the software we need. Since there are none of the modern conveniences that you take for granted when you're programming on a computer, writing and debugging software for a single board system like ours is a bit more involved. But, as with most things in life, there are alternatives and we'll look at all of them as we go about putting the hardware together. For the moment, however, let's take a quick run through the 8088's instruction set and see what we have to work with.

Even though its external data bus is only eight bits wide, it would be a serious error in judgement to think of the 8088 as being "just an eight-bit CPU with some sixteen-bit muscle''. It may look like an eight-bit machine when you're wiring up support chips and laying out the PC board, but the software knows differently. The instruction set of the 8088 has all the features of the older eight-bit CPU's as well as a whole collection of powerful new sixteen-bit instructions.

INSTRUCTION SET GROUPS

CPU designers are always faced with two opposing goals when it comes time to create the instruction set. They want it to be as powerful as the hardware will allow while still making it as easy as possible to use. No way.

The sixteenth Law of Life and Design:

> ## COMPLEXITY IS THE PRICE OF FLEXIBILITY

That's just the way it is.

The 8088 can understand over 95 separate instructions. And if that number doesn't stagger you, consider also that there are more than 24 ways to have the 8088 generate an address. These range from simply including the address in the instruction to instances where the CPU is told to calculate the address by doing arithmetic based on the values stored in several of its registers.

Trying to learn how to program by reading a detailed description of the complete instruction set is like teaching yourself a foreign language by reading a dictionary. Forget it—it can't be done. A more realistic approach—and the one we're going to follow—is to break the instructions into logical groups and discuss each one of them in general. This will give us a basic appreciation of what the 8088 can do and we'll be able to take a closer look at instructions that are unique to the 8088. These include the arithmetic set, the string manipulation set, and all the other goodies that make the CPU such an ideal choice for a stand-alone system.

If you put ten programmers in a room and ask them to arrange the 8088 instruction set into logical groups you're sure to wind up with eleven different lists. So if you've got some CPU development time under your belt, I guarantee that you're going to disagree with how I've broken down the instruction set. And if this is the first time you've played around with microprocessors, by the time you've worked your way through this book, you'll have more than enough burned into your brain to disagree as well. Guaranteed.

DATA ACCESS AND TRANSFER INSTRUCTIONS

Microprocessors spend most of their time accessing memory locations and moving data from place to place. Just about every CPU around has instructions that are equivalent to some of the fourteen that you'll find in this group. The *mnemonics* may be different but they all do pretty much the same basic job—getting a piece of data and moving it around. All of these instructions, with the exception of IN and OUT, are designed to move data between registers, memory, and the stack. IN and OUT, of course, are I/O instructions.

The most interesting instruction in this group is *XLAT* since it's the basis for any kind of table lookup operation. With older CPU's, the job of designing an indexing system for a table of data usually meant writing separate routines that would take a byte and use it as the offset into a table. You needed subroutines that would do the arithmetic (or logical operations) to convert the byte to a place marker in your table. Routines like that take a lot of instructions and, what's really bad, a lot of CPU time as well.

DATA ACCESS AND TRANSFER INSTRUCTIONS	
GENERAL PURPOSE	
MOV	Move 8 or 16 bit data
XCHG	Exchange 8 or 16 bit data
XLAT	Replace index with data
PUSH	Store data on the stack
POP	Get data from the stack
INPUT/OUTPUT	
IN	Get data from a port
OUT	Send data to a port
LOAD POINTER ADDRESS	
LDS	Load a register and DS
LES	Load a register and ES
LEA	Load a register with address
FLAG INSTRUCTIONS	
PUSHF	Copy flag register to stack
POPF	Copy flag register from stack
LAHF	Copy flag register to AH
SAHF	Copy AH to flag register

Table 4-1. The Data Access and Transfer Instructions.

With the 8088, however, you can pick the byte you want from a table by preloading one register with the offset. As soon as you issue the XLAT instruction, the 8088 will dive into the table, and replace the index byte you had in the register with the data byte you wanted. If you've got a couple of tables set up in memory, you can specify the table you want to search by preloading the start address of the table in a second register. Let's see how this is done since the mechanics of this operation are typical of a lot of the 8088 instruction set.

To keep things simple, let's say you wanted a stand-alone system to do quick conversions from letters to their equivalents in Morse code. The first thing you would do is convert the Morse code into something that can be stored in memory. Fortunately, the dots and dashes of Morse code are easy to encode—the dots become zeros and the dashes become ones. By reserving one byte for each character, you can build a complete table of Morse code data. Once you've got that done, you're ready to write the software that takes a keyboard character and translates it into Morse code.

The 8088 has to know where the table is stored in memory and we give it that information by loading the DS, (*Data Segment*), register with the base address of the segment we're using to store the table, and then putting the starting address of the table itself in the BX, (one of the general purpose Data Registers), register. This, by the way, is one of the instances where the 8088 designers have assigned a specific job to a particular data register.

Now that the table is loaded in memory and we've told the 8088 where it's located, the stage is set for the software. The flowchart is very simple. The program accepts an input character and puts its assigned value in *AL*, (the lower half of the accumulator). The rest of the program revolves around the XLAT instruction.

When the 8088 executes the XLAT instruction, it takes the eight-bit input code we put in AL and adds it to the starting address of the table we've already stored in BX.

The CPU takes this new number and combines it with the value in DS to produce an absolute twenty-bit address. As soon as the address is calculated, it takes the data from that location and puts it into AL, overwriting the input data your program put there initially.

This may all sound a lot more complicated than it really is. As is often true, the explanation of this software is more involved than the software itself. Here's a listing of the code—see if you can follow what's happening.

```
;The SETUP part of the code loads the segment registers with the
;base addresses of the 64K blocks of memory we'll be using for the
;code that takes the input character and looks up the Morse Code.
```

```
SETUP:    CLI                           ;Disable interrupts temporarily
                                        ;so we're not interrupted while
                                        ;we're setting up the registers.
          MOV     AX,DATASEG            ;Put the base address of the 64K
          MOV     DS,AX                 ;data segment we want in DS.
          MOV     AX,CODESEG            ;Put the base address of the 64K
          MOV     CS,AX                 ;code segment we want in CS.
          MOV     AX,STACKSEG           ;Put the base address of the 64K
          MOV     SS,AX                 ;current stack in SS.
          MOV     BX,TABLELOC           ;Load BX with the offset address
                                        ;of our Morse Code Table.
          STI                           ;Re-enable interrupts.
```

```
; This is the main part of the code.  It takes an ASCII character
; from the keyboard and uses the ASCII code as an index into the
; data table we've already stored at address TABLELOC.  We have our
; keyboard set up at I/O port #05h and our output device at port #06h.
; Our hardware is set so that a 00h is present at the keyboard if no
; key has been pressed.  The key that indicates we're finished with
; the Morse code conversion returns an FFh when it's pressed.
```

```
START:    IN      AL,05h               ;Get a character from keyboard.
          JZ      START                ;If a 00, no key was pressed so
                                       ;go back and try keyboard again.
          CMP     AL,0FFh              ;Check to see if we're finished.
          JNZ     DONE                 ;If so, get out of the routine.
          XLAT                         ;Find the Morse code equivalent
                                       ;to the ASCII character from the
                                       ;keyboard and put it in AL.
          OUT     06h,AL               ;Send the Morse code out port 6.
          JMP     START                ;Do it all over again.
DONE:     RET                          ;We're finished converting code.
```

You can see from the listing that the working part of the program is only a couple of bytes long. If you're new to microprocessors, you don't have the experience to appreciate how simple this is, but if you've done single board design with some of the older CPU's, the simplicity of this operation on the 8088 is a real eye opener. All you have to do is load your table, establish the pointers, and build the I/O routines. It doesn't take a lot more to manage two, three, or any amount of separate tables either. If you can fit them all in one 64K segment, the only extra step is to put the table address in

BX. Switching segments will give you access to any location in the 8088's one meg address space—and doing that is simply a matter of adding another instruction.

BIT MANIPULATION INSTRUCTIONS	
LOGICAL OPERATIONS	
AND	AND 8 or 16 bit data
OR	OR 8 or 16 bit data
XOR	XOR 8 or 16 bit data
NOT	NOT 8 or 16 bit data
TEST	TEST 8 or 16 bit data
ROTATE INSTRUCTIONS	
ROL	Rotate data left
ROR	Rotate data right
RCL	Rotate left through carry
RCR	Rotate right through carry
SHIFT INSTRUCTIONS	
SHL	Logical shift to the left
SHR	Logical shift to the right
SAL	Arithmetic shift to the left
SAR	Arithmetic shift to the right

Table 4-2. The Bit Manipulation Instructions.

BIT MANIPULATION INSTRUCTIONS

People who are only familiar with high level languages like BASIC, PASCAL, or, (for nose-up-in-the-air types), FORTH and LISP, usually have a hard time with this group of instructions. When they see the light and make the move to a real man's language like assembler, bit manipulation is always the place where they slow down. Most other instructions have some rough analogue in high level languages but the only way to even approach this set is to do some really crude arithmetic. Here, as everywhere else, you'll find machine language more powerful, more flexible, and more satisfying. The reason for this is simple—the seventeenth Law of Life and Design.

> ### MACHINE LANGUAGE GIVES
> ### YOU TOTAL CONTROL OF EVERYTHING

You may have to burn some new pathways in your brain but there's no doubt whatsoever that the end product is worth the effort. You'll be able to walk down the street with a new spring in your step and you'll be admired by all your friends and neighbors . . . strangers will ask for your autograph.

Heady stuff . . . but, onward.

SHIFTs and ROTATEs are old stuff to any seasoned microprocessor veteran but what sets the 8088 version apart is the fact that the instructions will accept an argument. This is a feature that any experienced programmer can appreciate since SHIFT instructions are kind of like TV commercials—you never find one by itself. This is because the traditional use for these instructions was to do a bit of arithmetic—the old SHIFT and ADD shuffle for multiplication or SHIFT and SUBTRACT for division.

There were obviously some veterans on the 8088 design team since you can tell the 8088 to SHIFT or ROTATE a specified number of bits in either direction. One peculiar aspect of this addition to the instruction set, which we'll get to in a little bit, is that the major use for it has been pretty much eliminated by the enhanced group of arithmetic instructions. That's only an opinion but you'll be able to judge for yourself when we get there.

One new addition to this group of instructions is "TEST" and a very useful instruction it is indeed. Most of the uses for the logical operators usually involve looking for loop exits or data matches. You compare the value in a particular register or memory location against a value stored in the accumulator and then look at one of the flags to see whether the condition you're testing for is true or not. In BASIC this would be one of your standard "IF-THEN" statements.

The problem with this type of instruction has always been that doing one of these logical operations always trashes the value in the accumulator. Now "trashing" may be a strong word but it's true that the original value in the accumulator is always overwritten by the result of the logical operation you've just performed. The TEST instruction will AND the contents of a designated byte with the accumulator, transfer the appropriate results to the Flags (also called the Status) register, but leave the original value in the accumulator unaltered.

This new instruction isn't as mind blowing as some of the other 8088 innovations but it's typical of the mindset of the guys who designed the instruction set. The key word behind all of the new additions is flexibility. There are lots of ways to get the 8088 to carry out a particular job and it's up to the person who's writing the software to decide which way to go.

FLOW CONTROL INSTRUCTIONS

No matter where you look in the instruction set, you're bound to run across command variations you wish had been present in some of the older eight-bit CPU's. You would expect a newer, more powerful, CPU to have newer, more powerful instructions, but experienced designers take a particular pleasure seeing new variations of old familiar ones.

The 8088 has a wide range of JUMP commands based on just about every conditional test you can imagine (and some you can't). All the usual options are there as well as some new ones designed to work with the 8088's string manipulation commands. What's really the most interesting subset in this group and the ones that deserve the most attention are the LOOP commands. The name may be new but, in actual fact, they're really useful variations on instructions you may have seen before.

If the starship Enterprise crash landed on Earth and you found some of its computer junk in your backyard, you might not be able to make head or tail out of the hardware but I'll bet you a new pair of tennis shoes you'd find the following sequence in the software:

```
                MOV   CX,PERSONNEL COUNT        ;Load number to beam down
BEAM AGAIN:     MOV   AX,COORDINATE BUFFER      ;Get entered coordinates
                MOV   NEW COORDINATES,AX        ;Set proper coordinates
                CALL  BEAM DOWN                 ;Activate transporter
                DEC   CX                        ;One less to beam down
                JNZ   BEAM AGAIN                 ;Is anyone left
                RET                             ;If not, we're done
```

Fortunately, Starfleet regulations require that all source code has to be kept in the system and, as evidence of how advanced they are, each line of code must be fully commented.

This may be buried in the middle of some space-age software but you don't have to be a member of the Galactic Federation to see that Starfleet didn't base their hardware on the 8088—or whatever Intel will be producing in the 25th century.

Table 4-3. The Flow Control Instructions.

FLOW CONTROL INSTRUCTIONS	
CONDITIONAL OPERATIONS	
JAE	Jump on above or equal if CF=0
JNB	Jump on not below if CF=0
JA	Jump on above if CF and ZF=0
JNBE	Jump on not below or equal if CF and ZF=0
JC	Jump if CF=1
JNC	Jump if CF=0
JBE	Jump on below or equal if CF=1
JNA	Jump on not above if CF or ZF=1
JB	Jump on below if CF=1
JNAE	Jump if not above or equal if CF=1
JE	Jump if equal
JZ	Jump if zero
JLE	Jump if less than or equal
JNG	Jump if not greater than
JL	Jump if less than
JNGE	Jump if not greater than or equal
JGE	Jump if greater or equal
JNL	Jump if not less than
JG	Jump of greater than
JNLE	Jump if not less than or equal
JNE	Jump if not equal
JNZ	Jump if not zero
JNO	Jump on not overflow if OF=0
JO	Jump on overflow if OF=1
JS	Jump on sign if SF=1
JNS	Jump on not sign if SF=0
JP	Jump on parity if PF=1
JPE	Jump on parity even if PF=1
JNP	Jump on not parity if PF=0
JPO	Jump on parity odd if PF=0
UNCONDITIONAL OPERATIONS	
JMP	Jump to another address
CALL	Run a subroutine
RET	Return from a subroutine
LOOP OPERATIONS	
LOOP	Decrement CX and loop until CX=0
LOOPE	Decrement CX and loop if CX and ZF<>0
LOOPZ	Decrement CX and loop if CX and ZF<>0
LOOPNE	Decrement CX and loop if CX<>0 and ZF=1
LOOPNZ	Decrement CX and loop if CX<>0 and ZF=1
JCXZ	Jump if CX=0

Somewhere in the very first program ever written for the very first microprocessor ever produced you're going to find a routine that looks exactly like the one I've just listed. Counting loops are a basic part of just about every single piece of software no matter what it's designed to do.

The 8088's LOOP instructions are a natural extension of the CPU's conditional branching commands and using them can make the routine I listed above smaller and more efficient.

```
             MOV   CX,PERSONNEL COUNT        ;Load number to beam down
BEAM AGAIN:  MOV   AX,COORDINATE BUFFER      ;Get entered coordinates
             MOV   NEW COORDINATES,AX        ;Set proper coordinates
             CALL  BEAM DOWN                 ;Activate transporter
             LOOP  BEAM AGAIN                 ;Beam down everyone
             RET                             ;We're done
```

The LOOP instruction automatically decrements the CX register and repeats the specified loop until CX is zero.

As you can see, the source code is more intuitive with the LOOP instruction. If you're shrugging your shoulders and yawning because you don't think that there's much of a difference between the two examples, it's because there's an additional subtlety to the LOOP instruction that's not immediately obvious.

The LOOP instruction decrements CX as it works its way through the count—this is similar to the first example. The subtle detail I'm referring to takes place when LOOP gets CX down to zero and lets the routine fall through to RET, the next instruction. If you use the first example, the DEC instruction will transfer the result of the subtraction to the flags—after all, the JNZ instruction looks at the flags to see what it should do. LOOP, on the other hand, doesn't pay any attention to the flags—it decides what it should do by watching the CX register directly.

You'll remember that the TEST instruction was unique because it would affect the flags but leave the register alone. LOOP does a similar sort of thing—it affects the registers but leaves the flags alone. If you're wondering what's so terrific about all this it means you've forgotten how important a feature flexibility is. And the eighteenth Law of Life and Design should be a permanent part of your brain:

> ## IT'S THE DETAILS THAT MAKE OR BREAK YOU

The chances of writing software that works is directly proportional to the subtleties in the instruction set. There's some conventional wisdom floating around that says you can do everything you want with every microprocessor but don't you believe it.

If you were writing 8080 or 6502 stuff, there's no doubt that you could write routines to mimic the 8088 LOOP and TEST instructions. There's also no doubt that the routines would involve using lots of buffers and stack activity—in any event, it's for sure that the one thing they wouldn't be is simple. And the more convoluted your software, the greyer your hair will be when you finally, (if ever), get it working.

CPU CONTROL INSTRUCTIONS

The 8088 has a good complement of instructions to set and clear all the flags that are used during normal program operation. For the most part, the flag controls are similar to the ones that you'd find on the 8080 or 8085. The new addition to this set concerns itself with the DF flag. STD and CLD set and clear the Direction Flag to determine whether strings will be autodecremented or autoincremented when they're processed.

CPU CONTROL INSTRUCTIONS	
EXTERNAL OPERATIONS	
HLT	Halt until interrupt or reset
LOCK	Lock bus for one instruction
WAIT	Wait until TEST pin active
ESC	Code for external CPU
INTERRUPT OPERATIONS	
INT	Run interrupt routine
INTO	Interrupt if overflow
IRET	Return from interrupt routine
FLAG OPERATIONS	
STC	Set the carry flag
CLC	Clear the carry flag
STD	Set the direction flag
CLD	Clear the direction flag
STI	Set the interrupt flag
CLI	Clear the interupt flag
CMC	Complement the carry flag
MISCELLANEOUS	
NOP	Do absolutely nothing

Table 4-4. The CPU Control Instructions.

The only members of this group that are worth a special mention are the instructions that have to do with external devices—HALT, WAIT, LOCK, and ESC. The reason they're interesting is that they point out one of the basic ideas inherent in the design philosophy of the 8088. Let's take a look at the instructions themselves and then we'll be able to see what they have to say about the 8088's design.

HALT is a command that Intel has included in the instruction set since the days of the 8008. When a HALT is issued, the CPU stops dead in its tracks and does absolutely nothing—for all practical purposes it's just sitting there and executing an endless stream of NOP's. What's really going on is that the 8088 is waiting for an external interrupt so you have to be careful and make sure things are set up properly before the command is issued.

Pity the poor soul whose program doesn't enable interrupts before the HALT instruction is executed—he's trapped. Anytime you want a HALT condition, always precede it with an STI (*Set Interrupt Enable Flag*). As a matter of fact, think of this sequence as really being one instruction.

This peculiarity has always been part of HALT. No one at Intel will admit it, but as far as I'm concerned it's a real defect in the design of the instruction set. Since it's been around for such a long time, however, I suspect one of two things—either cleaning it up involves a lot of brain damage or Intel doesn't want to take the chance of messing around with the source code compatibility of the 8088 and it's ancestors.

In any event, issuing a HALT without first enabling interrupts is a sure recipe for disaster. The only way to get things going again is to reset the 8088 so slipping up and putting yourself in a spot like that can just ruin your entire day.

The WAIT instruction is similar to a HALT in that it causes the 8088 to stop what it's doing and, logically enough, wait, but it's really a HALT instruction with a safety valve. Issuing a WAIT will put the CPU in an idle state but instead of effectively executing a series of NOP's, the 8088 will repeatedly look at the state of the TEST line, (pin #23), and wait for it to go low before going on to its next instruction. If the interrupt flag is set, (allowing the CPU to respond to interrupts), the 8088 will service the interrupt and then return to the wait condition.

If you issue a $\overline{\text{LOCK}}$ instruction, The CPU will hold the $\overline{\text{LOCK}}$ line low during the execution of the next instruction. This signal is only available when the 8088 is operated in $\overline{\text{MAXIMUM}}$ mode, (pin #33 tied low). The $\overline{\text{LOCK}}$ pin will only remain low for the duration of the next instruction and it's a way to let other hardware know that the 8088 has a real need to keep control of the bus.

I've saved the ESC instruction for last since it, more than any of the others, gives you a clue to the design philosophy behind the 8088. The ESC instruction is very close to an NOP far as the 8088 is concerned. When it's issued, the 8088 will access the location specified in the instruction and put the memory contents on the data bus—and that's all. From the 8088's point of view, it would seem that this instruction is rather pointless but, as someone or another once said, there's more to this than meets the eye.

Although the 8088 is a powerful stand-alone microprocessor, it was really designed to be a member of a processing team. We've seen that there are only so many signals you can squeeze into a forty-pin package. Well, it's also true that you can only stuff so much into the instruction set. I don't know what the limits are, but it's a safe bet that the more you put in, the longer it's going to take the 8088 to get anything done.

The 8088 was designed to do general data management. If you ask the chip to move and manipulate data, it has the muscle to get the job done in an economical and time efficient manner. But no matter how powerful it is, there are very definite limits to what it, or any other microprocessor, can be expected to do. The Intel design team recognized this and decided to use a parallel microprocessor approach to solve the problem.

Parallel processing means that microprocessors have joined the medical profession in entering the age of specialization. Well, the 8088 is just like the family doctor. It knows how to do a lot of things but if you want a particular operation done better and faster, you'll call in a specialist. The two areas where the 8088 can use the help of a specialist are in number crunching and I/O processing.

No matter how fast the 8088 operates it still has a hard time with arithmetic. Remember that its sixteen-bit register widths are a limit to the kind of precision it can deliver. Not only that, but the ability to do heavy duty arithmetic requires a very specialized instruction set and we've already seen why it wasn't designed into the 8088. Intel's solution to this problem was to give the 8088 the ability to recognize when instructions that show up on the bus are aimed at another CPU. The 8088's mechanism for doing this is the ESC instruction.

Remember that the only 8088 activity generated by an ESC is to read the desired location and get the data on the bus. The rest of the instruction is treated like an NOP. The coprocessor, on the other hand, monitors the bus and recognizes the ESC instruction as something it knows how to do. This means that both the 8088 and the coprocessor can share and receive instructions on the same bus. It also means that a system using both chips can have two instructions being executed at the same time.

The only coprocessing superstar that Intel has produced so far for the 8088 is the 8087 math coprocessor. The 8089 high speed I/O processor never became a popular chip since most designers chose the more familiar route of using DMA controllers. When it comes to pure number crunching, however, the 8087 is a real mind blower since its instruction set can recognize a series of special purpose commands designed specifically for math. Using one of these chips can speed up arithmetic operations by a factor of 100 and, since the 8087 has eight eighty-bit registers, the precision is much greater than that possible with the 8088 alone.

In order for the 8088 to use a coprocessor, however, it has to be configured to work in the $\overline{\text{MAXIMUM}}$ mode so it'll be a while before you get there. $\overline{\text{MAXIMUM}}$ mode operation is a lot easier to understand once you've got a handle on $\overline{\text{MINIMUM}}$ mode.

ARITMETIC INSTRUCTIONS	
ADDITION OPERATIONS	
ADD	Add data
ADC	Add data with carry
INC	Increment a location by one
AAA	ASCII adjust for addition
DAA	Decimal adjust for addition
SUBTRACTION OPERATIONS	
SUB	Subtract data
SBB	Suntract data with borrow
DEC	Decrement a location by one
NEG	Subtract number from zero
CMP	Compare data
AAS	ASCII adjust for subtraction
DAS	Decimal adjust for subtraction
MULTIPLICATION OPERATIONS	
MUL	Multiply unsigned data
IMUL	Multiplyy integer data
AAM	ASCII adjust for multiply
DIVISION INSTRUCTIONS	
DIV	Divide unsigned data
IDIV	Divide integer data
AAD	ASCII adjust for division
CBW	Put sign of AL in AH
CWD	Put sign of AX in DX

Table 4-5. The Arithmetic Instructions.

ARITHMETIC INSTRUCTIONS

Even though an 8087 adds lots of mathematics megamuscles it doesn't follow that the 8088 is limited to counting on its silicon fingers. The instruction set has a wide range of arithmetic functions, some of which are carryovers from the 8085 and some of which are new. If you want superspeed and high precision when you're doing math, an 8087 is what the doctor ordered, but for most applications we'll see that a stand-alone 8088 is fine.

There are three features of the arithmetic group that are worth a special mention—the first is an extension of 8085 features and the second two are entirely new.

Intel has given the 8088 a sizeable repertoire of instructions to do BCD and ASCII arithmetic. Where the 8085 could only convert the number in the accumulator to BCD, the 8088 has separate instructions for converting either the result of addition, (DAA), or subtraction, (DAS). If you're coming to the 8088 from the 8085, be aware that the 8085's DAA instruction isn't the same as the 8088's. The former is a blanket instruction to Decimal Adjust the Accumulator and the latter is a *Decimal Adjust for Addition*.

One of the new features in the 8088 is the ability to directly do ASCII arithmetic. What this really means is that the CPU has a few instructions tailored specifically to handling an unpacked decimal number. The difference between packed and unpacked decimal numbers is always a bit confusing so let's take some time to look at it more closely.

Decimal data can be coded into hex in two ways—either as packed (standard BCD) or unpacked (also referred to as ASCII) numbers. A packed decimal number is stored in one full byte and can be anywhere from 0 to 99. The tens digit is stored in the high half of the byte and the units digit is stored in the low half. That means that if you want to store a decimal number such as 52 in packed decimal, the numerals that would go into memory are exactly the same ones—52 in decimal is coded as "0502" in hex. The classic case of what you see is what you get.

HEX	PACKED	UNPACKED
00	00	0
01	01	1
02	02	2
03	03	3
04	04	4
05	05	5
06	06	6
07	07	7
08	08	8
09	09	9
0A	INVALID	INVALID
0B	INVALID	INVALID
0C	INVALID	INVALID
0D	INVALID	INVALID
0E	INVALID	INVALID
0F	INVALID	INVALID
10	10	INVALID
11	11	INVALID
12	12	INVALID
1A	INVALID	INVALID
45	45	INVALID
8E	INVALID	INVALID
99	99	INVALID
100	INVALID	INVALID
101	INVALID	INVALID

Table 4-6. Packed and Unpacked Decimal Numbers.

Unpacked decimals are very similar to packed ones, except they're single digits so the only legal values are 0 to 9. They're stored in a full byte but the high nibble is always 0—only the lower half has any significance. You would store 1 as 01, 2 as 02 . . . but I'm sure you get the idea. If you're thinking that the numbers 0 to 9 are the same in packed and unpacked decimal, you're right—they are the same. If you're also wondering why someone went through all the brain damage of creating the distinction between packed and unpacked decimals since they're so similar, I'm sorry to tell you that the answer just isn't all that satisfying.

That same someone noticed that the ASCII code, (in hex), for the numbers are almost the same as the numbers themselves—the ASCII code for 0 is 30h, for 1 it's 31h, and so on. The reason that Intel designed special instructions to handle unpacked decimals is because the 8088 has, as we'll see, powerful instructions for manipulating ASCII strings and it was considered a good idea to be able to do ASCII arithmetic as well—and it is a good idea at that.

In order for any of these instructions to work, however, the byte you're using has to be converted to a valid unpacked decimal number before the instruction is executed. This involves setting the high half of the byte to 0. And since the operation leaves the high half of the byte at 0, it has to be set to 3h if you want the result to be in ASCII rather than unpacked decimal. If you remember that an unpacked decimal is just the number's ASCII code with a 0 instead of a 3 in the upper half you won't have any trouble keeping it straight in your mind.

The second new feature in the 8088's instruction set is one that a lot of programmers really liked—the ability to do multiplication and division with a single instruction. The traditional way that this had been done with earlier microprocessors was to "shift and add" for multiplication and "shift and subtract" for division. This is fine for cases where you want to multiply or divide by relatively small numbers in the eight-bit range, but it can get really tedious when you have to deal with sixteen-bit double precision. Everybody who's snooped around some object code has probably seen the evidence of this—a long series of shift instructions followed by some adds or subtracts.

The 8088 can be told to multiply or divide eight or sixteen-bit numbers with a single instruction and it can handle either signed or unsigned numbers. Before we take another step, however, it's a good idea to do what we just did—go through the difference between the two kinds of numbers.

HEX	SIGNED	UNSIGNED
0000	+00	00
0500	+1280	1280
1000	+4096	4096
1500	+5376	5376
2000	+8192	8192
2500	+9472	9472
3000	+12288	12288
5000	+20480	20480
7000	+28672	28672
7FFF	+32767	32767
8000	-32768	32768
A000	-24576	40960
C000	-16384	49142
F000	-4096	61440
F500	-2816	62720
FF00	-256	65024
FFFF	-1	65535

Table 4-7. Signed and Unsigned Binary Numbers.

Unsigned numbers are scalar quantities—they tell you how much but they don't tell you what direction. These can be either eight or sixteen bits in length and since all the bits are used to build the number, an eight-bit unsigned number can be as large as 255 and an unsigned sixteen-bit number can go up to 65,535. Don't forget that these numbers aren't positive or negative—they only represent magnitudes. The common mistake here is to assume that the absence of a sign implies a positive number and we all know how much trouble you can get in by taking things for granted. It's time for the fifty fifth Law of Life and Design.

IF YOU ASSUME NOTHING, YOU'RE NEVER WRONG

Think about it.

Signed numbers (also known as integers), on the other hand, are vector quantities—they tell you how much and in what direction. Although they also can be either eight or sixteen-bit numbers, they cover a much different range than their unsigned relatives.

This is because the high bit in the byte is used to indicate the direction, (or sign), of the number. If the high bit is clear (0) the number is positive and if it's set (1) the number is negative.

This means that in the case of an eight-bit number, for example, only seven bits are available for the quantity. An eight-bit signed number therefore, has a range of plus or minus two to the seventh and a signed sixteen-bit number can span across plus or minus two to the fifteenth. The number zero is considered to be positive since its high bit is always clear (0).

The best way to keep this difference straight in your mind is to realize that no matter what kind of number you talk about, signed or unsigned, an equal number of bits gives you an equal range. Using one bit to indicate direction only means that a signed number covers a different range than an unsigned number. Even a heavy duty guy like Bertrand Russell will tell you that there are as many numbers from 0 to 65,535 as there are from −32,768 to +32,767, (don't forget that zero is a positive signed number). And if you didn't believe him, he probably could prove it.

STRING INSTRUCTIONS	
MOVS	Move 8 or 16 bit string data
LODS	Load 8 or 16 bit string data
STOS	Store 8 or 16 bit string data
SCAS	Search string for data
CMPS	Compare string data
REP	Repeat string instruction
REPE	Repeat while equal (ZF=1)
REPZ	Repeat while zero (ZF=1)
REPNE	Repeat while not equal (ZF=0)
REPNZ	Repeat while not zero (ZF=1)

Table 4-8. The String Instructions.

STRING INSTRUCTIONS

This is what really sets the 8088 off from the pack. When the CPU was first introduced some ten years ago (!!!!!!) news of this part of the instruction set made headlines everywhere except in the New York Times—I think it was an election year. It's all well and good to stuff the 8088 with all the things we've been talking about so far but, by and large, it had all been done before. Maybe not as well, as elegantly, or as completely, but there's no getting around the fact that it takes more than a fresh coat of paint and a new set of seatcovers to make people rush to the bank for a loan. You need something really new—nine cylinder engines, antigravity, stuff like that.

What made small systems designers lust after the 8088 was a group of five string oriented instructions. Nothing like it had ever been available before.

In a nutshell, the 8088's string instructions can save hours of brain time and programming hassles. As a matter of fact, this set of instructions was such a natural addition that most programmers found themselves wondering why it had never been done before. It's been done since by other companies with other microprocessors but you know what they say . . .

IMITATION IS THE SINCEREST FORM OF ROBBERY

and there aren't a lot of things as true as that.

Intel refers to these five string instructions as "primitives" since they, like the rest of the instruction set, are intended to be combined into complex commands. Although these command combinations are only a few bytes long, we'll see that they can do jobs that used to require a lot of bytes, a lot of time, and a whole lot of brain damage.

If you were paying close attention when you were working your way through the chapter on the 8088's architecture, you'll remember that two registers, SI (*Source Index*) and DI (*Destination Index*), are the ones used by string instructions. Whenever you want to use any one of these instructions to do any kind of stuff to strings, the 8088 will be expecting to have relevant addresses in both of these two registers. The actual data is simple enough—SI holds the current address of the string and DI holds the address you want the string moved to.

When you want to move or manipulate massive gobs of string data, it makes sense that you're going to need more than just these two registers. After all, multibyte operations involve three pieces of basic information— where to get data, where to put data, and how much data to handle. String instructions use the CX register to keep track of counting and the AX register for comparisons. Even though these instructions are really something new, they're designed to be very similar in use and syntax to the rest of the instruction set. If you have some previous microprocessor experience, you'll be comfortable with them immediately—if you don't have any experience at all, you won't find these instructions any more difficult to use than any of the others.

The MOVS (*Move String*) instruction can operate on either eight or sixteen-bit quantities and it does exactly what you'd expect. It takes the data at the location pointed to in SI and moves it to the address pointed to in DI. This is a straightforward memory move but there are a few subtleties involved. We've already talked about them, but let's go over them again here.

You might remember that the 8088's unique Direction Flag, (DF), is dedicated to string processing. If it's set to 1, executing any of the string instructions will cause the SI and DI registers to be decremented by one—automatically! If you clear the flag to 0, SI and DI will be automatically incremented. You may now be getting an inkling of what these instructions can do for you.

When you execute a MOVS instruction, therefore, two things happen in the CPU. The data gets moved and the registers are automatically updated. This is all setting the logical stage for the next part of the string subset—moving more than one eight-bit byte or sixteen-bit word at a time. And, just as the LOOP instructions gave you a one instruction answer to what had traditionally taken several bytes of code, a similar subset of instructions exists for string handling as well.

If you want to move a whole block of string stuff from one place to another, all you have to do is put a REP (*Repeat*) instruction in front of it. Consider the following piece of code.

```
BLOCK:    MOV    SI,PRESENT LOCATION    ;Where it is now
          MOV    DI,NEW LOCATION        ;Where to move it
          MOV    CX,STRING SIZE         ;How much to move
          REP                           ;Do all of it
          MOVS                          ;Move the data
          RET                           ;All done
```

This simple routine is, at the most, 15 bytes long and is capable of moving a 64K block of data from one location to another. The exact length of the routine depends on how we've defined the labels in the first three instructions, so they can be anywhere from two to four bytes long.

The reason we're able to get so much done with such a relatively short routine is that the REP instruction is actually ''Repeat the next string instruction until the CX register is equal to zero''. If you've written assembler code before, you might want to try writing a similar routine for the microprocessor of your choice. Even if you can keep the size of the routine as small as this example, I'll be willing to bet you'll have to think a few times to do it and, in any event, there's no way you can make it any more straightforward. You can try it in BASIC or some other high level language if that's what you know, but you'll have a hard time comparing the size of the routine.

The LODS (*Load String*) instruction takes a string byte or word and loads it into the accumulator. If you're thinking that this is like the MOV instruction found in the TRANSFER INSTRUCTIONS, you're almost right since the following instructions appear to be doing the same thing.

```
MOV     AX,SOMEPLACE          ;Load AX with data
LODS                          ;Load AX with data
```

Although the accumulator gets loaded in both cases, that's really where the similarity ends. Remember that LODS is one of the string instructions. This means the address from which it's going to get data (SOMEPLACE, in this example) is currently in the Source Index (SI) register. And once LODS is executed, it will automatically increment or decrement SI, depending on the state of the Direction Flag.

String instructions, since they're hardwired to look in specific registers for the relevant addresses, are smaller and execute much faster than general purpose data transfer instructions. We can see this more clearly by building the equivalent of a LODS instruction and counting up the bytes.

```
LOADSTRING:     MOV   AX,[SI]      ;Load the accumulator with the
                                   ;data found at the address
                                   ;stored in register SI
                PUSHF              ;Put the flag register onto
                                   ;the stack
                POP   BX           ;Put the flags into register BX
                TEST  BX,0200h     ;Check the current state of the
                                   ;Direction Flag
                JZ    INCREMENT     ;If a zero result the Direction
                                   ;Flag (DF) was clear (0) so we
                                   ;have to increment the Source
                                   ;Index (SI) Register
                DEC   SI           ;If we get here, DF was set (1)
                                   ;so we have to decrement SI
                RET                ;We're done
INCREMENT:      INC   SI           ;Increment SI
                RET                ;We're done
```

If you're a programming whiz, you can probably write some routine that's much more efficient than this one, but the result is going to be the same. Emulating a LODS instruction takes a lot of bytes any way you do it and in any event, when you realize that LODS does all this for you and is only one byte long to boot, there's not much more to say.

The companion to LODS is *STOS*. This instruction takes the byte or word in the accumulator and stores it in the location pointed to by the Destination Index (DI) register. As you would expect, after the byte has been stored, DI is updated as well.

The last operation you would frequently want to do with strings is to hunt through them for a particular byte or word. This is what the SCAS (*Scan String*) instruction does for you. When you execute SCAS, the 8088 will compare the contents of the location pointed to by DI with the value in the accumulator.

Issuing SCAS by itself will just compare a single location, but you can scan a range of locations by doing what we did with the MOVS instruction—just execute a REP before the SCAS.

If you see a small problem with this last paragraph, you've got the mind of a programmer. The hitch here is that the whole point of doing a comparison is to test the results and the only kind of test done by REP is to check if the CX register has reached zero. The people at Intel took care of this by providing *REPE* (Repeat as long as the zero flag is equal to zero) and *REPNE* (Repeat as long as the zero flag is not equal to zero).

You can try examples of this kind of searching when we get our system up and running since it's one of the instructions that can be used effectively (along with XLAT) when you're doing a lot of table lookups.

SUMMARY

When you read this, give yourself a couple of well deserved pats on the back because we've taken a look at the entire 8088 instruction set. I'll be the first to admit that a lot was left unsaid and a whole bunch of instructions were never even mentioned.

But that's OK . . . trust me.

There's no way in the world that you can become a software ace by just reading a book—that can only come with experience and the only way to get experience is to sit down and write code of your own. What you should have under your belt at the moment is an appreciation of the kinds of things the 8088 can do. If you're used to some of the older eight-bit microprocessors, you should also have a real respect for the added power inherent in the 8088 instruction set.

Once we get our hardware together, we'll be working on specific examples of 8088 code, so don't think that you have to understand all the details of putting together working software at this stage of the game. The general sort of awareness you've gotten so far will be transformed into reality later on.

I don't know about you, but I've had enough of software for a while. It's not well known, but too much time spent on theory can turn your brain to oatmeal. That's a scientific fact—you can look it up. So let's put the whole business of POP's and MOV's away for a while and turn to something that we can all really sink our teeth into—hardware.

5

Designing Hardware

DESIGNING A CIRCUIT AND ACTUALLY PUTTING HARDWARE TOGETHER IS A VERY PER-
sonal business. Everybody has their own way of doing things and the more
experience you've had getting your hands dirty, the more personal your method usually
gets. Some people like to work out all the details on paper first, some people like to
get stuff wired up before they touch a pencil, and some people don't write anything down
until they've got something working on the bench.

Whatever the case, whether you're building a light dimmer for your family or a Nitron
Beam for Ming the Merciless, there's one rule that absolutely everybody follows — the
first Law of Life and Design:

KNOW WHAT YOU WANT TO DO BEFORE YOU TRY TO DO IT

If you sit down at the bench without anything in mind, whatever you wind up with is
guaranteed to be mindless.

Sitting down to design a circuit around a microprocessor is a bit different than putting
together other kinds of circuitry. Remember that a board full of discreet components
does what it's designed to do while a board full of CPU type stuff does what you tell
it to do. The chameleon-like nature of a microprocessor-based circuit means that exactly
the same hardware can do very different kinds of jobs. It's all a function of the software.

We'll concentrate on building a basic single board 8088 circuit and dissect each
component as we add it to the system. Once we get the minimum system up and running, we'll start adding bits and pieces that will make it even more flexible. Each time
we add something to the circuit we'll stop and see what can be done with it. You'll see
that there's an awful lot of power in even the most minimal system. How much you
can do with it depends more on your imagination than the hardware. While I'll explore
several of the things that can be done with our project at each stage of development,
I'm sure you'll be a lot better at thinking up possible applications than I am.

Don't be afraid to experiment on your own. If you decide that you've got a handle
on what we're talking about, put the book aside and give it a try. The best way to find
out if you really understand something is to add your own ideas to mine and see if they
work. The worst thing that can happen is that you'll blow up an IC and, between the
two of us, that's not such a big deal.

If the truth be known, I've sent IC's off to the silicon afterlife as well, but remember
the twelfth Law of Life and Design:

so keep your eyes open, your mind open . . . and be adventurous.

A BASIC SYSTEM

Everybody has their own idea as to what components go into making a basic system — it has to do with what you consider to be important. For our purposes, the definition of a rock bottom circuit is like the one shown in Fig. 5-1. It's much too early in the game to start thinking about the details of the circuitry but what we're going to put together is covered in the block diagram.

As you can see, we've included all the elements needed to assemble a circuit that makes the 8088 come alive. Even though a basic system like this isn't about to win any awards for speed and power, you'll see that it still has more than enough muscle to do real world type jobs. Our minimum circuit described by the block diagram has all of the elements you'll find in much larger gee-whiz type systems.

I'm telling you right now that the key to being able to design a large 8088 based circuit is understanding the simple one we're going to put together. The only difference between this and something much more sophisticated is just size and complexity. That's not as silly as it sounds.

Even the world's most sophisticated 8088 system can be broken down into a block diagram resembling the one in Fig. 5-1. After all, no matter what you want a

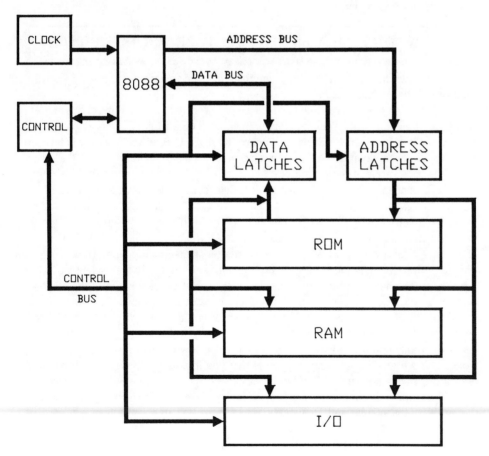

Fig. 5-1. Block diagram of the basic 8088 circuit.

54

microprocessor based circuit to do, there are a few elements you have to include to make the thing work. I have it on good authority that even systems built on Metaluna have:

1. Clock circuits
2. CPU circuitry
3. Address latches
4. Data latches
5. ROM
6. RAM
7. I/O

since these are the basic building blocks of any system. They may be bigger, they may be faster . . . chances are they may even be smarter, but that's only a matter of degree — the basic elements in the design are exactly the same.

Everything we're going to do with the 8088 will revolve around the circuit built from this block diagram so we're going to spend a lot of time seeing how it's put together and how it works.

THE BASIC APPROACH

The single most important element in the design of any circuit is the mind of the designer. There is no other aspect of electronics that depends so heavily on individual creativity. The designer's ability to take an idea from brain cells to breadboard is a function of good understanding and skill — coming up with the idea in the first place is an exercise of pure imagination.

If you've already got some bench time under your belt, you already know that lots of snags, and seemingly unsolvable problems crop up in the lifetime of a project. Working your way through them and finding ways to improve the design involve the same kind of creative energy that painters and sculptors draw on to show their particular vision of reality. Circuit design is an art form unique to this century.

But just as a painter has to know how to mix paints or a sculptor to work with the texture of his medium, a circuit designer has to bring an understanding of his materials to the bench. That's what we'll be doing here.

As we work our way through the details of this circuit, we'll be getting familiar with the ingredients of 8088 based designs but all we'll really be doing is describing the tools. The real measure of how well you understand them is to experiment on your own. When you feel that you've gotten a grasp on a particular aspect of the design, put this book aside and exercise your own imagination.

Don't worry about blowing things up — the parts are cheap but the lessons are invaluable. Don't lose sight of the fact that you don't really learn from your mistakes, you learn by understanding how to correct your mistakes. And in order to do that you have to keep good notes, observe carefully, and above all, you have to strictly obey the Golden Law of Life and Design:

THINK FOR YOURSELF

The only way to be 100% sure that you really have something straight in your mind is to successfully create your own version of it. And don't be put off by people who smugly point their fingers at their computers and accuse you of reinventing the wheel. There may be some truth in that but don't ever forget that reinventing the wheel means you'll know exactly how the wheel works.

Better cancel your plans for the weekend, we've got a lot of work ahead of us.

6

The Anatomy
of an 8088 Circuit

W E'VE SPENT A LOT OF TIME TALKING ABOUT THE 8088 BUT, AT LEAST SO FAR, JUST about everything we've been doing has been theoretical. The time has come to switch gears so, in the words of Shakespeare, let's get physical. We're going to flesh out the block diagram shown in Fig. 6-1 and, once we've gotten that straight, we're going to see what we can get it to do. But first let's talk a bit about procedure.

SETTING UP THE BENCH

It's impossible to build circuits with just parts, wire, and a host of good intentions—you need test equipment. Even if nothing goes wrong as you assemble each section of the circuit, you're not going to be able to learn anything if you don't have some way of snooping through the silicon. But, on the other hand,

REALITY HAS A HABIT OF GETTING IN THE WAY

since I'm the first to admit that good test equipment can put a real dent in your wallet.

In order to get around this problem, (and keep you solvent at the same time), I'm going to include real scope traces as well as data book type timing diagrams at important points in the development of the circuit. For those of you who are interested, there's a list of what equipment I used to design the circuit and a complete description of how these traces and measurements were made at the end of the book.

We'll treat each section of the circuit assembly as a construction project and I'll list all the components you'll need along with the minimum equipment you should have for testing and measurement. In the best of all possible worlds, you should have all of the following equipment on your bench.

1. An oscilloscope (30 MHz minimum bandwith)
2. A frequency counter (20 MHz minimum)
3. A multimeter
4. A 5 volt, 2 amp supply (regulated and filtered)
5. A logic probe
6. Data sheets for the chips being used
7. An EPROM burner
8. An IBM compatible computer

9. An 8088 family assembler or "DEBUG.COM", a mini assembler that comes on the DOS distribution disks

You can use any construction method you want to assemble the circuits but while things are in the development stage, it's best to use the tenth of an inch solderless breadboards. Most mail order houses and local electronic stores carry them. You should have several of the bus strips as well as regular component boards. You can buy packs of wire designed for use with these protoboards but it's just as easy, (and cheaper), to get some standard four conductor 24-gauge telephone wire and make your own.

When you're ordering parts, get several of each of the ICs since they're usually only available from mail order houses and it's a real bummer to be forced to wait a week to get a replacement for a three dollar chip. Besides, you'll need more chips and stuff as soon as you start laying out your own designs.

I'm ready if you are, so let's roll up our mental sleeves and take a detailed look at our circuit.

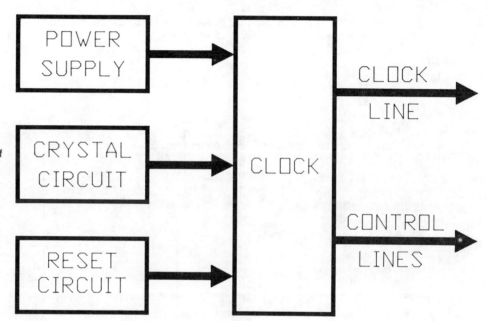

Fig. 6-1. Detailed block diagram of the basic 8284 circuit.

THE POWER SUPPLY

If you're lucky enough to have a good bench power supply you can skip this section but if you generally use a collection of batteries as a source of power on the bench, you'll find this section useful.

The 8088 circuit we're going to build is going to need a nicely regulated five volt supply and batteries just aren't going to do it. You can throw together a 7805 based regulator circuit, but depending on what you ultimately do with the 8088, there's a good chance you'll need more than the 1.5 amp maximum those regulators can supply. And remember that drawing the maximum current through a 7805 means lots of heat sinking and no margin for error. There are ways around this however.

The circuit shown in Fig. 6-2 is a versatile 5 volt supply you can put together with a minimum of parts searching. It will give you a source of ripple free power, can deliver up to 5 amps, has overload protection, and the output voltage can be varied from 5 to 20 volts using a singe trimmer.

PARTS
IC1 -   7805 regulator
IC2 -   741 op amp

Q1	-	MJ2955 PNP transistor
Q2	-	2N6594 PNP transistor
D1	-	1N4003 diode
R1	-	100 ohms, ½ watt
R2	-	10k trimmer
R3	-	.27 ohm, 2 watt
R4	-	.27 ohm, 2 watt
R5	-	2 ohm, 1 watt
C1	-	1000 μF, 50V
C2	-	.01 ceramic
C3	-	.01 ceramic
C4	-	100 μF, 50V
S1	-	SPST toggle switch
S2	-	SPST toggle switch
* T1	-	See text
* B1	-	See text
Misc	-	Suitable enclosure, wire, heat sinks for regulator and transistors, line plug, insulated output terminals.

EQUIPMENT

Multimeter

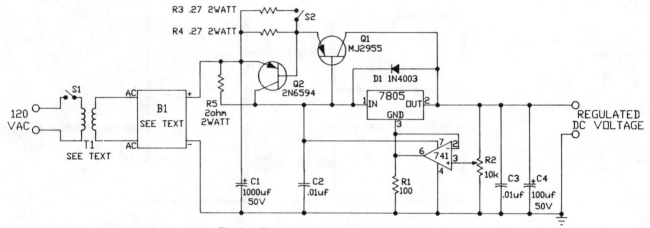

Fig. 6-2. The schematic of the power supply.

ABOUT THE CIRCUIT

It goes without saying, (but I'll say it anyway), that this supply can deliver enough power to do a lot of damage. Five volts may not sound like a lot to you, but at five amps, it can melt the tip on a screwdriver, so it doesn't take much imagination to figure out what it can do to you. Pay attention to what you're doing when you put the supply together.

In order to get the full output that this supply is designed to deliver, you're going to need an input transformer that can put out at least 25 volts and 8 amps. Several mail order houses have them in stock and there's even a chance to find them in a local shop. If you can't locate one and find yourself forced to settle for something with less muscle, that's okay, but remember that you can't pull power from the supply that you don't put in, in the first place. An 18-volt transformer is going to give you a maximum supply output voltage of about 15 volts.

For the purposes of the circuits in this book you're better off compromising on the voltage rating of the transformer instead of the amount of current it can supply since we'll never be needing more than 5 volts. Keeping that in mind, you should set your sights on a transformer that can deliver about 12 volts at 6 amps. Using this means that you'll only be able to get about 9 volts from the supply but that's more than adequate.

Once you've made your choice of transformer, you can decide how chunky a part you need for B1, the full wave bridge rectifier. Make sure it can handle the voltage from the transformer and can stand a current draw of at least 5 amps. Multiply your voltage and current numbers by 2 and use that as the specs for the bridge since the sixth Law of Life and Design clearly states that

SAFETY MARGINS ARE GOOD THINGS

If you're familiar with the 7805 regulator, you'll recognize a few of the components in the circuit as standard additions. C1, C3, and C4 are filters designed to soak up surges that appear on either the input or output of the supply. These include spikes generated by a sudden draw at the output or residual ac ripple at the input. Every regulator design includes parts like these since they do a good job of keeping the voltage nice and constant. Unfortunately, as we all know, there's no getting around the third Law of Life and Design that I've already mentioned — namely:

THERE'S NO SUCH THING AS A FREE LUNCH

since the price you pay for the line filtering is the added risk of blowing up the 7805. No kidding.

Imagine what happens when there's a short circuit at the output of the 7805. In this case, the 7805's output will be grounded and the short circuit current will be shunted safely to ground by C4. The 7805 will try to supply the short circuit current, (theoretically an infinite amount), until it reaches its thermal overload point and shuts itself down internally. It may get hot but, other than that, the regulator won't be damaged since it was designed with this type of eventuality in mind. Input shorts, however, are entirely different.

If the input of the 7805 is brought to ground, (a short circuit), the output of the regulator is going to be at a higher potential than the input, C4 is going to start to discharge its appreciable store of current into the regulator's output. This is definitely a bad thing since the 7805 was designed to source current, not sink it. The C4 current is going to flow into the output of the regulator and, if there's enough charge on C4, the internal short circuit protection of the 7805 is going to be swamped. This will reverse bias the pass transistor in the regulator's innards and, in a word, the chip will be history.

The way around this problem is provided by D1. As long as the circuit is operating normally, the voltage at the regulator's input will be greater than the voltage at its output. This means D1 will be reverse biased and do absolutely nothing in the circuit. If the 7805 input is shorted to ground, however, the output voltage will be higher than the input and D1 will be forward biased. Most of the C4 current will be shunted by D1 and passed to ground through the input short.

We're able to get up to 5 amps out of the supply because Q1 will take up the extra current demands when the regulator's 1.5 amp limit is reached. Q1 is configured as a simple switch and it's controlled by R5. All the current that's fed to the regulator flows through R5 and as long as the current stays below about an amp, Q1 is going to stay off. When the current gets past this point, however, it's going to generate enough voltage across R5 to turn on Q1 and the transistor will start to pass current through its collector emitter junction. Since the MJ2955 can safely handle more than 10 amps, it can easily meet the 5 amp specs of our supply. But supposing the load on the supply tried to draw even more than five amps of current — or what happens if there's a short? Enter Q2, stage left.

All the current that Q1 supplies flows through R3 or R3 and R4 combined. Since the base emitter junction of Q2 sits across these resistors, it works exactly the same way as Q1. It stays off until the current flowing in the resistors generates a large enough voltage drop to turn it on. When that happens, it will lower the voltage across R5 and Q1 will turn off. In other words, Q2 is our guaranteed short circuit protection. If the draw gets too high, Q2 will shut the circuit down.

The voltage from our supply can be varied because of IC1. The op amp, (I'm using a 741 since they're cheap and available, but you can use just about any one you happen to have around), is set up as a noninverting buffer to isolate the output stage of the circuit from the regulator's ground leg. Changing the voltage at the op-amps's input by rotating R2, will change the voltage at the output. This changes the 7805's ground reference and tricks it into putting out a higher voltage. You'll always have 5 volts from the output of the regulator to the output of the op amp, but we're pulling the supply voltage from the regulator's output and system ground.

The down side of this kind of trickery is that the minimum voltage the circuit will put out will always be greater than 5 volts since the closest the regulator can get to ground is through the R1 voltage drop. Such is life.

By using a value of 100 ohms for R1, you'll be able to generate a minimum voltage of about 5.15 volts. This is well within the +/− 10% limit for the 8088 and most TTL parts so it won't be a problem.

Don't do any cavalier substitution of part values since there's a considerable amount of math involved in calculating the numbers shown and changing one value will mean recalculating all the values. If you're interested, you can follow the calculations (they're all based around Ohm's law and aren't all that difficult) and change whatever circuit parameters you want. The values for R3, R4, and R5 are all interrelated so just keep in mind that if you change one you'll have to check them all.

You can use your favorite construction method for assembling the circuit — there's nothing critical at all. Just remember that you'll be connecting it to ac line voltage so take reasonable precautions such as housing everything in a plastic box instead of a metal one and make sure that all wires are properly covered. If you do it all properly, you'll wind up with a versatile supply that's not only perfect for all the things we're going to do, but most other bench projects as well.

Look at the Math

Calculating the correct resistance for R5 can be done one of two ways — the easy way and the hard way. Even though there's a difference in the assumptions made for each method, the practical results are just about the same. If you take a good look at the circuit, you'll see that the emitter base junction of Q1, along with R3 and R4, should be considered in the determination of R5 since they sit in the circuit with the emitter collector junction of Q2. This makes things a bit hairy since the impedance of the transistor is going to change with current flow, voltage, temperature, and the other circuit parameters. For all intents and purposes however, the effect of Q1's emitter base junction is minimal compared to the voltage drop across R5 so we can safely do things the easy way and ignore Q1. Having made this assumption, we can calculate the value of R5 by a straight application of Ohm's law. The 7805 can easily handle half an amp but let's play it safe and have Q1 turn on when the current flow in the regulator exceeds 250 mA. The turn on voltage for Q1, as it is for any silicon transistor, is .65 volts. Since we want it to turn on when the current flow is 250 mA, we can get the value for R5 from Ohm's Law.

$$R5 = E/I$$
$$R5 = .65/.250$$
$$R5 = 2.6 \text{ ohms}$$

This isn't really the end of the story, however, since what we have just calculated is the total resistance needed to have Q1 turn on at a draw of 250 mA. You can see from the schematic that R3 and R4 are in series with R5 across Q1's emitter base junction. The value of 2.6 ohms is therefore the total resistance we need. In order to find the correct value for R5, we have to work out the value for the parallel combination of R3 and R4. Fortunately, this isn't that hard to do. If we want Q2 to start conducting, (to turn off Q1), when the draw goes past 5 amps, we can get the R3/R4 value from Ohm's law by making assumptions similar to the ones we just made above. We can ignore the effect of having the emitter base junction of Q2 in parallel with R3/R4 and just do the same sort of arithmetic we did before.

$$R3/R4 = E/I$$
$$R3/R4 = .65/5$$
$$R3/R4 = .13 \text{ ohms}$$

Now that we have this number we can get the final value for R5 by a little subtraction.

$$R5 = Rtotal - R3/R4$$
$$R5 = 2.6 - .13$$
$$R5 = 2.47 \text{ ohms}$$

The schematic lists R5 as 2 ohms since that's a standard value but doing that will change the trip point of Q1. You can get the actual trip point of the circuit exactly the way we just calculated the resistor values. It's a good exercise to do since going through it will help you understand exactly how the circuit operates. Once you've done that, you can check your answers by powering up the circuit and measuring the results with your meter. If you've done everything correctly, the measured values will be within .2 volts of the calculated ones.

THE CLOCK

We've already talked a bit about the 8088's clock requirements and you'll remember that the closer the clock is to the maximum operating frequency of the CPU, the closer the waveform has to be to the ideal clock. This means 10 nanosecond transition times and a 33% duty cycle. It's certainly possible to design an oscillator that puts out a waveform meeting these requirements, but doing that means violating the second Law of Life and Design - to wit:

DON'T WORK HARD, WORK SMART

so let's use the part specifically designed for the job - the 8284 clock generator.

PARTS

1	-	8284 clock generator
1	-	14.31818 series resonant crystal
1	-	1N914 diode
2	-	510 ohm resistors
1	-	4.7k ohm resistor
1	-	10k ohm resistor
1	-	4.7μF capacitor
1	-	12 to 15 pF capacitor
1	-	SPST normally open pushbutton
1	-	.1μF mylar capacitor

MINIMUM EQUIPMENT
Multimeter
Logic Probe

ABOUT THE 8284

The 8284, shown in Fig. 6-3, has two main jobs — one for us and one for the 8088. It makes our life easy by providing a single chip answer to a circuit design and it generates ideal waveforms for the 8088. It's one of a family of IC's Intel designed to work with the 8088. Other members of the family include latches, transceivers, and other parts that are the essential ingredients of any microprocessor-based circuit.

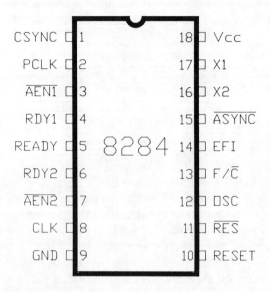

Fig. 6-3. The 8284 pinouts.

Using an 8284 does more than just provide the correct clock for the 8088. It also takes care of the reset circuitry, controls the 8088's ready line, provides an extra synchronized clock at TTL level that's half the system clock with a 50% duty cycle, and has a fully buffered TTL version of the crystal frequency on one of its pins. Useful stuff.

There are three options for clock generation with the 8284. You can hang a crystal across two pins, force feed it with an external oscillator, or slave it to another 8284. This last option comes in handy when you're designing multiprocessor circuits.

The X1 and X2 inputs, (pin #16 and pin #17), are the inputs of the internal crystal oscillator. The output of the oscillator is fed to a divide by 3 circuit and then brought to the outside world through a buffer. The divided clock is also sent to a divide by two circuit and then goes out to another pin.

The CLK output, (pin #8), is the main system clock for the 8088. The frequency is one third of the oscillator output and has a duty cycle of 33%. The OSC output, (pin #12), is a TTL level, buffered version of the internal oscillator. The PCLK output, (pin #2), is a TTL level frequency that's half the CLK output with a 50% duty cycle.

$\overline{AEN1}$ and $\overline{AEN2}$, (pin #3 and pin #7), are the Address Enable active low inputs that control the 8284's two Bus Ready lines. Both these inputs, ($\overline{AEN1}$ and $\overline{AEN2}$), are mainly used in multiprocessor systems where several CPU's have access to the busses.

RDY1 and RDY2, (pin #4 and pin #6), are used by external devices on the bus. By making them active, (high), the device can let the CPU know that it's finished using the bus. The RDY line the 8284 will look at is controlled by the $\overline{AEN}$ inputs. $\overline{AEN1}$ selects RDY1 and $\overline{AEN2}$ selects RDY2.

The $\overline{ASYNC}$ line, (pin #15), controls the 8284's READY output. The 8284 has two internal flip-flops that are used to synchronize the RDY inputs to the system clock. By tying $\overline{ASYNC}$ low, you get two stages of synchronization for the READY output. Tying it high will bypass the first flip-flop and just give you one stage. If you're hanging external devices on the bus that can't meet the CPU's required Ready timing, you would make $\overline{ASYNC}$ low. When the devices are fast enough, the $\overline{ASYNC}$ line can be tied high. If you're confused about this, go back and reread the section on the 8088's Ready timing that appeared in Chapter 3.

The READY output, (pin #5), connects directly to the Ready input of the 8088. When this line is low, the 8088 will add wait states to the instruction cycle so slower devices can have more time on the CPU system busses. READY line timing for "normally ready" and "normally not ready" devices is determined by the setting of $\overline{ASYNC}$. As before, if any of this sounds mysterious to you, review the Ready section in Chapter 3.

The $F/\overline{C}$ and EFI lines, (pin #13 and pin #14), tell the 8284 where to look for the main clock. If you tie $F/\overline{C}$ (*Frequency/Crystal*) low, the 8284 will take the master clock from it's internal oscillator and tying it high causes the 8284 to look for an input frequency on the EFI (*External Frequency In*) pin.

The $\overline{RES}$ input, (pin #11), is the 8284's reset line. The reason you can use a simple RC network to generate a reset pulse is that the $\overline{RES}$ line is squared up by an internal Schmitt trigger and locked to the system clock by an internal flip-flop before it goes out to the 8088.

The *RESET* output, (pin #10), feeds the Reset input of the 8088. Since it's controlled by the 8284, the actual reset pulse is tailored perfectly for the 8088.

The *CSYNC* input, (pin #1), comes into play when you're designing a system with multiple 8284's being driven by one master clock. When this line is high, the 8284 will reset its internal counters and put a high on the CLK and PCLK outputs. Bringing *CSYNC* low re-enables the internal counters and clock pulses will appear at the outputs. If you use this *Clock SYNCronization* line, the 8284 will expect its master clock to be fed in on the EFI input. Generally, the control signal sent to CSYNC is derived from and in sync with the master clock. Setting things up like this will guarantee that the outputs of all the 8284s in the system will be in phase. Systems like ours that have only one 8284 and make use of its internal oscillator have to tie CSYNC to ground because we want its counters to be enabled all the time.

Don't get the impression that the 8284 is designed exclusively for use with microprocessors in general or the 8088 in particular. When you have a need for a general purpose clock generator, keep the 8284 in mind. The 8284 will work reliably with crystals from 12 to 30 MHz and, with a bit of creative gating, can be made to switch back and forth between two different frequencies. All you'd have to do is put one clock on EFI, a crystal across X1 and X2, and then switch the $F/\overline{C}$ pin between high and low to select one source or the other.

Logic switching between two frequencies can come in handy in a lot of circuit applications, that's how the two speed IBM clone computers work, but wait . . . there's more. When you toggle the $F/\overline{C}$ pin high and low, what you're really doing is changing the input to the 8284's internal frequency division circuitry. The 8284 will always put a buffered version of its internal crystal oscillator on the OSC pin, this is always available, regardless of how you happen to have $F/\overline{C}$ set!

Being able to get two asynchronous clocks from a single chip makes the 8284 a real candidate for silicon superstar status. Don't ever lose sight of the fact that flexibility is high on the list of really desirable things since the fourteenth Law of Life and Design is:

KEEP AS MANY OPTIONS OPEN AS POSSIBLE

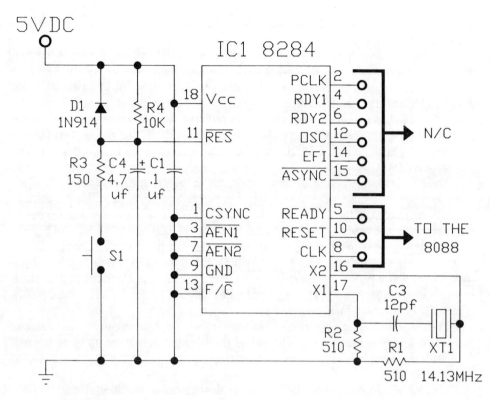

Fig. 6-4. Schematic of the 8284 circuit.

but let's take a look at the circuit.

ABOUT THE CIRCUIT

Since this is the first digital circuit we're putting together, you should take a moment to examine the schematic shown in Fig. 6-4. If you've never done digital design before you'll find it interesting to notice that the circuit is considerably cleaner and simpler than the power supply we just talked about. And the clock circuit has more passive components than most of the others we'll build!

This apparent circuit simplicity is misleading since a whole bunch of activity is going on inside those plastic IC packages but it is a fact that digital logic has less to deal with than analog stuff. You can get as much accuracy as you want with digital stuff, but no matter how many decimal places you want, you're still only dealing with ones and zeros. Analog stuff has to handle an infinite range of values. The bottom line is that, for a given problem, an analog solution will provide a more accurate answer but a digital one will be as accurate as you want.

Now that we have an understanding of how the 8284 works, there's not much that has to be said to describe the circuit. Only two pins have to be conditioned with passive components and once that's done the 8284 will, as they say, do its thing.

Since we're using the internal crystal oscillator, F/C is strapped low and EFI can be ignored. In the simplest case, you can hang any series resonant across X1 and X2, (as long as you pay attention to the 8284's upper and lower frequency limits), and the chip will start working. In practice, however, things are a bit more complex.

Because the internal oscillator is similar to an amplifier, it's a good idea to keep the resistance of the crystal circuit as low as possible. As it gets higher the oscillator gain will begin to drop and if it gets below one the circuit won't oscillate at all. It's better to be safe than sorry, so we have a capacitor in series with the crystal. This tends to cancel the effects of oscillator delays and frees you from the hassle of worrying about the crystal circuit.

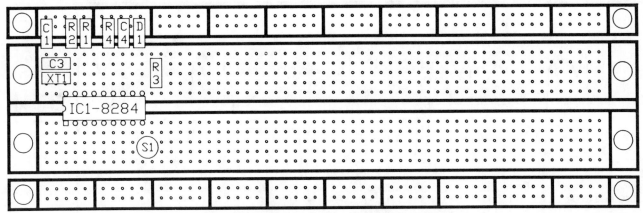
Fig. 6-5. Placement diagram for the 8284 circuit.

The value of the capacitor depends on the crystal frequency but since we're running at 14+ MHz we can use anything from 12 to 15 pF. The actual choice of the capacitor involves some math but any value in this range will more than satisfy our circuit requirements. The two 510 ohm resistors reduce frequency shifting due to such things as excessive stray board capacitance, temperature variation, and voltage fluctuations. In a well designed layout, you could probably get by without the resistors but the price you pay for the convenience of using solderless breadboards is a lot of stray capacitance.

The 8284 provides a convenient way of generating both power-up and manual reset pulses for the 8088. The minimum pulse width the 8088 wants to see on power-up is 50 microseconds and the pulse has to last that long *after* the system voltage has gotten up to the working Vcc value (5.1 volts in our circuit). Since there's no guarantee that any two power supplies will have the same rise time, designing a power-up reset pulse that only meets the minimum requirements is, in a word, idiotic. Especially since there's no limit on the maximum pulse width. In line with the ninth Law of Life and Design

ALWAYS IMAGINE THE WORST:

we're making the power-on reset pulse LLLOOONNNGGG -- the values shown in the schematic will generate a pulse of about 50 milliseconds — or some 1000 times longer than needed. You may think that this is a bit excessive but it can't hurt and, come on people, 50 milliseconds may be just short of forever as far as the 8088 is concerned but, let's get real here — 50 milliseconds is *not* a long time. Let's keep our sense of perspective.

Since the 8284 runs the $\overline{RES}$ input through a Schmitt trigger before it does anything else, we can feed it with a simple RC circuit and the length of the pulse will be real close to the RC product. In our circuit that would be 4.7 μF times 10k ohms. The diode, which works as a safety valve should the capacitor decide to dump its charge, is similar to the protection diode we used in the power supply.

A manual reset is provided by the pushbutton. When it's pressed, $\overline{RES}$ will be grounded, (made active), and the 8284 will send a reset pulse to the 8088.

Try to keep your leads as short as possible when you're building the clock generator since long leads create inductive and capacitive loading and, at best, the circuit will have to fight to oscillate in a stable manner. In the worst case you'll have so much noise and ringing on the line the clock may well turn out to be useless.

If you have a scope, you can compare the 8284 waveforms on CLK and PCLK against Fig. 6-6. These are real waveforms generated on my breadboard and captured with a digital scope. The ringing and other high frequency oscillation is due to the things we've been talking about but the waveforms are adequate for the 8088. If looking at the waveforms makes you a bit seasick you can turn to Fig. 6-7 which are the idealized

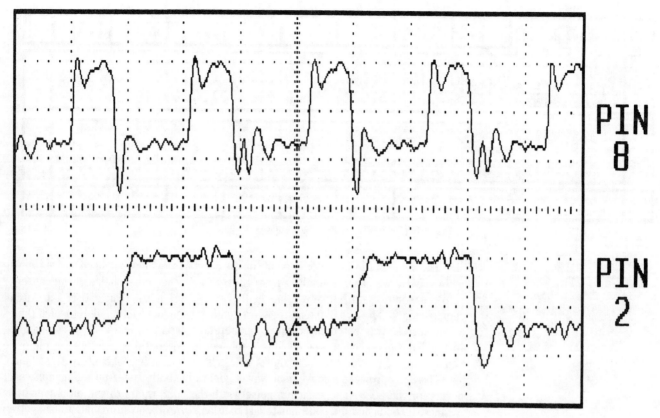

Fig. 6-6. Actual waveforms produced at pin #2 (PICK) and pin #8 (CLK) of the 8284.

waveforms. They may be clearer but never forget that they're not too in touch with reality.

You should particularly notice that the CLK's duty cycle is very close to the ideal 33% and PCLK, as we've already discussed, is half the frequency of CLK with a 50% duty cycle.

If you don't have a scope or frequency meter you can still get an idea of what's going on in your circuit by measuring the dc voltage. Since the CLK output has a 33% duty cycle, the dc voltage there will be approximately ⅓ the supply voltage. The key word to remember in that sentence is "approximately" since a look at Fig. 6-6 will show you that there's probably noise on the line, and that will have an effect on the reading. As long as the reading you get is within 10% of the calculated value, you're in the ballpark.

The same sort of check can be made on PCLK. This line has a 50% duty cycle and, once again, consider yourself home free if you get within 10%.

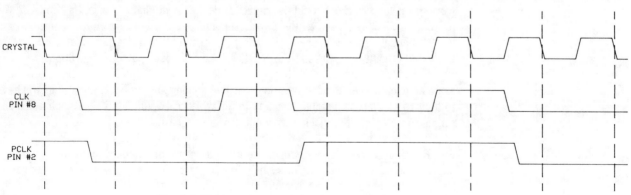

Fig. 6-7. Theoretical waveforms at pin #2 (PCLK) and pin #8 (CLK).

If you're reading zip, or something else unrealistic, on either of these lines, there's something wrong. Make sure the diode isn't in backwards and check the polarity on the capacitors. If they're all okay, carefully eyeball your connections, check the power supply, see if the 8284 is in correctly. Bent pins are a real possibility. If you find that the chip was in backwards, I'm sorry to tell you that you've probably had your first silicon fatality. You DO have another one around, don't you?

It's important to make sure that this circuit is working correctly because it has to drive everything else we'll be building. Once you have it up and operating, you're well on the way to building the rest of our 8088 based system.

7

Assembling The Parts

EVER SINCE I WAS A KID I'VE BEEN A HORROR MOVIE FREAK—BUT ONLY OLD HORROR movies. The people who make horror movies these days don't understand that there's more to it than just filling the screen with a bucket of leftovers from the butcher shop. That may be horrible but it ain't horror. Sending Igor to the cemetery with a shopping list and a meat cleaver . . . well, now we're talking horror. That's sort of what we're going to do now.

Our building of 8088 circuitry is real close to Dr. Frankenstein putting together a monster. Where we put the transceiver on the data bus, he puts the head of the girl on the body of the gorilla. No kidding.

Assembling the initial 8088 circuit is really just a matter of connecting the right parts together. If you're careful as you work you shouldn't have any mechanical problems. And that's very important since it's a lot harder to troubleshoot a microprocessor-based circuit than a dedicated one. Remember that the components on the board are only there as essential support for the 8088. The real work is being done by the 8088—and that work is the software we're going to store in the 2716. What makes troubleshooting so difficult is trying to decide whether the problem is coming from the hardware or the software.

But let's not start off under a cloud of pessimism—everything's going to be great. Trust me.

THE INITIAL 8088 CIRCUIT

The schematic in Fig. 7-1 is the first step we'll take in fleshing out the block diagram of Fig. 7-2. The reason we're calling it the "first step" is because a block diagram is only a general description while a schematic has to cross all the "T's" and dot all the "I's". The I/O shown in the block diagram can represent anything from the simple latch we're starting out with to something as involved as the engine control panel for the space shuttle.

The initial circuit we're putting together will do two things for us. On the one hand it's going to demonstrate the basic operation of any 8088 based circuit, and on the other hand it's going to show you the things that have to be taken into consideration when you're doing a design around the 8088. We've already covered a lot of the theory behind this so you shouldn't have trouble understanding any of it. All this stuff will be familiar to you from the previous discussion of the hardware aspects of the 8088. Trying to remember it all, however, is a first magnitude mistake since the tenth Law of Life and Design very clearly states that

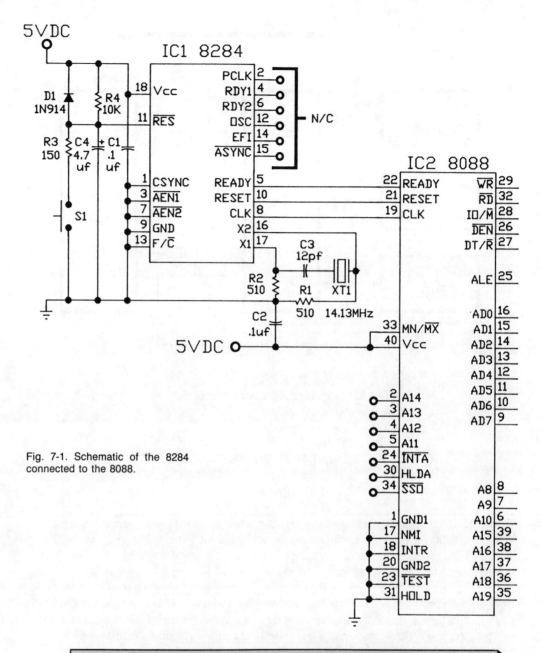

Fig. 7-1. Schematic of the 8284
connected to the 8088.

**DON'T WASTE BRAIN SPACE ON
STUFF YOU CAN LOOK UP SOMEWHERE**

Jamming everything into permanent head storage may be a great thing to do if you're
going to make a career of TV game shows but, let's face it, just how many microwave
ovens and sets of lawn furniture do you really need?So the sooner you put a bookmark
at the beginning of Chapter 4, the sooner we can get to work.

ADDING THE 8088

From everything we already know about the 8088, it comes as no real surprise to
say that there's not a lot it can do all by itself except drain batteries. That doesn't mean
it does nothing at all, however. A scope will show you that the 8088 is reacting to the
RESET line and that will be an indication that the chip is happy to be living on the
breadboard and listening to the 8284.

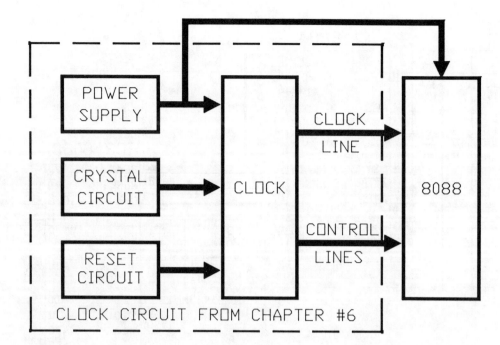

Fig. 7-2. Block diagram of the first part of the circuit.

PARTS

The 8284 clock circuit from Chapter 6.
A 5 volt power supply.
IC2 - 8088 (any speed)
C2 - .1μF capacitor

MINIMUM EQUIPMENT

Multimeter
Logic Probe

One of the things you should know by now is that while the 8088 is a powerful chip with lots of capability, it can't do much of anything without a lot of help. Plugging the 8088 in by itself may seem to be a pointless thing to do—and ordinarily it would be—but there's a good reason for doing it anyway.

Microprocessor-based circuits are complex. There's more going on than is evident from a simple parts count. The bus lines are moving, the control lines are going up and down—and all this is happening thousands of times a second. To make things even more complicated, everything has to happen at exactly the right time or it might as well not happen at all. Timing is everything.

When you consider all the variables that are involved in even as simple a circuit as the one we're putting together, it makes a lot of sense to isolate as many parts of the circuit as possible and test them individually. After all, let's not forget the nineteenth Law of Life and Design:

AVOID AMBIGUITY

since this can keep you from going prematurely grey whenever circuit snags appear. You stand a much better chance of finding the part of the circuit that doesn't work if you already know which parts of it do work.

While we're on the subject of troubleshooting, this is as good a time as any to warn you that the time is rapidly coming when you're going to need more than a multimeter to do meaningful snooping around the circuit. This is because we're getting to the point where timing is more important than voltage. Multimeters won't catch pulses that last less than a microsecond and even if they could, you still won't be able to tell *when* the pulse showed up.

When we get further into the circuit and we're sure that at least part of it is working, the 8088 can be programmed to do a good deal of the diagnostic work for us. A couple of words of software will hold a line high or low, and it's a simple matter to write a program that will sequentially clock the address and data lines. But that won't happen for a while yet.

If you plan on getting serious about microprocessor-based designs you're going to have to think of an oscilloscope as an essential tool rather than an expensive luxury. It's just about impossible to do any significant work without one.

BUILDING THE CIRCUIT

Don't even think of adding the 8088, (or any part), to the breadboard while the power is turned on. I know of no surer recipe for disaster than to add silicon to a board that's powered up. Turn off the power and, while you're at it, disconnect the power leads from the board as well. In actual fact, it's a good idea to be faced with a two step operation whenever you want to apply power to the board since it will give you a chance to think twice before you do it. Power indicators are nice things—LEDs can be very comforting—but they're really not a substitute for a moment of reflection while you run through a mental checklist.

Now that power is turned off, (and the leads are removed), plug the 8088 into the breadboard near the 8284. Make sure none of the pins get bent. ICs have standard pin spacing but they're usually a bit splayed out when you first get them. Hold the 8088 horizontally with one row of pins resting on the bench and GENTLY push down. This will bend one row of pins in slightly and make it easier to plug the IC into the breadboard.

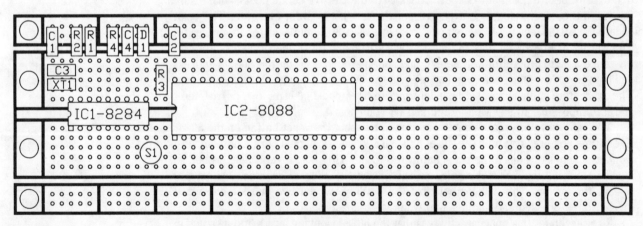

ALL BUS STRIPS ARE TIED IN PARALLEL
AND CARRY ONLY POWER AND GROUND

Fig. 7-3. Placement diagram for the 8088.

Make the connections shown in the following Table 7-1 and, since we're now at the point where an improper connection can fry the 8088, be very careful to make the right connections to the right pins—count the pins twice before you attach a wire to it.

Once you've made these connections and checked them several times, connect the .1 μF capacitor from pin #40 of the 8088 to the ground bus. That's all you have to do for this part of the circuit but we have one more thing to check before applying power to the board and it's a good thing to do whenever you make a change to the board.

Take your multimeter, put it across the power leads coming from the breadboard, and measure the resistance. What we're doing here is making sure we don't have a dead short since applying 5 volts to a dead short can only make other things dead. The

Pin #	Pin Name	Connect to
1	GND1	Ground
17	NMI	Ground
18	INTR	Ground
19	CLK	8284 pin #8 (CLK)
20	GND2	Ground
21	RESET	8284 pin #10 (RESET)
22	READY	8284 pin #5 (READY)
23	TEST	Ground
31	HOLD	Ground
33	MN/MX	5 Volts
40	Vcc	5 Volts

Table 7-1. Connections Made to the 8088 (IC2).

power supply we built is protected against this sort of thing but there's no profit in tempting fate.

CHECKING IT OUT

Now that we know everything is okay, apply 5 volts to the board and use your multimeter to measure the current being drawn by the breadboard. The exact number you get will depend on the particular 8088 you have, the layout of the board, and several other factors but you should see a draw of about 250 to 300 milliamps. Any reading out of this range is an indication that you've got a problem on the board and you'll have to correct it before going any further. Check all of the passive components—make sure they're the correct value, see if you've got them in backwards, etc., etc. The color coding for a 10k resistor looks exactly the same as a 300 ohm resistor if you read it backwards. There are at least 5 different ways to mark the value of a capacitor.

Take a logic probe, (or voltmeter), and snoop around a bit on the 8088's address and data pins. Not much will be going on since the 8088 isn't being told to do anything. The exact state of these pins will be indeterminate (they could be high, low, or tristated), and it's impossible to say what you'll find on your board.

You can, however, make something happen by using the reset button on the 8284. Every time you press it you'll see the 8088's RESET line go high. There's nothing very wonderful about this since the pin is hardwired to the 8284 but, if your logic probe has a pulse catcher, you'll detect a pulse on any one of the address lines as soon as you release the button. The ALE output, (pin #25), will show you two pulses—one when the button is pressed and another one when it's released.

The reason for this minimal activity is that the 8088 is looking for its first instruction at the power-up location of FFFF0h and, since we don't have anything anywhere, the 8088 isn't going to find anything there. Remember also that we haven't even demultiplexed the address and data busses so there's no telling what the busses are seeing at power up.

When the 8088 reset line goes high, the busses are tristated and, since there's an even money chance they were like that before RESET went high, you're not going to see any change. Releasing the reset button, however, is a different story. As soon as reset is inactive, the 8088 once again looks at FFFF0h for an instruction. That means this address will be put on the bus and that's exactly what you can detect when you release the reset button.

ALE, and several of the other control lines, are driven either low or high for at least one clock after RESET becomes active. This is indicated in Fig. 7-4 which shows you what happens when you use the reset button. Take the time to check them out before building the rest of the circuit. If you've seen pulses on the address and data bus you can be sure that everything's working okay but comparing the control line activity to

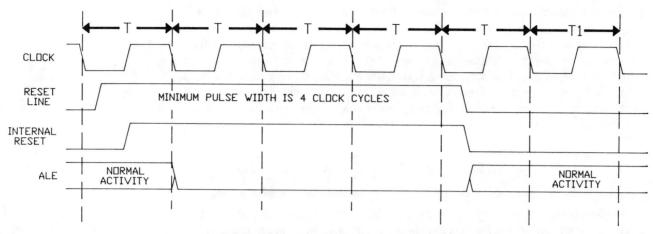

Fig. 7-4. 8088 activity when reset is triggered.

the timing diagram of Fig. 7-4 is a good thing to do since it's always comforting to verify reality against theory. Remember the thirty first Law of Life and Design:

YOU CAN NEVER BE TOO SURE

so do as much checking as possible at this stage of the game. It can't hurt anything and—who knows—it might help.

DEMULTIPLEXING THE BUS

There are several design approaches to handling the time multiplexing of the 8088's address and data lines. Small system designs can use bus devices that have their own internal latches. By triggering them with ALE, the address can be snatched from the 8088 at the time the full address appears on the bus. The data lines can be handled much the same way but this is less of a problem since data only appears on the bus toward the end of the machine cycle.

The problem with putting together a system like this is that bus timing becomes really critical and you have to be sure to use devices that can meet it. Granted the parts count will be reduced, but the amount of brain damage the design can cause just ain't worth it. Not only that, but trying to troubleshoot a system like this can be a one way ticket to the funny farm. Putting together a prototype system and making it work reliably is one of the hardest electronic design jobs imaginable and the only ones who go out of their way to make the job as difficult as possible are the legendary fish-faced people of Neptune and, as we all know, this is precisely the reason that their civilization collapsed.

Demultiplexing the busses is a much more intelligent way of going about the design—and that's exactly what we're going to do now. By adding a handful of silicon to the system, we can avoid the insanity that drove the Neptunians back to the caves.

PARTS
2 - 74LS373 Octal D Type Latches
1 - 74LS245 Octal Bus Transceiver
3 - .1 μF capacitors

MINIMUM EQUIPMENT
Multimeter
Logic Probe

The 8088 can directly control the 373s with ALE since ALE is active high and so is the Latch Enable control, (pin #1), of the 373s. If we tie these lines together, the 373s will latch the address when the 8088 indicates that the address bus has a valid address. The only other control on the 373 is Output Enable (pin #1). This is an active low signal that tristates the output pins. This can come in very handy when you have a bunch of devices sitting on the bus since a bit of control logic will make sure that only one set of 373's is active on the bus at any one time. Not taking care of this properly leads to the dreaded condition known as "bus contention" and, as the thirteenth Law of Life and Design clearly states:

BUS CONTENTION IS A REALLY BAD THING

For the time being, however, we're not going to have anything else on the address bus so we can tie the Output Enable lines low. In any event, since we want to make things as easy as possible for ourselves in developing the prototype, it's a very good idea to let the current address be available for as long as possible.

The 74LS245 is officially referred to as an octal transceiver but it's more accurate to think of it as an octal fuse. It isolates the 8088's data bus from the rest of the circuit and, like the 373, has outputs that can be tristated. The inputs and outputs of the 245 are set by the DIRection control (pin #1). If this line is high, the 245 will pass data from the "A" pins to the "B" pins and if the line is low, the direction will be reversed.

Once again, this is perfect for the 8088 since DT/$\overline{R}$ (pin #27) will always let the system know if the 8088 wants to transmit or read data on the bus. By connecting the 245's "A" inputs to the 8088 and using DT/$\overline{R}$ to control DIR, the 245's buffers will always be pointing in the right direction. The Output Enable control on the 245 is exactly the same as the one on the 373 but, rather than disabling it, we might as well use it since the 8088 can handle it directly with $\overline{DEN}$.

When the 8088's $\overline{DEN}$ line is active, it's an indication that the multiplexed address and data lines (pin #9 to pin #16) are being used for data. Using this signal to control the 245 outputs means that the 245 outputs will only be enabled when the 8088 expects to receive or transmit data. This is useful for our purposes and, remember, we get it for free. In a more complex system, the 245's outputs would have to be controlled differently since other devices will want to have access to the bus.

BUILDING THE CIRCUIT

Be as cautious here as always when you add these chips to the circuit we've built so far. Disconnect the power to the board, (a two step process, right?), and plug the ICs into the board as shown in the placement diagram of Fig. 7-5. The 373s we're adding now are IC3 and IC4—the 245 is IC5. Once the chips are on the board, make the connections shown in Tables 7-2, 7-3, and 7-4. After you've made all these connections add the three capacitors to the board. Each capacitor has one leg right next to the Vcc pin of the IC and the other leg connected to ground. These capacitors are used to soak up the spikes generated by the TTL chips whenever they change state.

In general, the rule of thumb is to use one .1 μF capacitor for every three TTL chips. As you can see, we're using one for each chip on the board. This is because we're laying out the breadboard with worst case operation in mind. Solderless breadboards are extremely convenient for prototyping, and they make switching things around so easy. It's worth putting up with the unavoidable noise and other garbage. That's the price you pay for the convenience.

Keeping this in mind, it's a good idea to do whatever is possible to minimize the stray capacitance and inductance that are the down side of this breadboarding method.

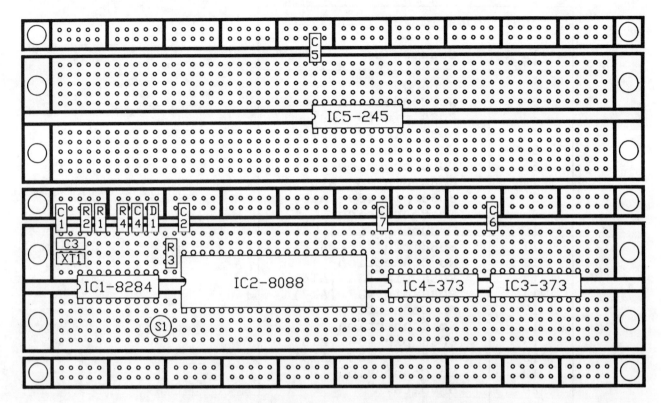

ALL BUS STRIPS ARE TIED IN PARALLEL
AND CARRY ONLY POWER AND GROUND

Fig. 7-5. Placement diagram for the bus demultiplexing and buffering circuit.

Table 7-2. Connections Made to
the 74LS373 (IC3).

CONNECTIONS TO IC3 (74LS373)	
Pin #	Connect to
1	Ground
2	No Connection
3	8088 pin #16 (AD0)
4	8088 pin #15 (AD1)
5	No Connection
6	No Connection
7	8088 pin #14 (AD2)
8	8088 pin #13 (AD3)
9	No Connection
10	Ground
11	8088 pin #25 (ALE)
12	No Connection
13	8088 pin #12 (AD4)
14	8088 pin #11 (AD5)
15	No Connection
16	No Connection
17	8088 pin #10 (AD6)
18	8088 pin #9 (AD7)
19	No Connection
20	5 Volts

CONNECTIONS TO IC4 (74LS373)	
Pin #	Connect to
1	Ground
2	No Connection
3	8088 pin #8 (A8)
4	8088 pin #7 (A9)
5	No Connection
6	No Connection
7	8088 pin #6 (A10)
8	8088 pin #39 (A15)
9	No Connection
10	Ground
11	8088 pin #25 (ALE)
12	No Connection
13	8088 pin #38 (A16)
14	8088 pin #37 (A17)
15	No Connection
16	No Connection
17	8088 pin #36 (A18)
18	8088 pin #35 (A19)
19	No Connection
20	5 Volts

Table 7-3. Connections Made to the 74LS373 (IC4).

CONNECTIONS TO IC5 (74LS245)	
Pin #	Connect to
1	8088 pin #27 (DT/R)
2	8088 pin #16 (AD0)
3	8088 pin #15 (AD1)
4	8088 pin #14 (AD2)
5	8088 pin #13 (AD3)
6	8088 pin #12 (AD4)
7	8088 pin #11 (AD5)
8	8088 pin #10 (AD6)
9	8088 pin #9 (AD7)
10	Ground
11	8088 pin #26 (DEN)
12	No Connection
13	No Connection
14	No Connection
15	No Connection
16	No Connection
17	No Connection
18	No Connection
19	No Connection
20	5 Volts

Table 7-4. Connections Made to the 74LS245 (IC5).

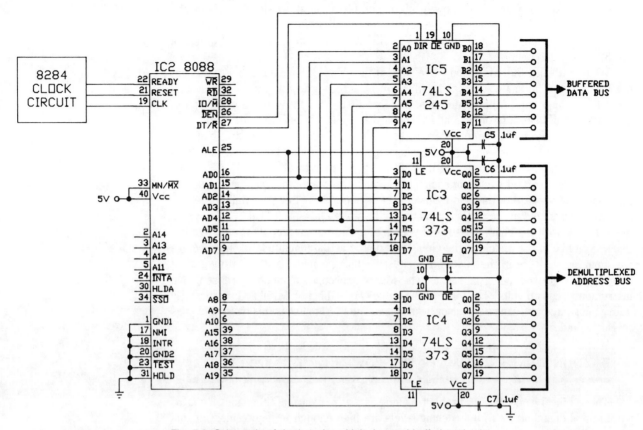

Fig. 7-6. Schematic of the bus demultiplexing and buffering circuit.

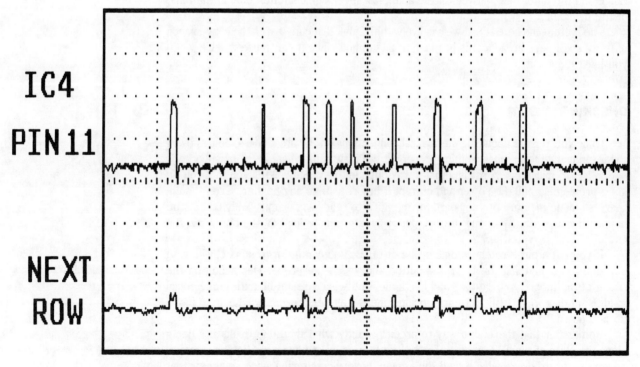

Fig. 7-7. Actual waveforms showing parasitic oscillation found in the row next to IC3 pin #11.

If you have a scope, you can see how much this problem can affect signal levels on the board. Power-up the circuit and put the scope probe in an unused row right next to one of the rows that has a clock of some kind on it. The row next to pin #11 of either of the 373s is a good choice.

What you'll see there is an inductive copy of the clock. It will be much weaker, but it will be there. This same sort of thing will show up across power as well. If you ground the scope at one end of the ground bus, and look at the V+ bus on the other end of the board, you'll see lots of hash and garbage that's roughly ghosting the sum of the main 14 MHz clock and every other frequency being generated on the board. Not only that, but another immense source of noise is generously contributed by the friendly folks at your local electric company—and they give it to you for free!

The 60 cycle world we live in squirrels it's inductive way into everything. You can get an idea of the size of the field by using a sensitive meter. Set your multimeter for ac volts and grab the probe that's connected to the Volts-Ohms jack. The reading you'll get will vary with the characteristics of your meter and the area in which you live but unless you live in the middle of the Gobi Desert, the actual magnitude of the readings will amaze you. I live in the middle of a city and, using a meter with a 10 meg input impedance I get a reading of half a volt. My oscilloscope, a much more sensitive instrument, reads 8 volts! The force of the inductive field is not trivial and, particularly with analog circuitry, can cause major headaches. The bottom line is this (with apologies to Darth Vader)

DON'T UNDERESTIMATE THE POWER OF THE FORCE

These things won't cause a problem as long as you're aware of them and all you're wiring up is digital stuff. TTL switching levels are high enough to ignore most of this noise and CMOS does an even better job. Analog circuitry, however, can really be thrown for a loop by this kind of stuff. Remember that analog circuit elements such as amplifiers and filters are often designed to respond to signals with levels anywhere in the supply range and the difference between noise and a low level signal is often only in the mind of the designer.

The bottom line here is that we can live with the junk that comes with the convenience of using solderless breadboards but keep it all in mind since it can cause trouble when you least expect it.

CHECKING IT OUT

Once you're sure about the mechanical connections on the breadboard, apply power to the circuit. If the circuit is working properly it will draw somewhere in the neighborhood of 325 to 375 milliamps. A reading that's way outside this range will tell you that you've got a problem so pull the power and correct it before you go any further. Even though there's still no memory on the board for the 8088 to read, you can probably make stuff happen because the 373s and the 245 put an indeterminate load on the bus when the circuit is first powered up.

If you put a pulse catching logic probe on ALE, you can get it to start clocking. If you don't see anything, hit the reset button and watch the probe. Depending on the phase of the moon, your latitude and longitude, and what you got in sixth grade social studies, after a while ALE will start clocking and the system busses will begin to move up and down.

Remember that there's no way to predict exactly what the 8088 thinks it's doing since the state of the TTL stuff is pretty close to random at power-up. Seeing it move, however, regardless of what it thinks it's doing, is very comforting since you know that everything is working. If you look at ALE on a scope, you'll see waveforms very similar

Now that we've got the bus demultiplexed, we've taken care of the nuts and bolts of the circuit. You've seen that the 8088 is actually doing stuff—lines are moving up and down—but the problem is that only the 8088 knows what it's doing. Letting the 8088 to those shown in Fig. 7-8. These are the actual waveforms captured by snooping around the circuit we just put together. In the interests of keeping the record straight, it took me an average of ten hits on the reset button before ALE started clocking.

If you've only got a multimeter, you can still get a good idea of what's happening in the circuit by measuring the dc voltage at ALE. You can see from Fig. 7-8 that ALE goes high every fourth clock and stays high for about half a clock cycle. This means ALE has roughly a 12% duty cycle and the dc voltage is going to be roughly 12% of the supply voltage. My system voltage is 5.1 volts and the dc voltage I read on ALE was .64 volts. That's pretty close and you should find much the same to be true on your breadboard.

Once you've got everything squared away and operating properly, it's interesting to compare the real life waveforms in Fig. 7-8 with the theoretical ALE timing shown in Fig. 7-9. The timing matches up but Fig. 7-8 clearly shows the noise, hash, and other miscellaneous garbage that's running around the breadboard beneath the signal levels.

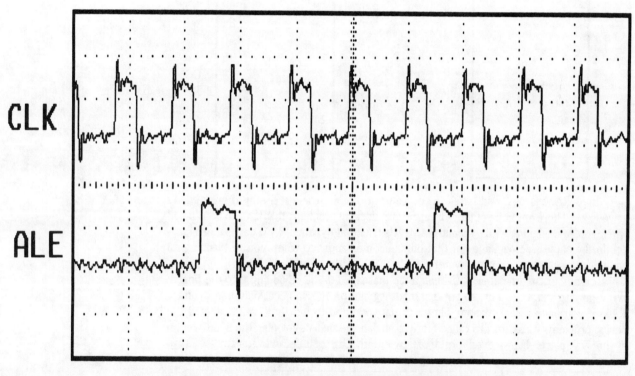

Fig. 7-8. Actual waveforms produced on ALE (8088 pin #25) and CLK (8088 pin #19).

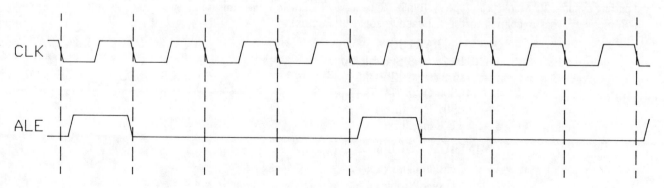

Fig. 7-9. Theoretical waveforms produced on ALE (8088 pin #25) and CLK (8088 pin #2).

do whatever it wants may be a terrific thing for people who are into microprocessor liberation, but I'm an old fashioned kind of a guy who likes to stay in control of things.

ADDING MEMORY

No matter what kind of microprocessor circuitry you're developing, this is one circuit element you can't forget (sorry about that). A microprocessor simply won't do anything without someplace to store programs and data. Most small systems like ours don't have or need the megabytes of memory it takes to operate as a "computer". That isn't to say that we don't have the capability of doing it should the need arise—we'll get into that later. For the moment, however, all we'll put on our system is 4K of memory—2K of ROM storage using an EPROM and 2K of RAM using a 6116 static RAM.

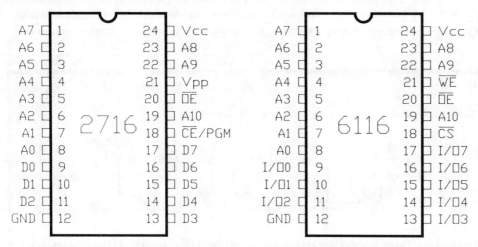

Fig. 7-10. Pinouts of the 2716 and 6116.

Static RAM is nice and hassle free. You put data in it and it'll stay there as long as you like. There are none of the refreshing and clocking problems that have to be handled when you're designing with dynamic RAM. It's true that dynamic RAM packs more storage in the same size package but that only becomes an issue when you're planning on having lots of memory in the system.

Remember that dynamic RAM has to be massaged if you're adding it to the board. We'll go into this later but, to put a temporary cap on the subject, only use dynamic RAM if you have a real reason. The circuitry you need to handle it is a bear and the design problems it creates can cause more brain damage than developing the 8088 system in the first place. Don't ever forget the twentieth Law of Life and Design:

GO OUT OF YOUR WAY TO AVOID HASSLES

and putting dynamic RAM in a prototype system is the best way I know to violate this rule.

Remember what happened to the fish-faced people of Neptune.

PARTS
1 - 6116 2k × 8 Static RAM
1 - 2716 2k × 8 EPROM
1 - 74LS00 Quad NAND Gate
1 - 74LS04 Hex Inverter
4 - .1 µF Capacitors

MINIMUM EQUIPMENT
Multimeter
Logic Probe

Everything that we've added to our circuit so far has been relatively straightforward. We plugged the right chips on the board, made the right connections, and that, as someone once said, was that. The CPU was able to directly control everything using the control signals it generates internally. Adding memory to the system, however, is a bit more involved.

The 8088 has no idea what kind of memory is living in its address map. We can put RAM, ROM, or even I/O devices anywhere we want on the bus but we need some method of generating the different kinds of control signals needed by each different type of memory. If we want to read from RAM, for example, we have to enable the RAM and disable any other device that's on the bus before we issue the read command. A different set of signals are necessary if we want to write to RAM and other considerations show up if we want to talk to an I/O port. These signals have to originate in the 8088 but, as you know by now, the number of control lines on the 8088 is rather limited.

Putting memory in the system, therefore, really means that we have to design two different additions to the circuitry we've put together so far. Besides connecting the various memory devices to the system bus, we also have to design the control circuitry that will select and enable the memory or I/O we want the 8088 to address.

If you've ever looked through the schematics for a microprocessor-based circuit, you've probably noticed that in addition to all the microprocessor support chips, lots of gates and other simple logic was scattered around the circuit. Chances are you were looking at the control logic—making head or tail out of it, however, is a lot more difficult than just recognizing it. A microprocessor circuit of medium complexity can use hundreds of simple gates to generate all of the signals needed to have things operate properly. Since having a lot of gates in the system can cause lots of design problems, there's a trend these days to use small PROM's, PAL's, or if you've got the bucks, ASIC's to cut the amount of logical glue the system needs.

Our system, fortunately, isn't that complex . . . yet. The lines we have to generate to control the devices we'll be hanging on the bus, can be created with a handful of gates—it also makes the whole process much more understandable as well. Just keep in mind that the difference between what we have to do and what has to be done, in a much larger system, is only one of degree, not kind. Both the approach to the problem and the considerations for the design are exactly the same—for everything from a microprocessor-based electric toothbrush to the space shuttle.

Before we even begin to design the control circuitry we have to lay out the memory map for our system. This means deciding where the various memory devices are going to live in the 8088's total address space of 00000h to FFFFFh. Since we're only using 4K of memory split evenly between ROM and RAM, it makes sense to use the memory map in Fig. 7-11. The reason the memory is split like this has to do with the characteristics of the 8088.

There are lots of ways to classify microprocessors—standard ones include maximum operating speed, bit size, addressing range—but one not so obvious method is determined by what the microprocessor does at power-up. Remember the thirtieth Law of Life and Design:

EVERYTHING HAS TO START SOMEWHERE

and that's true of microprocessors as well.

When you first power-up a microprocessor, it has to look somewhere for it's first instruction. Some CPU's, such as the 8080 and Z-80, expect their first instruction to be waiting for them at 0000h when they get turned on or reset. Other microprocessors,

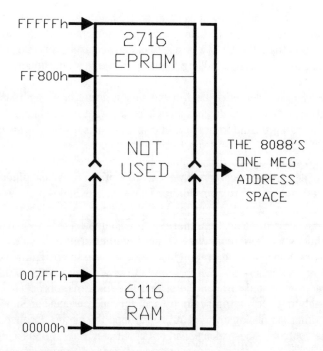

Fig. 7-11. The initial memory map for the circuit.

like the 6502 and 8088, wake up and look at what is referred to as the "power-up location". This is an address, hardwired into the CPU, that the microprocessor will put on the bus when it's first powered up. The difference in the power-up routines for "bottom up" CPU's like the Z-80 and "top down" CPU's like the 8088 determines the configuration of the memory map.

Since the 8088 will automatically execute the instruction it finds at absolute address FFFF0h, it's convenient to put all the permanent memory at the top of the CPU's address range. Most designers put an absolute jump instruction there that points to another address lower down in memory. Remember that, in the normal course of things, the 8088 executes sequential instructions in memory and there are only sixteen locations from the power-up location of FFFF0h to the end of the 8088's addressing range at FFFFFh.

By putting the ROM at the top of memory we can permanently store an instruction at the power-up location and, since the ROM we'll be using is 2K (07FFh) in size, the 8088 will be able to address it at any location from FF800h (FFFFFh minus 07FFh) to FFFFFh. The RAM in our system is the same size but, since we'll be mapping it in at the bottom of the 8088's memory range, it will be addressable anywhere from 00000h to 007FFh.

Locating these two memory devices in the system memory map isn't a simple matter of connecting up the address and data lines. Both the ROM and RAM have to be looking at the 8088's lower 11 address lines since they're the ones that will cover the 2K memory range (2 to the eleventh is 2048). If you study Fig. 7-12 you'll see that the only

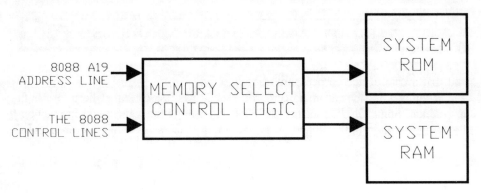

Fig. 7-12. Differences in RAM and ROM addressing.

difference there is in addressing the RAM and the ROM shows up on the 8088's upper address lines (A11 to A19). Since both memories only have 11 address pins and they're connected to the same 8088 address pins, any memory access in our system will address both the RAM and the ROM and the two of them will start putting data on the bus at the same time. Definitely something to avoid.

The way to avoid that is to build the kind of control circuitry we were talking about before. We need logic that will watch all of the 8088's control lines and be smart enough to know when we want to talk to each kind of memory, (or I/O for that matter), and do the enabling and selecting for us—automatically.

The best way to design this sort of stuff is to treat each one of the control lines separately so let's start with the RAM.

The 6116 has two control pins and one write enable pin. The $\overline{\text{Chip Select}}$ line (pin #18) enables the entire chip. When it's active, the chip goes to sleep, (the low power standby mode), and the outputs are floated. The $\overline{\text{Output Enable}}$ line (pin #20) controls the data you'll see on the output pins. This pin is necessary because the 6116 uses the same pins for data in and data out. The reasons for this are the same as the ones we discussed when we were looking at the address and data lines of the 8088—there's just not enough pin space on a 24-pin package to provide separate input and output lines. When OE is low the data lines will be output pins and when it's high, the lines will be input pins. The Write Enable line (pin #21) is the strobe for the chip's internal latches. When the chip is selected and this line is brought momentarily low, the 6116 will store the data that's presented at the currently addressed location. When this pin is high the output pins will carry the data currently stored at the addressed location.

This is as good a time as any to remind everyone of the fourth Law of Life and Design—namely;

THERE'S NO SUBSTITUTE FOR A DATA SHEET

because there's more to learn about this chip than the information we just went through in the last paragraph. Data sheets may frequently be difficult to read, and I'm the first one to admit that they have a lot of information you'll never need, but it's also true that they do have all the information you'll ever want. Working without one is an absolute guarantee of brain damage.

We can tie the $\overline{\text{Chip Select}}$ pin to the $\overline{\text{Output Enable}}$ pin because we don't have a need to separately control the data pins. We can use both of them to remove the chip from the bus when we don't want it there. When we do select the chip, the data it puts on the bus will be controlled by the write enable pin. As long as we keep it high, we'll be getting the stored data and if we pulse it low we'll write new data.

Designing all the control logic is a matter of seeing what signals you're given and figuring out how to combine them to get the signals you want. When we analyze what we want to do with our RAM, it turns out that we need three signals—enable, read, and write.

The first consideration is to find some way to make sure that the RAM is only enabled when the 8088 wants to talk to it. If you take a look at Fig. 7-12, you'll see that we can use any one of the address lines from A11 to A19. Considering the way we've mapped our memory, these lines will be low when we're talking to the RAM and high when we're talking to the ROM. By picking A19, the most significant line, we can do a bit of planning ahead. This line is low when we talk to the bottom 512K of the 8088's address space and high when we talk to the upper half. That means we'll be able to add 512K of RAM and 512K of ROM without changing any of the circuitry. This is a good thing . . . believe me.

Now that we have a way of identifying RAM access, we have to go a step further because there are two different types of devices living in the address space occupied by RAM—RAM and I/O. Since we'll be doing reads and writes to both these devices, our control circuit has to be sure that only one of them are selected at a time. This isn't difficult because, as we saw earlier, the 8088 uses it's IO/M̄ line to tell the system what kind of operation it's performing.

All the players in the RAM control logic have been identified so we can work out how to stick them together with logical glue to make the control signals we're looking for.

The only time we want the RAM selected is when both the 8088's A19 and IO/M̄ lines are high and that's exactly what the circuit shown in Fig. 7-13 does for us. The RAMSEL line will turn on the system RAM whenever the 8088 wants to talk to it. The same sort of analysis is used to generate RAMR̄W̄, the control line that tells the RAM whether we want to do a read or write.

Creating control signals for the ROM is a similar process. As a matter of fact, if you analyze the generation of ROMSEL as shown in Fig. 7-13, you'll see that there's only a one inverter difference between it and RAMSEL. The ROMRD line is produced by gluing the IO/M̄ and RD lines from the 8088. When we want to do a read from ROM, ROMSEL will enable the appropriate memory and ROMRD will enable it's outputs. One side advantage of treating the EPROM like this, by the way, is that the chip draws about 25% of normal operating current when it's in standby (not enabled). The down side is that it takes a bit longer to access since the memory has to be enabled before it can be read. No free lunch—remember?

TRUTH TABLE FOR THE MEMORY CONTROL LOGIC									
INPUTS				OUTPUTS					
IO/M̄	A19	W̄R̄	R̄D̄	RAMSEL	RAMR̄W̄	ROMSEL	ROMR̄D̄	IOSEL	COMMENTS
LOW	LOW	HIGH	LOW	LOW	HIGH	HIGH	LOW	LOW	READ RAM
LOW	LOW	LOW	HIGH	LOW	LOW	HIGH	HIGH	LOW	WRITE RAM
LOW	HIGH	HIGH	LOW	HIGH	HIGH	LOW	LOW	LOW	READ ROM
LOW	HIGH	LOW	HIGH	HIGH	LOW	LOW	HIGH	LOW	NO OPERATION
HIGH	X	X	X	HIGH	HIGH	HIGH	HIGH	HIGH	I/O OPERATION

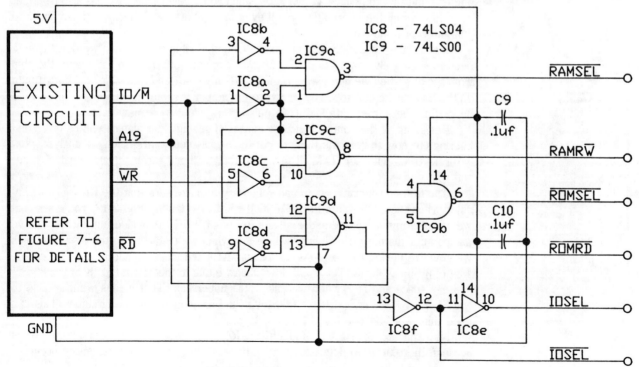

Fig. 7-13. Schematic of the memory control logic.

BUILDING THE CIRCUIT

Lay all the parts out as they're shown in Fig. 7-14. Even though we haven't programmed the EPROM yet, keep it on the breadboard while you wire things up since it's convenient to know exactly where the pins are. You'll notice, in Fig. 7-15, that the pin assignments of the 2716 and 6116 are almost exactly the same. This isn't a coincidence since they were designed to be pin compatible. The idea behind it is that you use a prototype system like ours to work out the code and then burn it in an EPROM. But that's still a ways down the road.

When you have the parts placed on the board, make the connections shown in Table 7-5 through Table 7-8—and don't forget to do our famous two step removal of power before you start.

Once you've made the connections and checked them to make sure that they're correct, add the .1 μF capacitors.

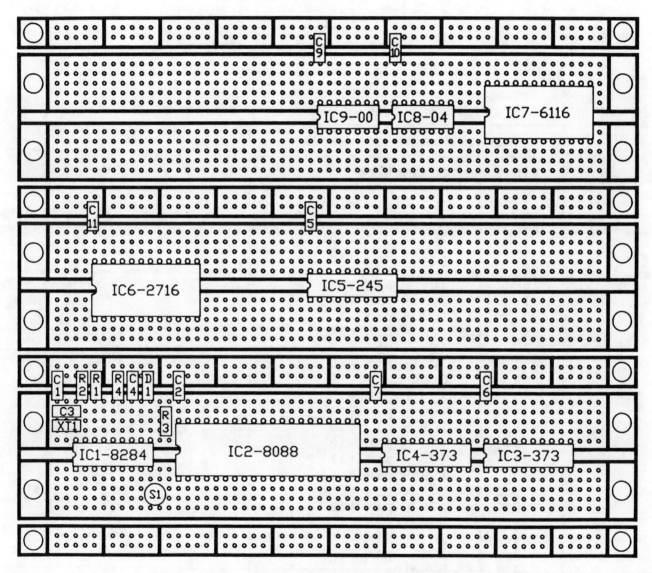

ALL BUS STRIPS ARE TIED IN PARALLEL

Fig. 7-14. Placement diagram for the memory control logic.

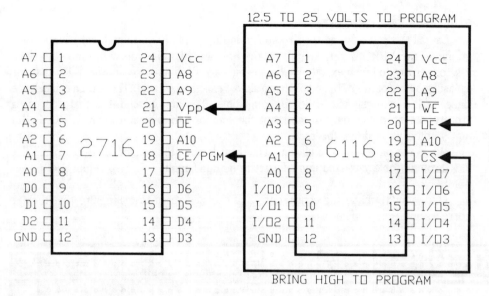

Fig. 7-15. Pinout similarity of the 2716 and 6116.

CONNECTIONS TO IC6 (2716)	
Pin #	Connect to
1	IC3 - pin #19
2	IC3 - pin #16
3	IC3 - pin #15
4	IC3 - pin #12
5	IC3 - pin #9
6	IC3 - pin #6
7	IC3 - pin #5
8	IC3 - pin #2
9	IC5 - pin #18
10	IC5 - pin #17
11	IC5 - pin #16
12	Ground
13	IC5 - pin #15
14	IC5 - pin $14
15	IC5 - pin #13
16	IC5 - pin #12
17	IC5 - pin #11
18	IC9 - pin #6
19	IC4 - pin #6
20	IC5 - pin #12
21	5 Volts
22	IC4 - pin #5
23	IC4 - pin #2
24	5 Volts

Table 7-5. Connections Made to the 2716 (IC6).

Table 7-6. Connections Made to
the 6116 (IC7).

CONNECTIONS TO IC7 (6116)	
Pin #	Connect to
1	IC3 - pin #19
2	IC3 - pin #16
3	IC3 - pin #15
4	IC3 - pin #12
5	IC3 - pin #9
6	IC3 - pin #6
7	IC3 - pin #5
8	IC3 - pin #2
9	IC5 - pin #18
10	IC5 - pin #17
11	IC5 - pin #16
12	Ground
13	IC5 - pin #15
14	IC5 - pin $14
15	IC5 - pin #13
16	IC5 - pin #12
17	IC5 - pin #11
18	IC9 - pin #3
19	IC4 - pin #6
20	IC9 - pin #3
21	IC9 - pin #8
22	IC4 - pin #5
23	IC4 - pin #2
24	5 Volts

Table 7-7. Connections Made to
the 74LS04 (IC8).

CONNECTIONS TO IC8 (74LS04)	
Pin #	Connect to
1	8088 pin #28 (IO/M)
2	IC9 - pin #1
3	IC4 - pin #19
4	IC9 - pin #2
5	8088 pin #29 (WR)
6	IC9 - pin #10
7	Ground
8	IC9 - pin #13
9	8088 pin #32 (RD)
10	No Connection
11	IC8 - pin #12
12	IC8 - pin #11
13	8088 pin #28 (IO/M)
14	5 Volts

CONNECTIONS TO IC9 (74LS00)	
Pin #	Connect to
1	IC8 - pin #2
2	IC8 - pin #4
3	IC7 - pin #18
4	IC8 - pin #2
5	IC4 - pin #19
6	IC6 - pin #18
7	Ground
8	IC7 - pin #21
9	IC8 - pin #2
10	IC8 - pin #6
11	IC6 - pin #20
12	IC8 - pin #2
13	IC8 - pin #8
14	5 Volts

Table 7-8. Connections Made to the 74LS00 (IC9).

We've finally reached the point where there's no way you can do any sort of meaningful circuit testing by simply turning on the power and probing various points on the board. You can still see various lines moving up and down but that's no indication that everything is okay. The last additions we made to the circuit have made the signal timing as important as the signals themselves and it's impossible to check this without knowing exactly what's supposed to be happening on the board. Fortunately for all of us, we've also finally reached the point where the 8088 can be used to help us check out the board. All we need is a small program that will give us a visual indication if everything is working properly. Unfortunately, that presents a slight problem.

Now, adding a visual indicator is no problem since it only means a bit of primitive I/O. By this time we can design that sort of thing with our eyes closed. All we need is a simple latch to grab data off the bus when the 8088 sends it out a port—we've even got the latch control circuitry already waiting for us on the board. What presents us with the problem is getting a program into the system.

We've designed our system with the idea of using EPROMs as storage for the software. Before we start writing software for the circuit, however, it's nice to know that the hardware is working. You don't know the meaning of the word ''frustration'' until you've tried running homemade software on homemade hardware. Naturally enough the whole thing doesn't work and it's murder to pinpoint the problem since you can't be sure which part is messed up—hardware or software. That's why we're putting together our system step by step.

The last thing we're going to do before we start talking about the software we can run on this initial 8088 circuit is add enough to the board to check out everything we've done so far. That means adding a latch for I/O and software to activate it.

ADDING SOME I/O

There are lots of differences in the design considerations between a small board system like ours and a large computer system that's built around the 8088. If you were forced to point to the most significant one, however, it would be a difference in the design philosophy, not the electronics. Small single board systems are usually dedicated to a particular job and larger systems are designed to do more general work. It's the difference between a controller and a computer.

We've seen that no matter what kind of system you plan on putting together, there are certain basic elements that appear on the board. So far we've talked about latches, memory, control circuits, and so on, but there's one major area left to discuss—I/O.

All systems have to communicate with external devices and, if the truth be known, this is usually more of a consideration for a small system like ours than it would be for a large commercial system. The reason is that while computer systems have to deal with a number of peripheral devices such as disk drives, keyboards, and other standard things you're already familiar with, small dedicated systems usually are designed to deal with dedicated and occasionally oddball I/O.

Our first step into the wonderful world of peripheral control is going to be a simple octal latch that can grab the data sent to it by using the 8088's OUT command—the doorway to I/O.

PARTS

1 - 74LS373 Octal D Type Latch
1 - .1 μF Capacitor
8 - LEDs (any size and color)
1 - 1k resistor

MINIMUM EQUIPMENT
Multimeter
Logic Probe

It's important to realize that what we're adding to the circuit now is the most minimal kind of I/O. As a matter of fact, calling it I/O at all is giving it more stature than it really deserves. All we're providing ourselves with here is a way of seeing if what we try to put on the bus with software really gets on the bus at all.

Adding the latch to the circuit means, more than anything else, that we have a way to use the 8088 to help us check out the circuit and find out, finally, whether everything is working properly. Of course we're going to need software to make it all happen, but let's take care of the latch first. Remember the twenty third Law of Life and Design:

TAKE IT SLOW

and nowhere is that more true than when designing prototypes.

BUILDING THE CIRCUIT

By this time, all of you have to be world class experts in adding new circuitry to the breadboard. So, following our now well established traditional procedures, put the 373 on the board as indicated in the placement diagram of Fig. 7-17, add the capacitor, the LEDs, and then make the following connections to the rest of the circuit as shown in Table 7-9. Make sure and connect the anodes of the LEDs to the Q outputs of the latch, the cathodes to a common bus, and the 1k resistor from the LED bus to ground.

You'll notice that the latch isn't being directly controlled by the 8088—there are two inverters on the IO/M line. The reason for this is the same as the one that makes a scope an essential piece of test equipment for microprocessor-based circuits—timing.

We've already seen that peripheral devices need special control lines that have to be derived from combinations of the signals that are generated by the 8088. And, as we've done so far, this is often a matter of using gates as logical glue. The price you pay for this is a timing delay since it takes a finite amount of time for each of the gates to decode input signals and change state.

Since the chip select lines of the memory we're using are being controlled by gate delayed signals, we have to do the same thing for the latch. The two inverters together

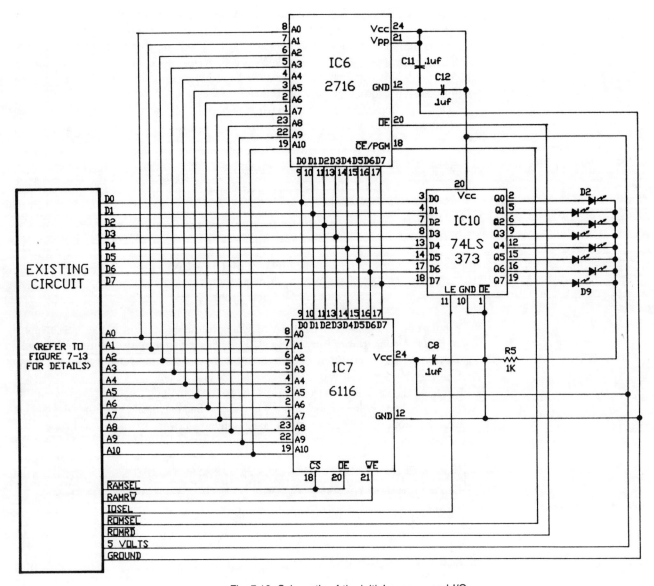

Fig. 7-16. Schematic of the initial memory and I/O.

produce a total delay of about 16 nanoseconds and that's enough to synchronize the latches with the rest of the circuit.

No matter what system you've worked out for circuit testing with a multimeter, it's just about impossible to determine that the circuit isn't working because of a 16 nanosecond timing error. If you want to get involved with circuits like these, you're going to have to do some serious thinking about a scope.

ADDING SOME FIRMWARE

Now that we've got all this stuff on the board, we have a circuit that's just about complete enough to actually start doing work—all we're missing is the software. To be absolutely correct, software stored in permanent memory is referred to as "firmware"— and that's the job we've assigned to the EPROM. If you're fortunate to have a way to program EPROMs, you can skip the rest of this section since all we'll be talking about here is building a circuit that we can use in place of the EPROM to hold a small program for the 8088.

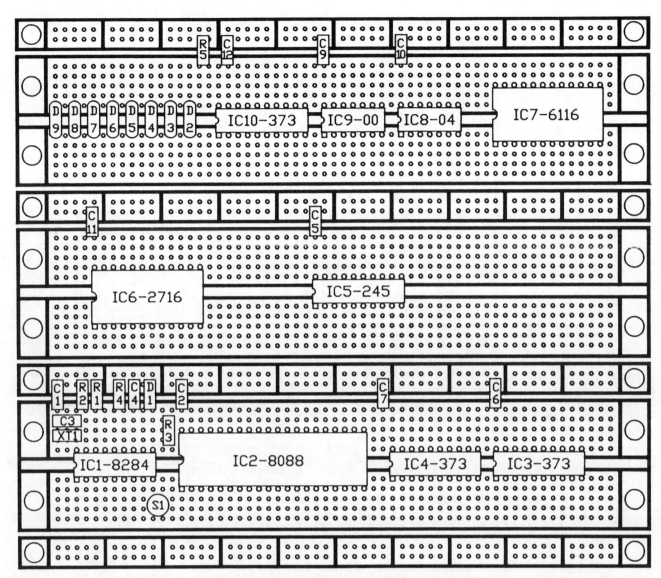

Fig. 7-17. Placement diagram for the initial memory and I/O.

The first program we're going to feed to our circuit is shown in Fig. 7-18. If you have access to an assembler, you can type in the program and assemble it but, if you don't, use the hex listing that accompanies the listing. That's what you'll get when you assemble the program. We'll be getting into a much more detailed discussion of producing software for the 8088 so don't worry if you can't follow everything that's going on in the listing.

PARTS

1 - 4051 CMOS 1 of 8 Analog Switch
1 - 74LS244 Octal Buffer/Line Driver
22 - 1N914 Switching Diodes
8 - 2.2k Resistors
2 - .1 μF Capacitors

MINIMUM EQUIPMENT

Multimeter
Logic Probe

CONNECTIONS TO IC10 (74LS373)	
Pin #	Connect to
1	Ground
2	LED
3	IC5 - pin #18 (D0)
4	IC5 - pin #17 (D1)
5	LED
6	LED
7	IC5 - pin #16 (D2)
8	IC5 - pin #15 (D3)
9	LED
10	Ground
11	IC8 - pin #10 (LE)
12	LED
13	IC5 - pin #14 (D4)
14	IC5 - pin #13 (D3)
15	LED
16	LED
17	IC5 - pin #12 (D1)
18	IC5 - pin #11 (D0)
19	LED
20	5 Volts

Table 7-9. Connections Made to the 74LS373 (IC10).

```
;              **************************************************
;              *                                                *
;              *  A TEST PROGRAM FOR THE 8088 BREADBOARD         *
;              *                                                *
;              **************************************************
;
;
;              TITLE    Light an LED on an I/O Port
;******************************************************************************
;*        Set variables, segments, equates, and location                     *
;******************************************************************************
BOB           SEGMENT                        ;Define the Code Segment.
              ASSUME  CS:BOB,DS:BOB,SS:BOB    ;Set all segment registers to
                                             ;the same location.
;
;******************************************************************************
;*                  The beginning of executable code                         *
;******************************************************************************
;The 8088 looks for its first instruction at FFFF0h when it's first powered up
;or reset.  Since the 2716 is enabled by any address that brings A7 high, the
;power up location is actually going to be location 07F0h in the EPROM.  This
;is because even though the 2716 adresses only cover 0000h to 07FFh, the chip
;will be enabled by any address from 80000h up.  This includes the 8088's power
;up location as well so we have to ORG the program at 07F0h.
;------------------------------------------------------------------------------
              ORG     7F0h                   ;The 2716 location for the 8088
                                             ;powerup instruction of FFFF0h
START:        MOV     AL,00000001b           ;This will light the zero light
                                             ;on the 373's output.
AGAIN:        OUT     10h,AL                 ;Since the 373 is enabled by
```

Fig. 7-18. MATRIX.ASM—A diagnostic program for the circuit.

```
                                                    ;IO/M directly, it will respond
                                                    ;to any port reference.
              JMP       AGAIN                        ;Go light the LED again
;
;*****************************************************************************
;*                      The end of the program                             *
;*****************************************************************************
;
BOB           ENDS                                  ;Tell assembler this is the end
                                                    ;of code for this segment.
              END       START                       ;Tell assembler this is the end
```

<u>Hex Dump of MATRIX.ASM</u>

```
0000 - 00 00 00 00 00 00 00 00 00 00 00 00 00 00 00 00
0010 - 00 00 00 00 00 00 00 00 00 00 00 00 00 00 00 00

0020 - 07CF are filled with zeros

07D0 - 00 00 00 00 00 00 00 00 00 00 00 00 00 00 00 00
07E0 - 00 00 00 00 00 00 00 00 00 00 00 00 00 00 00 00
07F0 - B0 01 E6 10 EB FC 00 00 00 00 00 00 00 00 00 00
```

Fig. 7-18. (continued)

Making a phony baloney ROM like this is really the kind of thing that should be avoided when you're doing any serious work with the circuit since it takes lots of work and lots of diodes. But if you don't have immediate access to an EPROM burner, there's no other way to get a program onto the board. This addition to our circuit is really a temporary measure to find out once and for all whether the circuit you've been putting together actually works.

BUILDING THE CIRCUIT

There's no sense making room for this on the breadboard because it's not going to be a permanent part of the circuit. As soon as we know for a fact that the 8088 circuit is working we're going to dump this part of it. The best approach to using this ROM replacement circuit is to build it on a separate piece of breadboard and then make the appropriate connections to the main circuit.

Don't forget to take the EPROM out of the circuit before you start hooking this circuit to the main board. Leave the connections you made for the EPROM on the board since they're handy points to make these temporary connections and, in any event, we'll be using EPROMs later on.

Once you've finished wiring these two ICs, add the two capacitors, and connect one end of all the resistors to ground.

You've got to be careful in adding the diodes. Make sure and put them on the board only where it's indicated in the schematic. If you make a mistake you'll be altering the program data for the 8088 and, take it from me, you'll have a hard time identifying the problem. Remember the rule . . . take it slow.

The easiest way to lay out the diodes is to connect each of the 4051 outputs to two rows on the breadboard. That will give you eight tie points for the anodes of the diodes. Assign two more breadboard rows for each of the 244 inputs and use the diodes to connect the two sets of rows together.

Once you've put the diodes on the board, take a minute and check your work once more against the table listing the correct connections since it only takes one mistake to render the whole circuit useless.

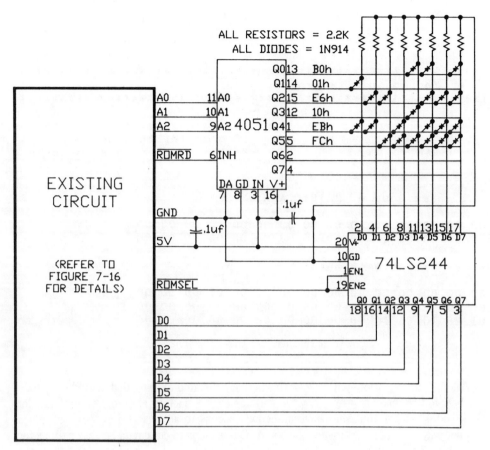

Fig. 7-19. Schematic of the 4051 diode ROM.

CONNECTIONS TO THE 4051	
Pin #	Connect to
1	See Figure #7-19
2	See Figure #7-19
3	5 Volts
4	See Figure #7-19
5	See Figure #7-19
6	IC9 - Pin #11 (ROMRD)
7	Ground
8	Ground
9	IC3 - pin #6 (A2)
10	IC3 - pin #5 (A1)
11	IC3 - pin #2 (A0)
12	See Figure #7-19
13	See Figure #7-19
14	See Figure #7-19
15	See Figure #7-19
16	5 Volts

Table 7-10. Connections Made to the 4051.

CONNECTIONS TO THE 74LS244	
Pin #	Connect to
1	IC9 - pin #6 (ROMSEL)
2	Rd0
3	IC5 - pin #11 (D7)
4	Rd1
5	IC5 - pin #12 (D6)
6	Rd2
7	IC5 - pin #13 (D5)
8	Rd3
9	IC5 - pin #14 (D4)
10	Ground
11	Rd4
12	IC5 - pin #15 (D3)
13	Rd5
14	IC5 - pin #16 (D2)
15	Rd6
16	IC5 - pin #17 (D1)
17	Rd7
18	IC5 - pin #18 (D0)
19	IC9 - pin #6 (ROMSEL)
20	5 Volts

Table 7-11. Connections Made to the 74LS244 Buffer.

4051 DIODE CONNECTIONS - ANODE TO 4051									
4051 PINS	4051 OUTPUT	D0	D1	D2	D3	D4	D5	D6	D7
13	0					X	X		X
14	1	X							
15	2		X	X			X	X	X
12	3					X			
1	4	X	X		X		X	X	X
5	5			X	X	X	X	X	X
2	6	<--------- NOT USED ---------->							
4	7	<--------- NOT USED ---------->							

Table 7-12. The Diode Connections for the 4051.

By tying the 4051's input pin high, the chip will sequentially put a high on each of the addressed outputs. Anyplace that we have a diode connecting the 4051 output to the data lines will put a high on the data line. As the 8088 steps through the 4051 address pins, it will put a high on each successive output and the diodes will cause a different combination of ones and zeros to be put on the data bus. As you've probably realized by now, each 4051 output is a byte of the program data that's listed in Fig. 7-18. Since the program is only six bytes long, we're only using the first six outputs of the 4051. You can see from the listing that the last instruction jumps back to the beginning of the program—the whole program is just an endless loop—not a terrific thing from the point of view of programming but a great thing for debugging the hardware.

We've already created the needed control signals since they're the same as the ones we'll be using for the EPROM later on. The 4051 INH input (pin #6) turns off all the 4051 outputs when it's high so we can connect it to the ROMRD line. When the 4051 outputs are off, all the inputs to the 244 will be low so we still need some way to disconnect these lines from the 8088 data bus. Fortunately, the 244 outputs can be tristated.

When ROMSEL is inactive, (which it will be unless we specifically address the ROM), the 244 will float its outputs. Selecting the ROM will enable the outputs and put our 4051 controlled data lines on the 8088 data bus.

THE ACID TEST

So now it's time to do the deed. Once you've finished breadboarding the diode based ROM and have it all connected to the main board, there's nothing left standing in the way. If everything has been done properly, you'll be able to see the 8088 doing some work. When power is applied to the circuit, the 8088 will light the ''0'' position LED—and that's all. Doesn't really seem like all that much, does it?

Don't be put off, however, since this is really only the beginning and the eightieth Law of Life and Design states:

A CIRCUIT OF A THOUSAND PARTS STARTS WITH A SINGLE LED

although it seems to me that this sounds strangely familiar.

You can snoop around the circuit while it's working but how much you'll be able to learn depends entirely on the test equipment you use. A scope, particularly a dual trace model, will let you examine the timing relationships between the various signals being generated on the board. If you have access to a scope like this put one probe on IC10 pin #11 and the other probe on the AD0 line (pin #16) of the 8088.

The 8088 line will be moving rapidly up and down since what you're looking at is a multiplexed address and data line. The IC10 line is low when the 8088 is talking to memory and high when it's talking to I/O. If you can get a stable trace, (and you should be able to if you set the scope to trigger on the IC10 line), you'll see that no matter

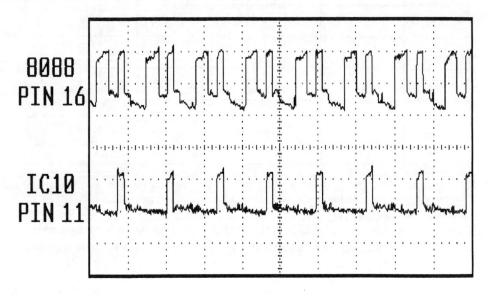

Fig. 7-20. Actual waveforms appearing on AD0 (8088 pin #16) and IOSEL (IC10 pin #11).

what the 8088 line is doing, it's always high when the IC10 line is high—that's because the program is lighting the LED during each I/O cycle. So there you have it.

One hundred years of electronic development, an uncountable number of man-years of research and dollars for development. All this, and more, so we could light an LED on a breadboard.

It's worth it . . . but we all know that there's a lot more work to do.

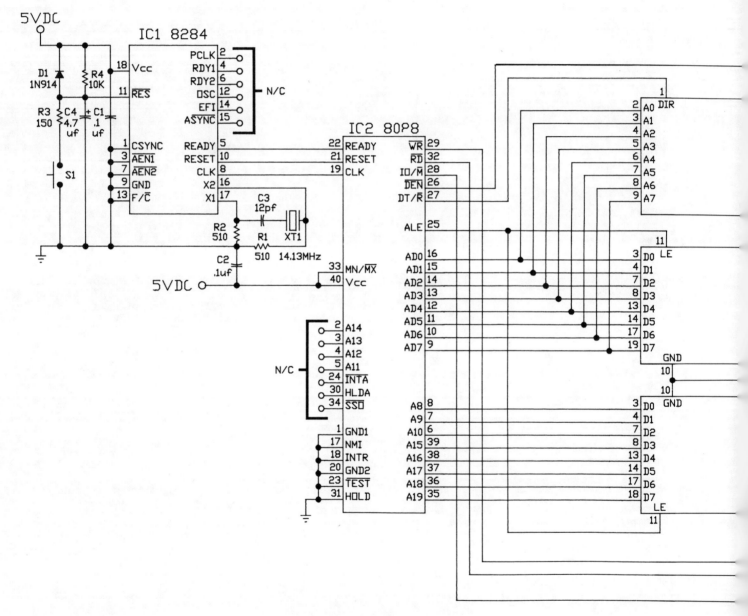

Fig. 7-21. Complete schematic of the basic circuit.

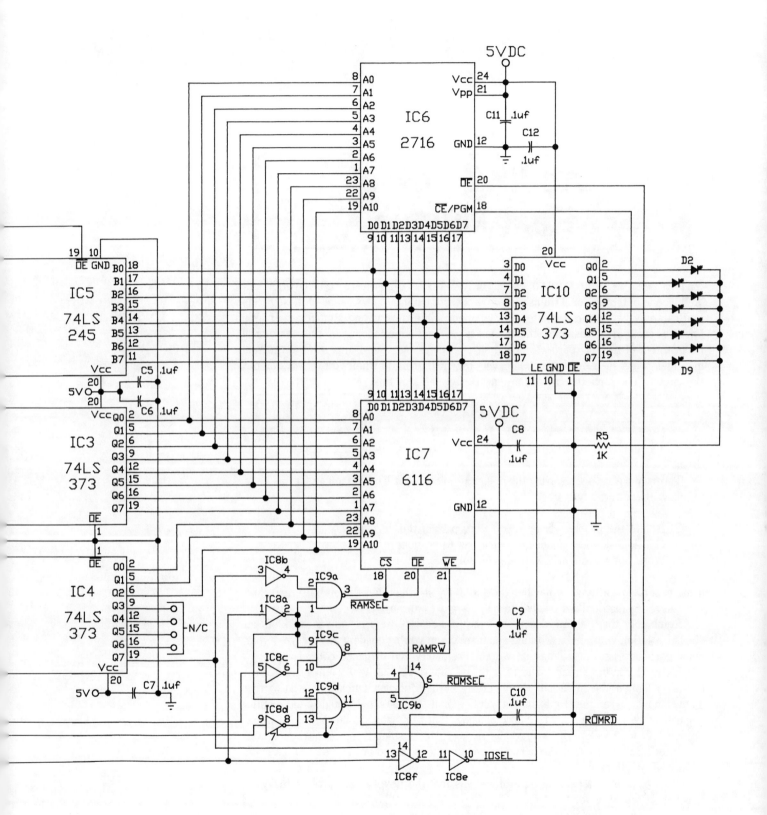

99

8

Adding Some
Real Muscle

N OW THAT WE'VE GOTTEN THIS FAR, THE TIME HAS COME FOR ME TO LET YOU ALL IN
on one of the essential truths of microprocessor circuitry. This is one of those things
that can only be appreciated after you've spent some time wiring stuff together. We
know by now that designing the circuit takes an understanding of the anatomical
peculiarities of the microprocessor and support chips but, more importantly, the real
ingredient for a successful design is having the right attitude when you're working out
the circuit. The fortieth Law of Life and Design hints at this:

BE LOGICAL

and we've been working with this point of view all the time we've been developing the
circuit.

The way we've been solving the design problems that have arisen so far has been
to follow these three steps:

1. Isolate the problem from every other part of the design.
2. Get a clear understanding of what has to be done.
3. Work out a straightforward design solution.

using paper, pencil, (you remember those don't you—they don't need batteries), and
any reference material we needed to help us get to an answer.

Remember that the first design isn't the final design. Before you can work out an
elegant solution you need a working solution. When you're building a prototype, your
initial goal is to get something that works. Profundity and elegance come later.

If any of you have read ''The Plague'' by Albert Camus, you might remember a
character named Joseph Grand, a civil servant in the Municipal Office who was writing
a novel in his spare time. He had been working on it for years and would spend months
anguishing over each word. The choice of using ''but'' or ''and'' in one sentence would
occupy him for weeks. He wanted the novel to be absolutely perfect when it was
submitted. So perfect that the publisher would read it, stand up, and say to his staff,
''Hats off, gentlemen.''

The result of this painstaking attitude was that the novel could never actually be
finished—it would never be, to use Grand's own word, ''flawless''.

This is exactly the same trap that a lot of circuit designers fall into. They're probably not familiar with the twenty first Law of Life and Design:

since "perfect" is really a point of view and not some kind of objective standard.

As we continue adding hardware and software to the circuit we're building, you will undoubtedly think of alternative ways of doing the same thing that seem more logical to you. As a matter of fact, I'd be surprised if you didn't since they occurred to me as well.

My goal in this book isn't to wow everyone with slick circuits and neat ways of designing the system. I'm not looking for anyone to say "Hats off, gentlemen". What I hope you all get from these exercises in design is a basic understanding of how to approach the subject of microprocessor circuitry—how to get the right attitude, the right point of view.

But that's enough soapbox stuff—let's get back to work.

ADDING SERIOUS I/O

The 373, (IC10), we put in the circuit to make sure everything was working properly is not, to put it mildly, the last word in I/O. It's a great diagnostic tool but, since we ultimately want to do more than light some LEDs, we have to add circuitry that has a lot more muscle.

Serious I/O means serious silicon.

Now that we have a working circuit, adding real I/O, or any other hardware for that matter, is more involved than it was when we were just starting out. The reason for this is that we have to pay more attention to the system map. Deciding what kind of devices to hang on the circuit is only half the problem, we have to decide where we want them to live as well. We touched on this briefly when we were adding memory to the system.

You'll remember that we mapped the RAM in from 00000h up and the ROM in from FFFFFh down. We also decided to use the A19 line as the toggle that would automatically select either one or the other. The result of doing this was to split the memory map in half. The top 512K is reserved for ROM and the bottom 512K is reserved for RAM. In larger computer systems, this memory arrangement would be incredibly screwy since RAM space is considered to be a lot more important. The main use for a single board system like ours, however, is to handle dedicated jobs—in other words we're putting together a controller and most of the applications you'll find for it will be put in ROM. Of course, people use dedicated systems for jobs that never crossed the mind of the system's designer.

So why split the memory map exactly in half? Three reasons. The first is that it's the most flexible arrangement, the second is that it takes the least amount of design time, and the third reason is just that—hey, I'm a democratic kind of guy. The same sort of consideration has to be done with I/O.

The 8088 has a huge I/O space—it can address 65,536 different ports. There's a software catch in this since it's faster and easier to address the first 256 ports, (00 to FFh), than the rest of them so we want to put all the important stuff down at the bottom. Besides, let's get real here, 256 ports is a lot of ports.

This is terrific but, just as with memory, there's only one pin on the 8088 that lets you know when a read or write is aimed at a memory location or an I/O port. Accessing a port means the 8088 will bring the IO/$\overline{\text{M}}$ line high, put the port's address on the bus, and finally activate either the $\overline{\text{RD}}$ or $\overline{\text{WR}}$ line. It's good to have lots of I/O in the system—it gives you flexibility, power, and the opportunity to control just about anything you can think of.

There's no doubt about it, ports are great . . . but you need a way to uniquely deal with each one you have on the board. You need the same sort of control logic for I/O that you do for memory.

BASIC I/O CONTROL

The more I/O you put on the board, the more control circuitry you're going to need. This is because you'll need a way to uniquely select each individual port whenever it's addressed. The address bus, after all, is the only way the 8088 has to tell you which port it wants to talk to. It's up to you to make sure that when the 8088 is talking to port #3, for instance, that's the *only* port connected to the bus. Having more than one port enabled at a time can be useful in some circumstances, but unless you're careful about what's happening, you can be faced with serious problems in bus contention and that, as we know, is a no-no of the first order.

TRUTH TABLE FOR I/O CONTROL LOGIC					
INPUTS			OUTPUTS		
IOSEL	RD	WR	IORD	IOWR	COMMENTS
LOW	HIGH	LOW	HIGH	LOW	WRITE TO I/O
LOW	LOW	HIGH	LOW	HIGH	READ FROM I/O
LOW	LOW	LOW	---	---	IMPOSSIBLE STATE
LOW	HIGH	HIGH	---	---	IMPOSSIBLE STATE
HIGH	X	X	HIGH	HIGH	MEMORY OPERATION

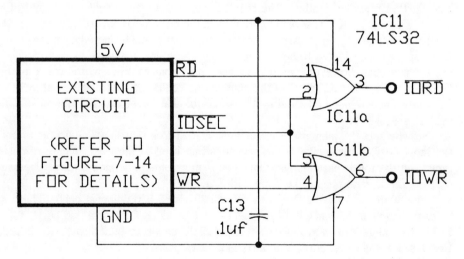

Fig. 8-1. Schematic of I/O control circuit.

The first step in designing the I/O control circuitry is simple. We need some logic to decode the 8088 signals and provide us with two lines—one to indicate an I/O write and another to indicate an I/O read. The way to do this is to follow exactly the same procedure we did when we had to generate similar signals for memory. Just as we used gates to get the $\overline{\text{RAMRD}}$, RAMWR, $\overline{\text{ROMSEL}}$, and $\overline{\text{ROMRD}}$ signals, we'll do the same sort of thing to generate $\overline{\text{IORD}}$ and $\overline{\text{IOWR}}$.

We want the $\overline{\text{IORD}}$ signal to be produced whenever we're doing a read to an I/O port and that means we have to use a combination of the IO/$\overline{\text{M}}$ and RD lines from the

102

8088. There are several ways to gate the 8088 lines and generate IORD signal but you have to keep in mind the devices you'll be enabling with $\overline{\text{IORD}}$. Most I/O will expect to see a signal that's active low so we can save ourselves some future hassles by making $\overline{\text{IORD}}$ an active low signal. The way we're going to do this is shown in Fig.8-1.

As you can see from the accompanying truth tables, the OR gates in IC11 create the two signals we need. The only time they'll generate $\overline{\text{IORD}}$ and $\overline{\text{IOWR}}$ is when the 8088 is talking to an I/O port. But these two signals are also only a part of what's needed to control I/O. We also need logic to select the I/O port we want to address since any system that's designed to do real work has to have a good stable of available I/O lines.

The minimal I/O we added to the circuit in the last chapter was only a primitive port designed to help debug the system—and as we continue on with this, you'll see that it can still provide us with a convenient eye into the circuit. All the rest of the I/O we'll be putting on the board has to be a lot more sophisticated if we want it to do useful things for us.

Now that we have the basic I/O signals to work with, the time has come, as someone once said, to think of other things—real I/O ports and a way to automatically distinguish between them.

THE 8255

I/O ports are the 8088's window to the real world and, if we wanted to, it's perfectly possible to build them with discreet parts. An output port can be made with a latch, (we've already done that), and an input port can be as simple as a tristating buffer. But doing things like that can make the problem of designing addressing logic as complicated and timing critical as dealing with the Department of Motor Vehicles—and just as frustrating.

Not only that, but it would also mean that an output port would always be an output port and an input port would always be an input port. Since the key is to be flexible and we've already seen that it's a good thing to keep your options open, it makes sense to build the ports around the 8255. An 8255 . . . what's an 8255?

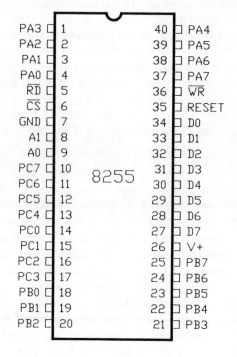

Fig. 8-2. The pinouts of the 8255.

The 8255 is a jack-of-all-trades type of I/O device. Inside its 40-pin package it has four separate registers. The first three can be individually programmed to be just about every type of I/O port you can imagine. The fourth port is the one that makes this part so flexible and the ideal candidate for I/O in a microprocessor based design. It's also the reason the 8255 is officially classified as a *"Programmable Peripheral Interface"* or, to its friends, a PPI.

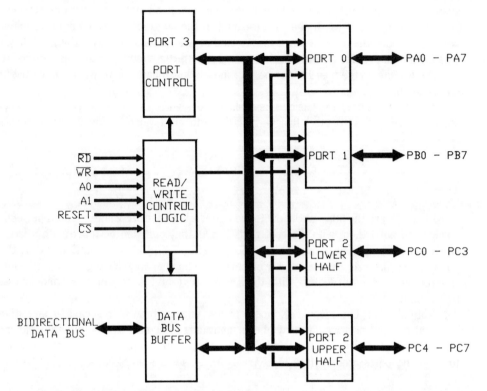

Fig. 8-3. Block diagram of an 8255.

By writing different values into the command port, you can define the functions of the other three ports. This includes making them either inputs or outputs for simple data transfers, or bidirectional ports for handshaking data transfer. Since the characteristics of the ports depend on the control word loaded in the command register, the 8255 can be dynamically configured by software. What makes this so terrific is that it can be done whenever you want. All you have to do to change the way the 8255 is set up is stuff port #4 with the word that defines the setup you want. And, catch this, programming the 8255 is simply a matter of having your software write a byte to the command port—that's right, all you need is the "OUT" command of the 8088. One unexpected benefit of using the 8255 is summed up in the ninety third Law of Life and Design.

> **SOFTWARE, UNLIKE LIFE,**
> **LETS YOU CHANGE HORSES IN MIDSTREAM**

The 8255 has three basic modes of operation—basic I/O, strobed I/O, and bidirectional I/O. There are many options in each of these three modes that determines the characteristics for each of the ports and I strongly urge everybody to read through the 8255's data sheet to get a feel for the things this chip can do. There's no point in trying to jam all of it in your brain, but it's a good idea to get a general idea of what has to be done to initialize the 8255.

Once we get the 8255 on the breadboard we'll see exactly what has to be done to initialize it to work in a particular way, but before we can do that we have to design the hardware needed to drive it and that means we have to get started with the decoding circuitry needed to select the individual ports as they're addressed by the 8088.

I/O DECODING

Since the 8088 can address more than 65,000 ports, a basic part of any I/O subsystem is the logic that makes sure the 8088 is connected to the correct port when it does an I/O operation. The 8255 has four ports so the first step in designing the circuit is to decide where they're going to live in the system's enormous I/O space. These are the first four ports that we're adding to the circuit so I suppose we ought to be logical about it and map them into the circuit as port #0 through port #3. The first three are the 8255's general purpose programmable I/O ports and the last one, port #3, is the 8255 command register.

In order for the 8088 to be able to talk to any of the ports we're adding to the circuit, several signals have to be generated and sent to the 8255's control pins. We've already arranged automatic $\overline{IORD}$ and $\overline{IOWR}$, so the only line we're still missing is the one needed to control the "Chip Select" pin of the 8255.

A high on the 8255's chip select line will cause it's data pins to float. We need this feature to avoid data bus contention with all the other devices we have in the system that use the data bus at one time or another. The circuitry we're designing has to put a low on the 8255's chip select pin every time the 8088 wants to talk to one of the first four ports.

The natural silicon choice to do this job is a data selector that watches the lower three lines in the system address bus, (A0 to A3), and, if other conditions are met, put a low on the 8255's chip select. The control of the 8255, therefore, is really handled by the data selector we choose to watch the bottom of the address lines.

Let's take a minute to see exactly what happens when the 8088 is told to address one of the ports contained in the 8255.

1 The address of the port is put on the address bus.
2 The IO/$\overline{M}$ line goes high to indicate an I/O operation.
3 Either the 8088's $\overline{RD}$ or $\overline{WR}$ line is activated.

If the 8088 is doing a write to a port, one other thing will happen as well—the data will be put on the system data bus.

There are several ICs that we can use as selectors and the things you have to consider when you're deciding which one to use are the chips's operating characteristics, special requirements, and, no less important, whether you can get it in onesies, cost, and how many of the mail order houses carry it. There are always ways to get chips that are perfectly suited for the job you want to do but the only suppliers that handle them are the mail order houses on Neptune (the prices are okay but the shipping charges are murder.).

What we're looking for is a decoder and, since I have some spare ones around, the 74LS259 is as good a choice as any. This chip is extremely flexible since it can be set up to work as a one of eight decoder and has an internal eight-bit latch as well. By configuring it properly in our circuit, not only will it control the chip select input of the 8255, but, by writing the appropriate software, it can stay selected even after we've finished the I/O operation.

This might not seem to be terribly useful but there's a variation on the fifteenth Law of Life and Design that's right to the point:

STAY FLEXIBLE

and since you can never tell what you'll want to do with the finished circuit, it's a good idea to keep your options open.

By tying the 259's reset pin to the 8088's A7 line and its enable pin to an inverted version of the 8088's IO/$\overline{M}$ line, the 259 will work as a one of eight decoder and select an output by decoding the bottom three lines of the address bus (A0 to A2). The 259 is hardwired to put a low on all its unselected outputs so we have to tie its "D" pin

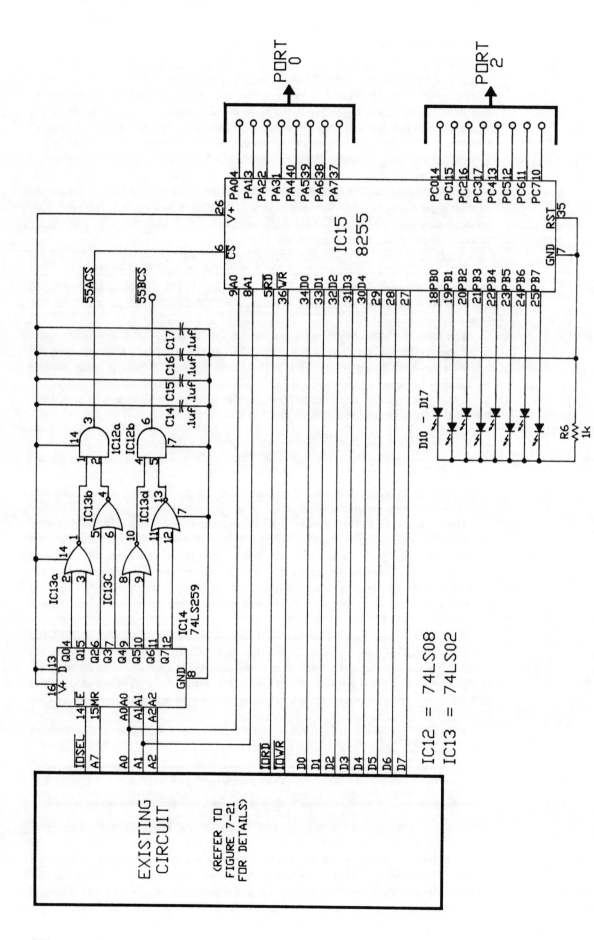

Fig. 8-4. Schematic of the 8255 decoding circuit.

to V+. This will make the selected output to go high and distinguish it from the unselected outputs.

Now that we have the 259 decoding the I/O address for us, we need a bit more logic to have it control the 8255. Since the 259 selects up to eight outputs, we have to arrange things so that the first four of them relate to the 8255. Remember that we've mapped the 8255 as the first four ports in the system. This means that whenever any of the first four 259 outputs goes high, we want it to enable the 8255. The simple gating arrangement of NOR and NAND gates shown in Fig.8-4 gets the job done perfectly.

You might be wondering why we're using two chips, (the 74LS02 and the 74LS08), to do a job that could be handled by a single four input NOR gate. Good question. There are four answers—two main and two ancillary.

The main reasons are first that since we're still designing the circuit, extra gates come in handy and it's a good idea to have spare ones lying around the circuit. The second main reason is that the two gate packages we're using are standards and most people are going to have them lying around the house—quad input NOR gates are a bit more specialized and, while they're not hard to find, they're not as common as the two ICs we're using. Besides, you can always change things around once you've locked in the basic circuit design. Don't forget what we talked about earlier. The first job is to get things working—perfection comes later.

The two ancillary reasons are practical ones. A two chip layout gives us a way to further decode the port addresses. By looking at the outputs of the NOR gates, we can detect when either of the first two or second two ports are being selected. This might not seem to be a useful thing at the moment but that's only at the moment and, as when you put the completed circuit to work, you can never tell what signals will come in handy. The second practical reason is that when you're designing a circuit, you want as many test points as possible since the more you have the easier it is to find out what's wrong with the circuit. Remember that we're still a good ways from putting a cap on the design.

If you look at this decoding circuitry, you'll realize that we've not only arranged for the port selection, but we've gotten something for free as well. The 259 is a one of eight decoder and by laying it out to decode the first four ports, we've also given ourselves a way to decode the second four ports as well. One look at Fig. 8-4 will show you that all we have to do to get three more I/O ports is to put another 8255 on the breadboard and connect its chip select pin to pin #6 of the 74LS08. The $\overline{WR}$, $\overline{RD}$, and data lines of the second 8255 can be put in parallel with the first 8255. It's great to get stuff for free.

BUILDING THE CIRCUIT

Now that we know what we're going to do to get some real I/O into the system, the time has come to actually wire everything in place on the breadboard. Once we get that done we can run some software that will let you know if you've done everything correctly. Lay the parts on the breadboard in the positions shown in the placement diagram of Fig. 8-5. The 74LS32 will be IC11, the 74LS08 will be IC12, the 74LS02 will be IC13, the 74LS259 will be IC14, and, finally, the 8255 will be IC15.

PARTS
1 - 74LS32 Quad OR Gate
1 - 74LS08 Quad AND Gate
1 - 74LS02 Quad NOR Gate
1 - 74LS259 Addressable Latch
1 - 8255 PPI
5 - .01 μF Capacitors
8 - LEDs of any kind
1 - 1k resistor (any wattage)

MINIMUM EQUIPMENT
Logic Probe

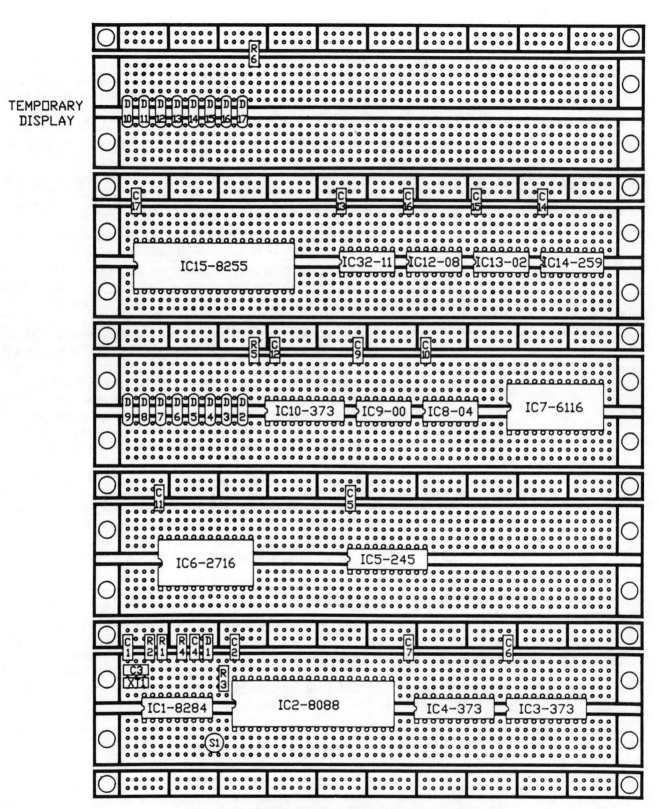

TEMPORARY
DISPLAY

ALL BUS STRIPS ARE TIED IN PARALLEL
AND CARRY ONLY POWER AND GROUND

Fig. 8-5. Placement diagram for the I/O circuit.

You'll notice that the days are finally gone when you could use a multimeter to see what the circuit is doing. When our design was much simpler you could get a reasonable idea of how it was performing by making a few intelligent assumptions about duty cycles and looking at the voltage of various points in the circuit. By the time you add these I/O parts however, our design has reached a level of complexity where the activity on IC pins is just too dynamic for simple voltage reading to tell you anything of real significance.

Even a logic probe can only tell you whether there's activity on a particular pin—it can't tell you what kind of activity. From this point on our circuit is serious enough to require the use of serious diagnostic equipment and by that I mean an oscilloscope. You can put the circuit together and, if you do everything correctly, you can get the circuit working without one, but there's unfortunately no way you can troubleshoot it without a scope.

Once you get past a certain complexity in a microprocessor based circuit, the timing relationships between circuit signals become just as important as the signals themselves, and a scope is just about the only instrument that will let you see this. You don't need a really expensive scope—a bandwidth of 20 MHz and dual trace are the two features that are the most useful. Things like delayed sweep, auto triggering, variable holdoff, and so on are nice to have but they're not needed for basic circuit snooping.

Wire the parts up according to Tables 8-1 through Table 8-5, being careful to count the pins correctly when you're making the connections. And don't forget that all the ICs on the breadboard should be facing the same direction. Lots of parts don't take kindly to being backwards and once they're covered with wire, it's easy to overlook this kind of mistake.

Table 8-1. Connections Made to the 74LS32 (IC11).

CONNECTIONS TO IC11 (74LS32)	
Pin #	Connect to
1	8088 pin #32 (RD)
2	IC8 pin #12
3	8255 pin #5 (IORD)
4	8088 pin #29 (WR)
5	IC8 pin #12
6	8255 pin #36 (IOWR)
7	Ground
8	No Connection
9	Ground
10	Ground
11	No Connection
12	Ground
13	Ground
14	5 Volts

Once you've finished wiring these parts into the breadboard, add the capacitors and the LEDs. The anode of the LEDs, (usually identified by a longer leg or a dot on the plastic), should be facing the 8255. Connect the cathodes to a common point and then to ground through the 1k resistor.

That's all there is to the hardware side of the I/O. Before you connect up power, it's a good idea to make sure you haven't connected power and ground together. Check to see whether there's a short between the legs of the power supply. The easiest way

CONNECTIONS TO IC12 (74LS08)	
Pin #	Connect to
1	IC13 pin #1
2	IC13 pin #4
3	8255 pin #6 (55ACS)
4	IC13 pin #10
5	IC13 pin #13
6	No Connection (55BCS)
7	Ground
8	No Connection
9	Ground
10	Ground
11	No Connection
12	Ground
13	Ground
14	5 Volts

Table 8-2. Connections Made to the 74LS08 (IC12).

CONNECTIONS TO IC13 (74LS02)	
Pin #	Connect to
1	IC12 pin #1
2	IC14 pin #4
3	IC14 pin #5
4	IC12 pin #2
5	IC14 pin #6
6	IC14 pin #7
7	Ground
8	IC14 pin #9
9	IC14 pin #10
10	IC12 pin #4
11	IC14 pin #11
12	IC14 pin #12
13	IC12 pin 5
14	5 Volts

Table 8-3. Connections Made to the 74LS02 (IC13).

to do it is with a multimeter, (I guess there's still a use for it). The exact reading you'll get is completely unpredictable since there's a wide variation in the amount of board capacitance and, even though we've been adding lots of small capacitors, there's absolutely no way to know what numbers you'll see. It's only important that you see some reading other than zero. In this case, electronic design is a lot like life since

SOMETHING IS BETTER THAN NOTHING

but it's only true some of the time.

CONNECTIONS TO IC14 (74LS259)	
Pin #	Connect to
1	IC3 pin #2 (A0)
2	IC3 pin #5 (A1)
3	IC3 pin #6 (A2)
4	IC13 pin #2
5	IC13 pin #3
6	IC13 pin #5
7	IC13 pin #6
8	Ground
9	IC13 pin #8
10	IC13 pin #9
11	IC13 pin #11
12	IC13 pin #12
13	5 volts
14	IC8 pin #12
15	IC3 pin #19 (A7)
16	5 Volts

Table 8-4. Connections Made to the 74LS259 (IC14).

CHECKING IT OUT

Every time we've reached this point in the past, there's been some simple test we could do to make sure everything was wired up and working properly. As the circuit gets more and more complicated, the testing procedures do as well. The days are past when we can power-up the circuit, and expect to get any meaningful information from a simple voltage measurement. Diagnostic routines are combinations of hardware and software. The more sophisticated the system becomes, the more we have to rely on software to run system checkouts.

When the only I/O we had in the system was the 373 latch, we could get around the software problem by hardwiring the program with a data selector and some diodes. The right place for the routine was in an EPROM but since we were only looking at six bytes we could still get by with building a phony baloney ROM. If you're one of the people who used the data selector/diode scheme in the last chapter, you know what a pain in the neck it is.

Now that we have the 8255 as the I/O device, the diagnostics are going to be more than just six bytes long. The most rudimentary test that we can do on the 8255 is shown in Fig. 8-6. It should be ten bytes long to run continuously, (a good thing), but there's a way we can use a fact of hardware to shave it by two bytes.

The 8255 has to be programmed before it can be used. That means we have to output a byte to its control register. Doing that takes four bytes—two bytes to load a byte in the accumulator and two bytes to send the value in the accumulator out the port.

The small routine we had in the last chapter was six bytes long and the data selector we used to Mickey Mouse an EPROM, a 4051, can only encode eight bytes. Since the core of the basic test routine for the 8255 is eight bytes long, (the last two bytes are a jump back into the program so it will run as a continuous loop), it's possible to fix the 4051 circuit so it can be used here. The jump instruction that occupies the last two bytes can be ignored because the 4051 will only be looking at the lower three address lines. As a result, it will cycle through all eight instructions over and over again. The program counter in the 8088 may think it's incrementing from 7h to 8h but the 4051, since it's not looking at the more significant address lines, will just go back to 0h.

In order to have this scheme work though, the RAM on the board has to be either disabled or removed because a low on the 8088's A7 line will enable it, put it on the

CONNECTIONS TO IC15 (8255)	
Pin #	Connect to
1	No Connection (PA3)
2	No Connection (PA2)
3	No Connection (PA1)
4	No Connection (PA0)
5	IC11 pin #3 (IORD)
6	IC12 pin #3 (55ACS)
7	Ground
8	IC3 pin #5 (A1)
9	IC3 pin #2 (A0)
10	No Connection (PC7)
11	No Connection (PC6)
12	No Connection (PC5)
13	No Connection (PC4)
14	No Connection (PC0)
15	No Connection (PC1)
16	No Connection (PC2)
17	No Connection (PC3)
18	LED #0 (PB0)
19	LED #1 (PB1)
20	LED #2 (PB2)
21	LED #3 (PB3)
22	LED #4 (PB4)
23	LED #5 (PB5)
24	LED #6 (PB6)
25	LED #7 (PB7)
26	5 Volts
27	IC5 pin #11 (D7)
28	IC5 pin #12 (D6)
29	IC5 pin #13 (D5)
30	IC5 pin #14 (D4)
31	IC5 pin #15 (D3)
32	IC5 pin #16 (D2)
33	IC5 pin #17 (D1)
34	IC5 pin #18 (D0)
35	Ground
36	IC11 pin #6 (IOWR)
37	No Connection (PA7)
38	No Connection (PA6)
39	No Connection (PA5)
40	No Connection (PA4)

Table 8-5. Connections Made to the 8255 (IC15).

bus at the same time as the output of the 4051, and result in bus contention. Bus contention, you should remember, is a super no-no.

There are several ways to avoid this but the easiest is to pull the chip from the board. If, for some reason, you don't want to do this, move the wire at IC9 pin #3 (RAMSEL) to pin #14 of the same IC. This will tie RAMSEL high, permanently disable the RAM, and eliminate the possibility of bus contention.

The test routine is about as simple as you can get. You can see from the listing that it's very similar to the routine from the last chapter. The only changes are the bytes

```
;         ***************************************************
;         *                                                 *
;         *         A TEST PROGRAM FOR THE 8255              *
;         *                                                 *
;         ***************************************************
;
;
;
                TITLE     Light an LED Through The 8255
;*****************************************************************************
;*          Set variables, segments, equates, and location                  *
;*****************************************************************************
BOB             SEGMENT                       ;Define the Code Segment.
                ASSUME   CS:BOB,DS:BOB,SS:BOB  ;Set all segment registers to
                                              ;the same location.
;
;*****************************************************************************
;*              The beginning of executable code                            *
;*****************************************************************************
;As with all the diode ROM programs, we have to ORG this program at the 8088
;startup location of FFF0h and limit the program to 8 bytes in length.
;----------------------------------------------------------------------------
                ORG      7F0h                 ;The 2716 location for the 8088
                                              ;powerup instruction of FFFF0h
START:          MOV      AL,90h               ;Load the 8255 setup value.
                OUT      03h,AL               ;Send it to the command port.
                MOV      AL,01h               ;This will light the first LED.
                OUT      01h,AL               ;Send it to 8255 port #1.
;----------------------------------------------------------------------------
;The 4051 will keep executing this program over and over since it only looks
;at the three least significant address lines.  The 6116 has to be disabled
;or removed as described in Chapter #8 or bus contention will result.
;*****************************************************************************
;*                  The end of the program                                  *
;*****************************************************************************
;
BOB             ENDS                          ;Tell assembler this is the end
                                              ;of code for this segment.
                END      START                ;Tell assembler this is the end
                                              ;of the program.
```

Hex Dump of TEST8255.ASM

```
0000 - 00 00 00 00 00 00 00 00 00 00 00 00 00 00 00 00
0010 - 00 00 00 00 00 00 00 00 00 00 00 00 00 00 00 00

0020 - 07CF are filled with zeros

07D0 - 00 00 00 00 00 00 00 00 00 00 00 00 00 00 00 00
07E0 - 00 00 00 00 00 00 00 00 00 00 00 00 00 00 00 00
07F0 - B0 90 E6 03 B0 01 E6 01 00 00 00 00 00 00 00 00
```

Fig. 8-6. TEST8255.ASM—A diagnostic program for the 8255.

at the head of the program to program the 8255 and the substitution of the port number from 10h to 01h, the 8255 port containing the LEDs.

If you've got your mind set on using the 4051 circuit from the last chapter, here's the modifications you have to make to use it—but this is it. After this, it's history. If you've grown fond of it you can bronze it and hang it from your rearview mirror. From now on the diagnostic software is going to have to live in an EPROM.

Put a diode every place there's an X in the table and follow the same precautions you did last time. Remember that it's hard to catch a mistake when you're doing this and one diode in the wrong place, or facing the wrong direction, will make the whole circuit useless and what it tells the 8088 to do is anyone's guess.

The single diode hanging on pin #5 of the 4051 is forming the byte that lights the LED. It's a good idea to move it from place to place and see if all the LEDs can light since that will tell you if all the bits in this 8255 port are working.

If you're like most earth people and burn the code into an EPROM, you can use this diagnostic program but it's not too exciting since the only thing it'll do is light an LED. A much more interesting diagnostic test is contained in Fig. 8-7. The operation of the routine is fully described in the comments and you should go through them carefully to make sure you understand what's happening.

```
;       ***********************************************
;       *                                             *
;       *      A TEST PROGRAM FOR THE 8088 BREADBOARD  *
;       *      WITH THE 8255 SET UP AS PORTS #0 TO #3   *
;       *                                             *
;       ***********************************************
;
;
;               TITLE     Sequence 8 LED's back and forth.
;
;---------------------------------------------------------------------------
;This program will sequentially light one of eight LED's connected to both the
;outputs of the 74LS373 (IC10) and the second port in the 8255 (port #1).  The
;LED's controlled by both chips will flash back and forth in response to the
;value put in the accumulator.  This will test the functioning of the 8255.
;---------------------------------------------------------------------------
;Eight new LED's are connected to the 8255 at Port #1 as follows:
;
;                    8255      Connection
;                    =====================
;                    PB-0      LED #0
;                    PB-1      LED #1
;                    PB-2      LED #2
;                    PB-3      LED #3
;                    PB-4      LED #4
;                    PB-5      LED #5
;                    PB-6      LED #6
;                    PB-7      LED #7
;
;The original LED's connected to IC10 will behave exactly the same as the ones
;connected to the 8255.  The new LED's are tied to ground through a 1k resistor
;and if the circuit is working properly both sets of LED's will light up in the
;same pattern as the program sequences from one to the next.
;
;****************************************************************************
;*                        SET THE 8088 SEGMENTS                            *
;****************************************************************************
BOB             SEGMENT                      ;Define initial segments.
                ASSUME  CS:BOB,DS:BOB,SS:BOB ;Set all segment registers to
                                             ;the same location.
                ORG 100h                     ;Set program start location.
                                             ;head of the program.
;
;****************************************************************************
;*                        INITIALIZE THE 8255                              *
;****************************************************************************
START:          MOV     AL,90h               ;This sets the 8255 to operate
                                             ;in Mode 0 (basic input output)
                                             ;with port 0 as an input and
                OUT     03h,AL               ;ports 1 and 2 as outputs.
```

Fig. 8-7. 8255.ASM—An LED sequencing program for the 8255.

```
;
;****************************************************************************
;*                 THE BEGINNING OF EXECUTABLE CODE                        *
;****************************************************************************
               JMP      SETUP
;
;****************************************************************************
;*                      TIME DELAY ROUTINE                                 *
;****************************************************************************
;The main loop consists of decrementing memory location 100h and the test being
;done by JNZ.  The DEC takes 32 clocks, The OUT takes 10 clocks, CMP takes 23,
;and JNZ, if a jump is executed, will take 16 clocks.   At 4.77 MHz, each clock
;lasts 200 ns so the main loop takes some 16 microseconds.  By doing it 3FFFh,
;or (16,383), times means the whole loop will take about quarter second.
;----------------------------------------------------------------------------
WAITASEC:      MOV      DS:[100h],3FFFh         ;Set up a timing delay constant
WAITASEC1:     DEC      WORD PTR DS:[100h]      ;Decrement the delay constant.
               OUT      01h,AL                  ;Send the current AL value out
                                                ;the port.  This instruction is
                                                ;in the timing loop to add to
                                                ;the time delay.
                                                ;Since the 373 is enabled by
                                                ;IO/M directly, (through the
                                                ;two inverters), it will latch
                                                ;data sent to any port address.
               CMP      WORD PTR DS:[100h],00h  ;Has RAM location 100h reached
                                                ;zero yet?
               JNZ      WAITASEC1               ;If not, go back to the loop.
               RET                              ;When zero is reached, exit the
                                                ;delay loop and return to the
                                                ;main part of the program.
;
;****************************************************************************
;*                    MAIN BODY OF THE CODE                                *
;****************************************************************************
SETUP:         MOV      CL,2h                   ;Store the multiplier.
BEGIN:         MOV      AL,00000001b            ;This value, 01h, will light
                                                ;the '0' LED's at both the 373
                                                ;and port #1 of the 8255.
               CALL WAITASEC                    ;Run the time delay loop and
                                                ;send the current AL value to
                                                ;the 373 and the 8255.
;
;----------------------------------------------------------------------------
;The number in AL can be changed by shifting, adding, loading the value in the
;register directly, and so on.  Multiplying, however, is one of the slowest
;operations that can be done on the 8088, (some 75 clocks), and using it to
;change the AL value allows the LED to be lit for the maximum length of time.
;----------------------------------------------------------------------------
NEXTLED:       MUL      CL                      ;Each multiplication moves the
                                                ;addressed LED over one bit.
                                                ;The first MUL changes data in
                                                ;AL from 00000001 to 00000010.
                                                ;After the last one, the data
                                                ;in AL is 10000000 which should
                                                ;light the bit '8' LED's.
               CALL     WAITASEC                ;Run the time delay.
               CMP      AL,80h                  ;AL will contain 80h if the '8'
                                                ;bit LED's are currently lit.
               JNZ      NEXTLED                 ;If this isn't true, the last
                                                ;LED's aren't lit yet so go
```

Fig. 8-7. (continued)

```
                                                            ;back, change the value in AL,
                                                            ;and run the delay loop again.
;
;------------------------------------------------------------------------------------
;When the 8088 gets to this part of the program the '8' bit LED's are currently
;lit so by dividing rather than multiplying, the LED's can be made to sequence
;in reverse order.
;------------------------------------------------------------------------------------
PREVLED:        DIV     CL                  ;This will produce a value that
                                            ;lights the previous LED.
                CALL    WAITASEC            ;Run the time delay.
                CMP     AL,02h              ;See if the second LED is lit.
                JNZ     PREVLED             ;If not, go back an LED.
                JMP     BEGIN               ;Go light the first LED again.
;
;********************************************************************************
;*                   T H E   B O O T   C O D E                                 *
;********************************************************************************
;This is the location in the 2716 that will be accessed at power up since the
;8088 looks for it's first instruction at FFFF0h.  The 2716 is enabled by any
;address that brings A19 high (8000h - FFFFFh) but the 2716's address lines are
;connected from A0 to A10 on the 8088.  This covers a range of 0000h to 07FFh.
;Since accessing the 2716 means A19 has to be high as well, the 8088 addresses
;used for talking to the 2716 are FF800h to FFFFFh even though the EPROM sees
;all 20 bit addresses with A19 high as the same - ie, 80000h equals F0000h.
;The 8088 power up location of FFFF0h is actually 07F0h in the 2716.  The boot
;instruction has to be ORG'ed at 08F0h since the assembler wants to ORG the
;above main code at 0100.  The result is that the 2716 will have the main code
;at 0000h and the boot code at 07F0h.
;------------------------------------------------------------------------------------
                ORG     8F0h                ;The 2716 location for the 8088
                                            ;power-up instruction allowing
                                            ;for the assembler's ORG 100
                                            ;requirement for the main code.
                JMP     START               ;Go to the main code located at
                                            ;0000h in the 2716.
                DB      00,00,00,00,00,00,00 ;Nul bytes to fill the 2716
                DB      00,00,00,00,00,00    ;with 00's after power up
                                            ;jump described above.
;
;********************************************************************************
;*                   THE  END  OF  THE  PROGRAM                                *
;********************************************************************************
BOB             ENDS                        ;Tell assembler this is the end
                                            ;of code for this segment.
                END     START               ;Tell assembler this is the end
                                            ;of the program.
```

Hex Dump of 8255.ASM

```
0000 - B0 90 E6 03 EB 15 90 C7 06 00 01 FF 3F FF 0E 00
0010 - 01 E6 01 83 3E 00 01 00 75 F3 C3 B1 02 B0 01 E8
0020 - E5 FF F6 E1 E8 E0 FF 3C 80 75 F7 F6 F1 E8 D7 FF
0030 - 3C 02 75 F7 EB E7 00 00 00 00 00 00 00 00 00 00
0040 - 00 00 00 00 00 00 00 00 00 00 00 00 00 00 00 00
0050 - 00 00 00 00 00 00 00 00 00 00 00 00 00 00 00 00

0060 - 07CF are filled with zeros

07D0 - 00 00 00 00 00 00 00 00 00 00 00 00 00 00 00 00
07E0 - 00 00 00 00 00 00 00 00 00 00 00 00 00 00 00 00
07F0 - E9 0D F8 00 00 00 00 00 00 00 00 00 00 00 00 00
```

Fig. 8- . Continued.

If you have access to an IBM compatible computer and an assembler, you can assemble the program yourself. If you can hand assemble the program for an EPROM, I've included the hex as well.

Whichever one you use, the first byte of code goes into location 000h of the EPROM—with one important exception. At the end of the listing, you'll note that the boot code has to be placed at location 7F0h in the EPROM. As is described in the listing, this will put the JUMP at location FFFF0h in memory which is where the 8088 will look for its first instruction.

If you're using an assembler, it will produce a hex file with all the bytes where they belong but if you're doing it by hand, remember that there's a big gap between the last byte of the main code and the first byte of the power-up instruction. It doesn't matter what bytes you have in between—the FFh's in a blank EPROM are fine—since the software will never look at them. An assembler will fill up all the intervening spaces with 00h—it makes things neater but it doesn't mean anything.

The fourteen bytes from the end of the power-up instruction to the end of memory are too little for anything useful. IBM uses them to store the release date of the ROM and we used them for the diagnostic routines coded in the handmade ROM but, in general, there's not much use for them.

You shouldn't have any trouble getting the 8255 working since we haven't done anything sneaky with the hardware. The only things that can be causing problems are bad or incorrect connections. Check all your wiring against the tables, (and the schematic for that matter), and take a second look at the orientation of the ICs. I've seen a lot of people mistake the molding mark on plastic IC packages for the pin #1 mark. There's absolutely no convention for which way the IC printing faces. The fact that the printing isn't upside down is no guarantee that the IC is right side up.

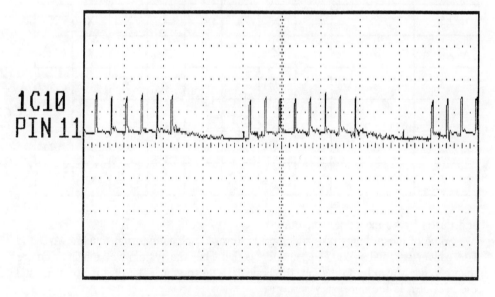

1C10
PIN 11

Fig. 8-8. IOSEL pulses generated while 8255.ASM is running.

And even if the circuit appears to be working correctly, leave it running overnight. You really want to remember the twenty second Law of Life and Design:

YOU CAN NEVER BE TOO SURE

since the oddball circuit glitches, (the ones that are the hardest to find), never show up when you're expecting them.

GOING FURTHER

If you stand back for a moment and take a look at the circuit in front of you, you'll realize that we've come a long way since we were talking about the power supply. Our system has grown from a simple clock circuit to a fairly complex design that can actually do useful work.

For example, you could:

1. Store the appropriate data in an EPROM and drive a sequencer with the I/O port to play music.
2. Build a burglar alarm by using the I/O ports as a combination of sensor inputs and relay outputs.
3. Use various pieces of hardware to monitor and display things like temperature, pressure, voltage, etc.
4. Set all three I/O ports as outputs and use the system as a programmable light show controller.

4051 DIODE CONNECTIONS - ANODE TO 4051									
4051 PINS	4051 OUTPUT	D 0	D 1	D 2	D 3	D 4	D 5	D 6	D 7
13	0					X	X		X
14	1					X			X
15	2		X	X			X	X	X
12	3	X	X						
1	4					X	X		X
5	5	X							
2	6		X	X			X	X	X
4	7	X							

Table 8-6. Diode Connections for Testing the 8255.

and this is by no means a complete list.

Some of these things take additional hardware such as external sensors, A/D and D/A converters, and so on. The point here is that while the system we've built has more than enough brawn to do the job, the brains are up to you. A lot of it is software and the rest of it is the necessary hardware.

Even though our circuit has made the transition from educational to operational, we're still short some pieces of basic hardware and we're not really taking advantage of some of the really heavy duty features of the 8088. By adding some more hardware to the system, we can make it much more powerful. So let's do it.

9

Adding A Display

EVERY TIME I'VE REFERRED TO THE SYSTEM WE'RE BUILDING I'VE BEEN CALLING IT A "microprocessor-based design", "8088 circuit", "single board system", or something similar. I've never used a specific term for it because it's not being designed to do any specific job. Light dimmers dim lights, amplifiers amplify, but circuits like ours only control. Control what, you might well ask.

Well, the simple answer is that they control whatever you decide they should control. Microprocessor-based circuits, (see, I did it again), can be built to do nothing in particular and everything in general. After all, exactly what does a computer do? By itself it doesn't do much but, given the appropriate software, it can do just about anything you want—including dimming lights.

If you had to put a label on the system we're putting together, it would be a "controller". What that means is that we're designing a circuit that contains two basic parts. The first is the 8088 along with all the support and glue it needs to make it come alive and the second is the circuitry that gives us a way to get data into and out of the system.

We've designed most of the basic elements that are needed for the first part of the system—this includes demultiplexing the address bus, buffering the data bus, and generating the fundamental control signals needed to control memory, I/O, and so on. There's not a lot of memory in the system at the moment—2K of RAM and 2K of ROM—but adding more is just a matter of spending more money and adding some more connections. Since we've already worked out the system memory map, all we have to do to bring it up to the maximum is plug in some more chips and wire them into the bus. The system is set for static RAM but dynamic RAM can be used as well—we'll talk about that a bit later on.

Now that we've started on the I/O and have a couple of real ports to play around with, we can add some of the peripheral devices that most people regard as being more in the way of system essentials than system luxuries.

The two most common are a display and a keyboard. Although these are extremely important for systems designed to work as a computer, they're less important for controllers like ours. As a matter of fact, we could add some hardware to the board to turn one of the I/O ports into a standard RS-232 port, and control our entire circuit by using an external terminal. But this can always be done later. What we need right now is some way to display such things as memory, port values, and other basic operating parameters of the circuit. This means a simple display and, once that's done, a simple keyboard.

Since these two things are peripheral devices, the easiest way to add them to the system is to hang them on I/O ports—and that's what we're going to do.

A BASIC DISPLAY

In the best of all possible worlds, the ideal display is a TV tube. You can get a lot of information up on the screen and, in most cases, it's nice and easy on the eyes. The down side of this is that it takes a good deal of time to design. For our purposes it's a lot smarter to use a simple seven segment LED type of display. Remember that we're not designing a computer, we're designing a controller. A display only has to show us what's going on in the circuit.

When we get to working out the software to drive our system, we'll talk about building a simple BIOS that any application software can use. All we'll need for that is a display that can show us values in hex and a seven segment LED is a great way to handle that. It's quick, cheap, and easily expandable if and when it becomes necessary. Alphanumeric displays—as opposed to standard seven segment ones—can always be substituted to give you a full range of characters on the display. They cost more and are more complex to drive but getting them to work is only more involved, not more difficult. Remember, cost is as important a design factor as function.

Making a seven segment display come alive is easy. There are lots of MSI parts that are designed specifically to handle them. The only hassle we'll have is due to what I've always regarded as an amazing shortcoming in the standard parts market.

Here it is people. You probably never expected to find a get rich quick scheme outlined in an electronics book, but that's exactly what this is.

Even though there are thousands of applications that use a seven segment digit for a hex display, there are virtually no standard ICs on the market to do the job. Motorola makes a part for this but it's hard to find, expensive, and all but impossible to buy in onesies. I've asked several IC manufacturers why BCD to seven segment drivers are common and binary to seven segment drivers are rare.

I never got an answer worth remembering. I suspect it's because it costs an arm and a leg to tool up for making a new chip. And any time a manufacturer is faced with adding to his product line, most of his considerations revolve around cost and payback. The main stable of parts produced by any manufacturer is built with a basic rule of business in mind:

> ## GO WITH THE FLOW

which is exactly opposite to the basic principle of the individual developer as expressed in the Primary Law of Life and Design:

> ## THINK FOR YOURSELF

and no matter what else you remember, that's the one you should write on the inside of your eyelids.

HARDWARE CONSIDERATIONS

Every display system designed around seven segment digits has to take binary information as an input and convert it to signal outputs that will light up the correct segments in the display. This is the part of the system that does most of the work. Standard MSI devices, such as the CMOS 4511, also have their output drive capability beefed up to supply the current needed by the LEDs, and other amenities like lamp test and blanking inputs. These things might be nice to have but, since we're designing our own from the ground up, they're not really necessary.

Any time you talk about a decoder, you're really talking about memory. All the standard LED decoder drivers have a lookup table somewhere in their innards that translates binary data at the input to character patterns at the output. Since this is the basic job the subsystem has to do, it's the first part of the circuit we'll get to work on.

Just as you have to plan memory and I/O maps, you have to plan display maps as well. Building a lookup table means knowing how many input and output lines you have to deal with. Since we're going to be working with binary data, we need at least four input lines. I say at least four lines because while we certainly want to be able to display all the hex digits from "0" to "F", it's not a bad idea to have the ability to display other segment combinations as well. This would include things like a dash, underscore, and any other character that might be useful. If we design our system to accept five input lines, we'll be able to output 32 different patterns on the display and that should be enough to take care of any special characters we might have in mind.

We're going to hang the display on one of the I/O ports so we have eight output lines to play with. Since five of them are already set aside, we have three left to control the rest of the display. We'll need more than one digit in the display so we might as well use the rest of the I/O lines as the control lines for display multiplexing. Three lines means we can control eight digits and that's an adequate display size for any single board system.

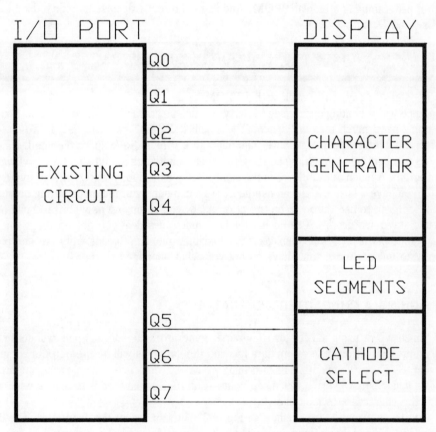

Fig. 9-1. How the I/O lines are assigned to the display.

Everybody refers to them as seven segment displays but, in actual fact, they're really eight segment displays since the decimal point is a separate LED with its own input. The amount of unique data you can show with a seven segment digit is pretty limited no matter how creative you are with segment combinations. While it's true that two to the seventh gives you 128 possible characters, the only ones who can keep all of them straight in their minds are the fabulous fish-faced people of Neptune we've mentioned so often before. The only reason they could do it was because they didn't have much else on their minds. The decimal point can come in handy, so in keeping with the law regarding flexibility, we'll design our system to take advantage of it.

Now that we've worked out our system's basic rules for generating characters we know that we need a decoder with five input lines and eight output lines. What we're really talking about here is a small 32 × 8 ROM. The address lines will serve as the inputs and the data lines will serve as outputs. If you hunt through the relevant data books, you'll find that there are several available ROM's that are exactly this size—what a coincidence! Unfortunately, they're all bipolar PROMs and they're all a pain in the neck to program. If you read the data sheets, you'll get the impression that all you need to burn them is a power supply, some switches, and a volt meter. Forget it—things are never that easy.

Unlike EPROMs, which are burned a byte at a time, bipolar PROMs are burned a bit at a time. Not only that, but since programming them involves actually burning a nichrome fuse, they need a lot of current and there's no going back. If you make a mistake, the only thing you can do with the chip is paint eyes on it and put it in the bottom of your fish tank.

Bipolar PROMs may have faster access times but we don't need the speed and EPROMs are erasable. I can't tell you how frustrating it is to make a mistake near the end of programming a bipolar PROM. And it goes directly against the sixty third Law of Life and Design:

GRIEF IS ONLY GOOD IN THE ABSTRACT

so, needless to say, we'll stick with EPROMs.

Since we're limiting our display to thirty two unique characters and the decimal point, we don't need much memory space. The smallest EPROM we can get, however, is a 2708 and even that contains more than thirty times the storage space we need. Using a 2708 is a bad idea though, since they're usually multivoltage chips and are awkward to program. A much better choice is the same 2716 we used for the ROM in our system.

If you have a burner that can handle 2708s and a supply of the chips sitting on your shelf, feel free to use them. If, on the other hand, you're buying new stuff to build our circuit, stay away from 2708s no matter how much of a deal you get on them since, while some occasional brain damage is unavoidable, only Neptunians went out and paid money to get it. And I don't have to tell you what happened to them.

DESIGNING A CHARACTER GENERATOR

Since we're using a 2716 for a character generator, the address pins will serve as the inputs that sit on the system data bus and the data pins will be the outputs actually driving the display segments. The first thing we have to do is make the pin assignments—decide which pins will drive which segments—and the second step is to decide what we want the characters to look like.

All this information is contained in Fig. 9-2. You can accept the characters I've designed but, should they offend your artistic sense of style and form, you can design your own. Use the form shown in Fig. 9-2 as a template for your own character set. The first part to fill in is the "Segment Display". Once you've drawn out the character set, put a "1" for the segments you want lit and a "0" for the others.

I'm using common cathode displays. If you plan on using a common anode display, you'll need a "0" for the lit segments and a "1" for the others. You'll also have to do some work with the multiplexing circuit we'll be building because it was designed with common cathode displays in mind.

CHARACTER GENERATOR TRUTH TABLE											
INPUTS		OUTPUTS									
BINARY DATA	HEX DATA	D7 DP	D6 'G'	D5 'F'	D4 'E'	D3 'D'	D2 'C'	D1 'B'	D0 'A'	HEX DATA	LED'S LIT
00000	00	0	0	1	1	1	1	1	1	3F	0
00001	01	0	0	0	0	0	1	1	0	06	1
00010	02	0	1	0	1	1	0	1	1	5B	2
00011	03	0	1	0	0	1	1	1	1	4F	3
00100	04	0	1	1	0	0	1	1	0	66	4
00101	05	0	1	1	0	1	1	0	1	6D	5
00110	06	0	1	1	1	1	1	0	1	7D	6
00111	07	0	0	0	0	0	1	1	1	07	7
01000	08	0	1	1	1	1	1	1	1	7F	8
01001	09	0	1	1	0	1	1	1	1	6F	9
01010	0A	0	1	1	1	0	1	1	1	77	A
01011	0B	0	1	1	1	1	1	0	0	7C	b
01100	0C	0	0	1	1	1	0	0	1	39	C
01101	0D	0	1	0	1	1	1	1	0	5E	d
01110	0E	0	1	1	1	1	0	0	1	79	E
01111	0F	0	1	1	1	0	0	0	1	71	F
10000	10	0	0	0	0	1	0	0	0	08	_
10001	11	1	0	0	0	0	0	0	0	80	.
10010	12	0	1	0	0	0	0	0	0	40	–
11111	FF	0	0	0	0	0	0	0	0	00	

Fig. 9-2. Translating the characters to the EPROM.

Since there's so much room in the 2716, you can hedge your bets a bit by programming it to be used with either common anode or common cathode displays. No matter how many characters your creative urges cause you to design, I doubt that you'll fill half the EPROM. That being the case, you can program a common cathode driver in one half of the EPROM and a common anode driver in the other. Switching from one to another can be done with a switch, hardwiring on the board or, if you really get into this, under software control (although I don't see what advantage this could possibly give you.)

It's always a problem to design a hex display for a seven segment digit since there's no way to clearly distinguish a "6" from a "b". The standard practice, which I've followed, is to use the "a" segment with the "6". This works well enough, but you have to make sure to remember what you've done so you'll know what you're looking at.

MULTIPLEXING THE DISPLAY

The last piece of hardware we need to finish the eight-digit display is the multiplexer. Since eight is a magic number for digital ICs, there's no shortage of chips we can use.

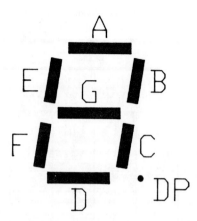

Fig. 9-3. A standard seven segment display.

You can see in Fig. 9-4 that we'll be using a 74LS138. This is a one of eight decoder with a versatile set of enable pins. We won't be using them, however, since we want the display to be enabled all the time.

The 138, IC17, will individually turn on each of the digits. Most display multiplexing is done to cut down on power requirements and, while that's a consideration here, it's not the main reason we'll be using this technique.

Remember that the display scheme we're using gives us a total of eight lines to control the digits. If all we were interested in was saving power, we could drive the 138 with a stand-alone clock but the result would be less control of the display. Using five of the I/O lines for data and three lines for the digits means that in addition to sending data, we can use software to illuminate any combination of digits we want. Some applications may have another use for the three I/O lines we're using to select the digits and if you have something like that in mind, feel free to rework the design. It's not a simple thing to do however, since the port is being used as an output port and unless you reprogram the 8255, there's no way to send data only to the three digit select lines. Data can only go out a byte at a time.

As the schematic shows, our display technique is using a minimal amount of hardware—the majority of control is done in software. In systems based around some other microprocessors, this might be a bit of a problem but it's a terrific choice for the 8088 since it has an extremely versatile interrupt setup.

The number to be displayed is sent on the lower five bits and the digit to display it on is selected with the upper three bits. The standard hex digits (0 to F) are carried on bits 1 through 4 and the digit selection is done on bits 5 through 8. You can think of bit 5 as being the toggle for an alternate character set. The only three characters I've defined that have bit 5 set are a blank, the decimal point, and a dash. You can add your own but the truth of the matter is that most of the time the data you'll be sending to the display will have bit 5 clear.

The schematic shows the current limiting resistors for the LEDs on the common cathodes. You could just as easily have them between the 2716 and the 138. I've hung them on the cathodes because it was an easy way to limit the total current for each digit. It does make the brightness of the display somewhat dependent on the digit being displayed—the more segments needed to form the character, the dimmer the display will be. Limiting the current through each segment gives you a more uniform display but it's not really noticeable and, in any event, the 138 maximum current is limited and I just didn't want to bother with the math. Remember the eighty second Law of Life and Design:

SOMETIMES IT'S JUST NOT WORTH THE TROUBLE

especially when it doesn't make any real difference.

124

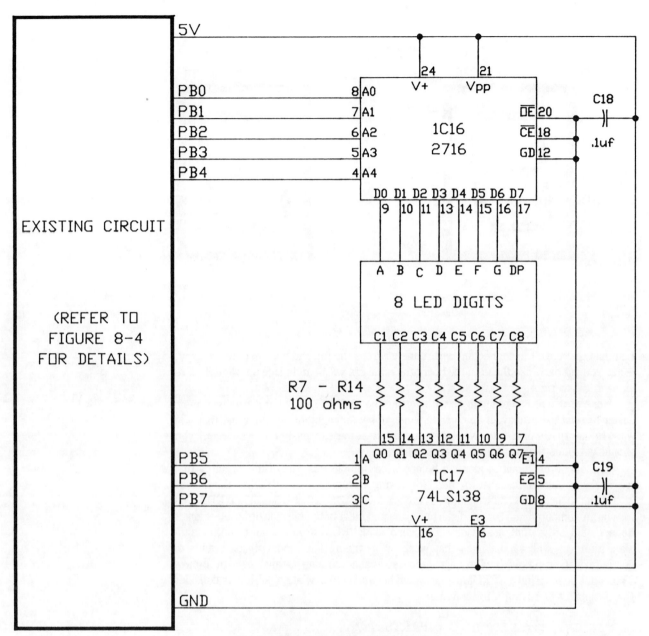

Fig. 9-4. Schematic of the display circuit.

BUILDING THE CIRCUIT

The scheme we're using for the display puts the major emphasis on software so we won't be having to add much in the way of hardware to the circuit. Unfortunately though, there's no getting around the fact that eight digits may mean a lot of wiring. You can cut the number of connections needed by using a multidigit display instead of eight separate digits. They can be of any size or color since the only characteristic required by the circuit in Fig. 9-4 is that the digits be common cathode ones.

There's one more thing to consider when you're choosing the digits to put on the breadboard and that's the orientation of the segments with respect to the pins. If you use digits that have the pins along the sides of the package it will be awkward to read them when they're put on the board since the numerals will be laying on their sides. A reasonable way around this problem is to use parts like the FND-500 series from

125

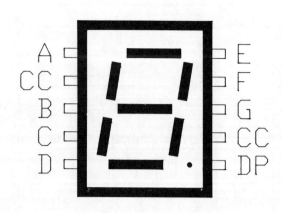
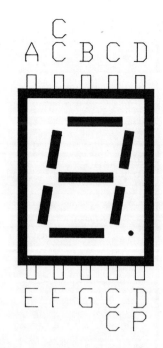

Fig. 9-5. Displays can have their pins arranged either vertically or horizontally.

Fairchild that have the connecting pins running across the top and bottom of the display. When you put parts like these on the board the numbers will be right side up when they're viewed left to right.

None of this has anything to do with getting the circuit to work but it makes it much easier to read the display. If you have a bunch of seven segment digits around that you want to use that's fine, but if you're going to buy some expressly for this circuit, you should get ones that have pins running horizontally.

The only other point to mention before we assemble this part of the circuit is that we've finally come up against the need for having a programmed EPROM—the display isn't going to be much good without it. There are lots of places that will program EPROMs for you. A computer club is a good starting place and most of the big mail order electronics houses offer programming services. They also sell EPROM programmers—both stand-alone units as well as the ones that work as peripherals for most major brands of computers. Getting involved in microprocessor-based circuits means that you'll have a constant need to burn EPROMs so it would be worth your while to seriously consider the possibility of buying a programmer.

PARTS

1 - 74LS138 1 of 8 Decoder
1 - Character Generator Eprom
8 - Seven Segment Common Cathode Displays
8 - 100 ohm resistors ¼ watt
2 - .1µF capacitors

MINIMUM EQUIPMENT
Logic Probe

The location of the parts on the breadboard is shown in the placement diagram of Fig. 9-6, but how you lay out the digits will depend on the display you use. I used displays with horizontal pins but if you're using some other ones you'll have to lay them out differently. The choice of the display layout is cosmetic though and has nothing to do with how the circuit works. Be careful when you're wiring it up, however, since it takes a lot of connections to get all the digits working.

REMOVE THE
TEMPORARY DISPLAY
FROM FIGURE 8-5

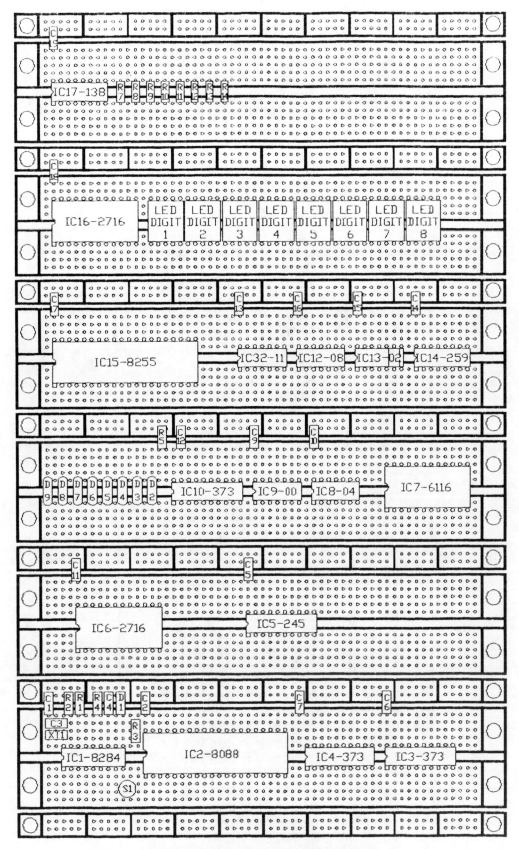

ALL BUS STRIPS ARE TIED IN PARALLEL
AND CARRY ONLY POWER AND GROUND

Fig. 9-6. Placement diagram for the display circuit.

CONNECTIONS TO IC16 (2716)	
Pin #	Connect to
1	No Connection
2	No Connection
3	No Connection
4	8255 pin #22 (PB4)
5	8255 pin #21 (PB3)
6	8255 pin #20 (PB2)
7	8255 pin #19 (PB1)
8	8255 pin #18 (PB0)
9	LED `A' Segments
10	LED `B' Segments
11	LED `C' Segments
12	Ground
13	LED `D' Segments
14	LED `E' Segments
15	LED `F' Segments
16	LED `G' Segments
17	LED Decimal Points
18	Ground
19	No Connection
20	Ground
21	5 Volts
22	No Connection
23	No Connection
24	5 Volts

Table 9-1. Connections Made to the 2716 (IC16).

CONNECTIONS TO IC17 (74LS138)	
Pin	Connect to
1	8255 pin #23 (PB5)
2	8255 pin #24 (PB6)
3	8255 pin #25 (PB7)
4	Ground
5	Ground
6	5 Volts
7	Digit #7 Resistor
8	Ground
9	Digit #6 Resistor
10	Digit #5 Resistor
11	Digit #4 Resistor
12	Digit #3 Resistor
13	Digit #2 Resistor
14	Digit #2 Resistor
15	Digit #1 Resistor
16	5 Volts

Table 9-2. Connections Made to the 74LS138 (IC17).

Once all the parts (including the current limiting resistors and decoupling capacitors) are on the board, take a second to check for a short on the supply pins. A bad connection will keep the display from working, but a general short circuit may blow things up and the seventy eighth Law of Life and Design clearly states:

ANYTHING THAT CAN BLOW UP WILL BLOW UP

because that's the way things are. Mistakes on a breadboard always operate on the "jelly side down" principle. If you've never heard of this before, all you have to do to find out exactly what it means is butter a piece of bread and drop it on the floor.

Once everything is on the board and connected, run the test program from the last chapter. Nothing meaningful will show up on the display but if the program operates properly, (as it did before the display parts were put on the board), you'll know the chances are good that you made no mistakes in adding the new parts to the breadboard.

CHECKING IT OUT

The addition of the display has increased the circuit complexity past the point where a six or eight-byte program will adequately test the circuit. It's certainly possible, and good practice for you as well, to write a small program that will put a particular hex number on any or all the digits in the display. In order to really exercise the whole circuit

```
;       ****************************************************************
;       *                                                              *
;       *    A TEST PROGRAM FOR THE 8088 CIRCUIT USING ADDRESSES        *
;       *    80h THROUGH 87h AS LOCATIONS FOR THE COUNTER DATA.         *
;       *                                                              *
;       ****************************************************************
;
;  ------------------------------------------------------------------------
;This program will use 80h - 87h to store an eight digit count, transfer the
;contents to the eight digits at port 1, and blank leading zeros.  The 8 digits
;are connected to Port #1 (B) on the 8255 and the bit assignments are:
;
;                     8255       Connection
;                     ==============================
;                     PB-0      2716 Chargen - A0
;                     PB-1      2716 Chargen - A1
;                     PB-2      2716 Chargen - A2
;                     PB-3      2716 Chargen - A3
;                     PB-4      2716 Chargen - A4
;                     PB-5      138 DigitSel - A0
;                     PB-6      138 DigitSel - A1
;                     PB-7      138 DigitSel - A2
;
;The first five lines, PB-0 to PB-1, select the character to be displayed and
;the last three lines, PB-5 to PB-7, select the digit to be turned on.  The
;program will count from 0 to 99999999 and then start all over again.
;  ------------------------------------------------------------------------
;
TITLE   Test RAM storage and digit display.
;
; **********************************************************************************
; *                           SYSTEM EQUATES                                      *
; **********************************************************************************
```

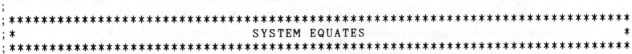
Fig. 9-7. COUNT.ASM—A diagnostic program for the display.

```
FIXED                   SEGMENT AT 0000h        ;All the variable storage will
                        ASSUME  DS:FIXED         ;be at the bottom of RAM.
        DELAY           EQU     DS:[100h]        ;Address of the delay constant.
        WAITCNT         EQU     0036h            ;The time delay constant.
        DISPLAY1        EQU     DS:[80h]         ;Digit #1.
        DISPLAY2        EQU     DS:[81h]         ;Digit #2.
        DISPLAY3        EQU     DS:[82h]         ;Digit #3.
        DISPLAY4        EQU     DS:[83h]         ;Digit #4.
        DISPLAY5        EQU     DS:[84h]         ;Digit #5.
        DISPLAY6        EQU     DS:[85h]         ;Digit #6.
        DISPLAY7        EQU     DS:[86h]         ;Digit #7.
        DISPLAY8        EQU     DS:[87h]         ;Digit #8.
FIXED                   ENDS                     ;No more variables.
;
;********************************************************************************
;*                      SET THE 8088 SEGMENTS                                  *
;********************************************************************************
BOB             SEGMENT                          ;Define initial segments.
                ASSUME  CS:BOB,DS:BOB,SS:BOB     ;Set all segment registers to
                                                 ;the same location.
                ORG 100h                         ;Set program start location.
                                                 ;head of the program.


;********************************************************************************
;*              INITIALIZE THE PORTS, STACK, AND DATA SEGMENT                  *
;********************************************************************************
START:          MOV     AL,90h                   ;This sets the 8255 to operate
                                                 ;in Mode 0 (basic input output)
                                                 ;with port 0 as an input and
                OUT     03h,AL                   ;ports 1 and 2 as outputs.
                MOV     AX,0070h                 ;Set the location of the stack
                MOV     SS,AX                    ;bottom at 00700h and set the
                MOV     SP,00F0h                 ;top of the stack at 000F0h.
                MOV     AX,0000h                 ;Tell the 8088 that the data
                MOV     DS,AX                    ;segment is at 00000h.
;
;********************************************************************************
;*                      ZERO OUT THE DISPLAY                                   *
;********************************************************************************
BLANK:          MOV     AL,00h                   ;Now load the value that will
                                                 ;cause the character generator
                                                 ;to send zeros to each segment.
                MOV     BYTE PTR DISPLAY1,AL      ;Store the number '0' character
                MOV     BYTE PTR DISPLAY2,AL      ;in each of the locations that
                MOV     BYTE PTR DISPLAY3,AL      ;are reserved for the numbers
                MOV     BYTE PTR DISPLAY4,AL      ;to be displayed in each of the
                MOV     BYTE PTR DISPLAY5,AL      ;displays.
                MOV     BYTE PTR DISPLAY6,AL      ;Once all the eight locations
                MOV     BYTE PTR DISPLAY7,AL      ;have been loaded, the display
                MOV     BYTE PTR DISPLAY8,AL      ;can be set to zeros by calling
                CALL    SCAN                     ;the digit scanning routine.
                JMP     GO                       ;It's SHOWTIME folks.

;
;********************************************************************************
;*                      TIME DELAY ROUTINE                                     *
;********************************************************************************
;The main loop consists of decrementing the memory location 100h and the test
;done by JNZ.  DEC takes 32 clocks, each CALL takes 23 clocks, the SCAN routine
;takes 240 clocks, the CMP takes 23 clocks, and JNZ, (if a jump is executed),
;will take 16 clocks.  The rest of the instructions that are outside the main
;loop add up to 35 clocks but since they're only executed once, they don't have
;much to add to the total delay time.  The delay from this routine is:
```

Fig. 9-7. (continued)

```
;      [(Total Loop Clocks X Loop Count) + Outside Loop Clocks] X Clock Time
;                                      or
;                    [(597 X Loop Count) + 35] X Clock Time
;
;At 4.77 MHz, each clock lasts 210 microseconds, so by executing the whole loop
;55h, (85 decimal) times, we'll get a delay of a hundredth of a second.  Since
;the counting loop in the main program that calls the delay loop takes about 31
;microseconds, subtracting that from the delay loop time will cause the display
;to increment at a rate of one count per hundredth of a second.
; ----------------------------------------------------------------------------
WAITASEC:       MOV     WORD PTR DELAY,WAITCNT   ;Set up a timing delay constant.
WAITASEC1:      DEC     WORD PTR DELAY          ;Decrement the delay constant.
                CALL    SCAN                    ;Put the current values in all
                                                ;eight of the displays.
; ----------------------------------------------------------------------------
;Since IC10 latches ANY data sent to ANY port, the LED's will change every time
;an OUT instruction is executed.  This program sends rapid data out port 1 so
;the LED's will flicker while it runs.  Keeping this OUT instruction inside the
;loop will slow things down but will also make the pulses long enough to be
;easily observed on a scope with a maximum sweep speed of 20 microseconds.
; ----------------------------------------------------------------------------
                CALL    SCAN                    ;Twice as often=twice as bright
                CMP     WORD PTR DELAY,00h      ;Is RAM location 100h zero yet?
                JNZ     WAITASEC1               ;If not, go back to the loop.
                RET                             ;When zero is reached, exit the
                                                ;delay loop and return to the
                                                ;main part of the program.


; ****************************************************************************
; *                   DIGIT MULTIPLEXING ROUTINE                             *
; ****************************************************************************
SCAN:           PUSH    AX                      ;Save the current accumulator.
                PUSHF                           ;Save the current flags.
; ----------------------------------------------------------------------------
;The next several instructions will sequentially load AL with the current value
;of the numbers from the page zero variables and output the current value to
;each of the corresponding digits at port 1.
; ----------------------------------------------------------------------------
                MOV     AL,DISPLAY1             ;Get the current digit 1 value.
                OUT     01h,AL                  ;Send it to the display.
                MOV     AL,DISPLAY2             ;Get the current digit 2 value.
                ADD     AL,20h                  ;Set the high byte for digit 2.
                OUT     01h,AL                  ;Send it to the display.
                MOV     AL,DISPLAY3             ;Get the current digit 3 value.
                ADD     AL,40h                  ;Set the high byte for digit 3.
                OUT     01h,AL                  ;Send it to the display.
                MOV     AL,DISPLAY4             ;Get the current digit 4 value.
                ADD     AL,60h                  ;Set the high byte for digit 4.
                OUT     01h,AL                  ;Send it to the display.
                MOV     AL,DISPLAY5             ;Get the current digit 5 value.
                ADD     AL,80h                  ;Set the high byte for digit 5.
                OUT     01h,AL                  ;Send it to the display.
                MOV     AL,DISPLAY6             ;Get the current digit 6 value.
                ADD     AL,0A0h                 ;Set the high byte for digit 6.
                OUT     01h,AL                  ;Send it to the display.
                MOV     AL,DISPLAY7             ;Get the current digit 7 value.
                ADD     AL,0C0h                 ;Set the high byte for digit 7.
                OUT     01h,AL                  ;Send it to the display.
                MOV     AL,DISPLAY8             ;Get the current digit 8 value.
                ADD     AL,0E0h                 ;Set the high byte for digit 8.
                OUT     01h,AL                  ;Send it to the display.
```

Fig. 9-7. (continued)

```
;*****************************************************************
;*                   MAIN BODY OF THE CODE                      *
;*****************************************************************
GO:             MOV     BYTE PTR DISPLAY1,00h   ;Load a '0' in digit #1
DIGIT1:         CALL    WAITASEC                ;Display the current values and
                                                ;refresh the digit display.
                MOV     AL,DISPLAY1             ;Get the current value in AL.
                CMP     AL,09h                  ;Have we reached '9'?
                JZ      DIGIT2                  ;If so, bump the next digit.
                INC     AL                      ;Add one to the value in AL and
                MOV     BYTE PTR DISPLAY1,AL    ;Store it away safely.
                JMP     DIGIT1                  ;And start again.
DIGIT2:         MOV     BYTE PTR DISPLAY1,00h   ;Put a zero in the first digit.
                MOV     AL,DISPLAY2             ;Get the current digit 2 value.
                CMP     AL,09h                  ;Is it a '9'?
                JZ      DIGIT3                  ;If so, bump the next digit.
                INC     AL                      ;Add one to the value.
                MOV     BYTE PTR DISPLAY2,AL    ;Store it away
                JMP     DIGIT1                  ;And start again.
DIGIT3:         MOV     BYTE PTR DISPLAY2,00h   ;Put a zero in digit #2.
                MOV     AL,DISPLAY3             ;Get the current value in AL.
                CMP     AL,09h                  ;Have we reached '9'?
                JZ      DIGIT4                  ;If so, bump the next digit.
                INC     AL                      ;Add one to the value in AL and
                MOV     BYTE PTR DISPLAY3,AL    ;Store it away safely.
                JMP     DIGIT1                  ;And start again.
DIGIT4:         MOV     BYTE PTR DISPLAY3,00h   ;Put a zero in digit #3.
                MOV     AL,DISPLAY4             ;Get the current digit 3 value.
                CMP     AL,09h                  ;Is it a '9'?
                JZ      DIGIT5                  ;If so, bump the next digit.
                INC     AL                      ;Add one to the value.
                MOV     BYTE PTR DISPLAY4,AL    ;Store it away
                JMP     DIGIT1                  ;And start again.
DIGIT5:         MOV     BYTE PTR DISPLAY4,00h   ;Put a zero in digit #4.
                MOV     AL,DISPLAY5             ;Get the current digit 5 value.
                CMP     AL,09h                  ;Is it a '9'?
                JZ      DIGIT6                  ;If so, bump the next digit.
                INC     AL                      ;Add one to the value.
                MOV     BYTE PTR DISPLAY5,AL    ;Store it away
                JMP     DIGIT1                  ;And start again.
DIGIT6:         MOV     BYTE PTR DISPLAY5,00h   ;Put a zero in digit #5.
                MOV     AL,DISPLAY6             ;Get the current value in AL.
                CMP     AL,09h                  ;Have we reached '9'?
                JZ      DIGIT7                  ;If so, bump the next digit.
                INC     AL                      ;Add one to the value in AL and
                MOV     BYTE PTR DISPLAY6,AL    ;Store it away safely.
                JMP     DIGIT1                  ;And start again.
DIGIT7:         MOV     BYTE PTR DISPLAY6,00h   ;Put a zero in digit #6.
                MOV     AL,DISPLAY7             ;Get the current digit 7 value.
                CMP     AL,09h                  ;Is it a '9'?
                JZ      DIGIT8                  ;If so, bump the next digit.
                INC     AL                      ;Add one to the value.
                MOV     BYTE PTR DISPLAY7,AL    ;Store it away
                JMP     DIGIT1                  ;And start again.
DIGIT8:         MOV     BYTE PTR DISPLAY7,00h   ;Put a zero in digit #7.
                MOV     AL,DISPLAY8             ;Get the current digit 8 value.
                CMP     AL,09h                  ;Is it a '9'?
                JZ      AGAIN                   ;BLANK is too far away.
                INC     AL                      ;Add one to digit #8.
                MOV     BYTE PTR DISPLAY8,AL    ;Store the incremented value.
                JMP     DIGIT1                  ;And start again.
AGAIN:          JMP     BLANK                   ;Blank everything and restart.
```

Fig. 9-7. (continued)

```
;   ---------------------------------------------------------------------------------
            POPF                                    ;Restore the previous flags.
            POP     AX                              ;Restore the previous AX.
            RET
;
; ***********************************************************************************
; *                      T H E   B O O T   C O D E                                 *
; ***********************************************************************************
;This is the location in the 2716 that will be accessed at power up since the
;8088 looks for it's first instruction at FFFF0h.  The 2716 is enabled by any
;address that brings A19 high (8000h - FFFFFh) but the 2716's address lines are
;connected from A0 to A10 on the 8088.  This covers a range of 0000h to 07FFh.
;Since accessing the 2716 means A19 has to be high as well, the 8088 addresses
;for talking to the 2716 are FF800h to FFFFFh.
;The 8088 power up location of FFFF0h is actually 07F0h in the 2716.  The boot
;instruction has to be ORG'ed at 08F0h since the assembler wants to ORG the
;above main code at 0100.  The result is that the 2716 will have the main code
;at 0000h and the boot code at 07F0h.
;   ---------------------------------------------------------------------------------
;
            ORG     8F0h                            ;The 2716 location for the 8088
                                                    ;power-up instruction allowing
                                                    ;for the assembler's ORG 100
                                                    ;requirement for the main code.
            JMP     START                           ;Go to the main code located at
                                                    ;0000h in the 2716.
            DB      00,00,00,00,00,00,00            ;Nul bytes to fill the 2716
            DB      00,00,00,00,00,00               ;with 00's after the power up
                                                    ;jump described above.
;
; ***********************************************************************************
; *                     THE END OF THE PROGRAM                                     *
; ***********************************************************************************
BOB         ENDS                                    ;Tell assembler this is the end
                                                    ;of code for this segment.
            END     START                           ;Tell assembler this is the end
                                                    ;of the program.
```

<u>Hex Dump of COUNT.ASM</u>

```
0000 - B0 90 E6 03 B8 70 00 8E D0 BC F0 00 B8 00 00 8E
0010 - D8 B0 00 A2 80 00 A2 81 00 A2 82 00 A2 83 00 A2
0020 - 84 00 A2 85 00 A2 86 00 A2 87 00 E8 1B 00 EB 54
0030 - 90 C7 06 00 01 36 00 FF 0E 00 01 E8 0B 00 E8 08
0040 - 00 83 3E 00 01 00 75 EF C3 50 9C A0 80 00 E6 01
0050 - A0 81 00 04 20 E6 01 A0 82 00 04 40 E6 01 A0 83
0060 - 00 04 60 E6 01 A0 84 00 04 80 E6 01 A0 85 00 04
0070 - A0 E6 01 A0 86 00 04 C0 E6 01 A0 87 00 04 E0 E6
0080 - 01 9D 58 C3 C6 06 80 00 00 E8 A5 FF A0 80 00 3C
0090 - 09 74 07 FE C0 A2 80 00 EB EF C6 06 80 00 00 A0
00A0 - 81 00 3C 09 74 07 FE C0 A2 81 00 EB DC C6 06 81
00B0 - 00 00 A0 82 00 3C 09 74 07 FE C0 A2 82 00 EB C9
00C0 - C6 06 82 00 00 A0 83 00 3C 09 74 07 FE C0 A2 83
00D0 - 00 EB B6 C6 06 83 00 00 A0 84 00 3C 09 74 07 FE
00E0 - C0 A2 84 00 EB A3 C6 06 84 00 00 A0 85 00 3C 09
00F0 - 74 07 FE C0 A2 85 00 EB 90 C6 06 85 00 00 A0 86
0100 - 00 3C 09 74 08 FE C0 A2 86 00 E9 7C FF C6 06 86
0110 - 00 00 A0 87 00 3C 09 74 08 FE C0 A2 87 00 E9 68
0120 - FF E9 ED FE 00 00 00 00 00 00 00 00 00 00 00 00
0130 - 00 00 00 00 00 00 00 00 00 00 00 00 00 00 00 00
0140 - 00 00 00 00 00 00 00 00 00 00 00 00 00 00 00 00
```

Fig. 9-7. (continued)

```
0150  -  07CF are filled with zeros

07D0  -  00 00 00 00 00 00 00 00 00 00 00 00 00 00 00 00
07E0  -  00 00 00 00 00 00 00 00 00 00 00 00 00 00 00 00
07F0  -  E9 0D F8 00 00 00 00 00 00 00 00 00 00 00 00 00
```

Fig. 9-7. (continued)

you'll need software designed with that in mind. You can write your own but the listing shown in Fig. 9-7 will not only test the display, but do some other things as well.

None of the programs we've used so far made direct use of the RAM in the circuit. The listing at the end of the last chapter made a CALL to the time delay routine and, since that involved a stack operation, we know that the RAM is working (remember that the 8088 builds the stack in RAM). This didn't really tell us anything since we left the RAM usage to the 8088.

The listing in Fig. 9-7 uses several locations in RAM as storage for the values to be displayed. Not only that, but the opening of the program, (at the label "START" in the listing), forces a location and size for the stack and also defines the data segment to be at 00000h. If you're new to assembler listings, you may find some of the syntax to be confusing. There's nothing I'd like better than spending time to describe the use of the assembler and assembly language programming in general, but the subject is much too complex to get into. There are lots of books that treat these subjects in detail and I strongly urge everyone to get some of them and take the time to become at least familiar with them.

I've made sure that the listings in this book are well commented so you shouldn't have any trouble following the flow of the programs. A few of the lines, such as the SEGMENT statements, are requirements for the assembler, not the 8088. If you don't understand what they are, don't worry about it since there's a good chance that the assembler you decide to use won't require them anyway.

As our circuit gets more and more complex, we'll need increasingly complicated software to drive it. You'll notice that several routines are used on each piece of software we run. This makes it easier to understand the listing and, as we'll see later, they (or variations on them) form the basis for a general BIOS for the circuit. We'll get into software later on, but if you want to make maximum use of the circuit we're building you're going to have to learn much more about assembler programming than we can possibly discuss here.

Since the listing in Fig. 9-7 will increment the display every hundredth of a second, we've reached a kind of milestone because the circuit will actually do a real world job—work as a stopwatch. When you run it, however, you'll discover that software based clocks leave a lot to be desired as far as accuracy is concerned.

The problem is that the count, in the program, is based on one third of the 14 MHz clock (4.77 MHz). If you want real accuracy, you have to divide by a lot more than three. This brings up an important point because one of the most useful things you can have on a single board system like ours is an accurate timebase. Fortunately that's not too difficult to do.

10

Clocks and
General Purpose Timing

Timing is everything—with life in general and microprocessor-based circuits in particular. If things don't happen at exactly the right time they might as well not happen at all. The heartbeat of the 8088 is the 4.77 MHz clock provided by the 8284 and all the circuitry we've designed so far is driven by it. But remember that the circuit we're building is being designed as a controller and a controller, no matter what else it does, should be able to control things.

We've spent a lot of bench and brain time adding I/O to the system and, even though that's a big part of controlling things, a complete controller needs more than just a way in and out of the system. In order to make our circuit as useful as possible we should have several clocks available . . . and not just random clocks either. Let's talk about that for a minute.

From the point of view of timing, there are two ways our circuit can see things happen—synchronously or asynchronously. In other words, events can either be locked to our system clock or not. In the best of all possible worlds, it's nice to keep things in phase with the system clock since it makes it much easier to process the data produced by the event. There's actually so much of an advantage to this arrangement that buffer circuits usually sit between the real world and I/O ports to delay or lengthen external events and bring them into phase with the system clock.

The details of this kind of circuit however, vary with the kind of event being monitored and aren't really the responsibility of our controller. What our responsibility is though, is to provide a series of clocks that are derived from the system clock.

Asynchronous, or random events are dealt with differently. There's no way to know when they're going to happen (think of a microprocessor-based burglar alarm). These can either be dealt with in software by using loops to repeatedly test a port, in hardware by using the 8088's READY and TEST lines, or by a combination of these using the interrupt handling facilities built into the 8088. Even these asynchronous events can often make use of clocks that are in phase with the system clock.

Whatever you plan on doing with the completed circuit, you'll find it a terrific convenience to have a wide assortment of frequencies available for use. Since it's so easy to have the circuit provide them for us, it doesn't make any sense not to do it. Besides, the forty third Law of Life and Design doesn't really give you any other alternatives:

> **YOU ONLY LIVE ONCE OR TWICE,**
> **MIGHT AS WELL TRY EVERYTHING**

and anyway, it only takes a couple of chips to get the job done so why not do it.

HARDWARE CONSIDERATIONS

This part of the circuit is the first we've talked about that doesn't have a particular job in the main circuit. Even if we use the clocks we're about to generate, their main purpose is just to be there for any peripheral device that gets hung on the main circuit.

Since these are going to be synchronous clocks, our first job is to find out what part of our system is going to supply the fundamental frequency for them. It should come as no big surprise to you that any time you talk about frequency generation on the board your eyes should go to the 8284. After all, not only is that its job but it's also the IC that's supplying the basic clock for the whole system.

The 8284 has two outputs that are designed specifically for the job we have in mind. The first one, OSC, is a buffered version of the main crystal frequency (14.318 MHz) and the second, PCLK, is half the CPU clock, or 2.386 MHz. Remember that the 4.77 MHz 8088 clock is one third the main crystal frequency so PCLK is one sixth the main crystal frequency.

We could get by with just buffering these two clocks and sending the buffered version out to the real world but there's no sense in shortchanging ourselves. By putting a divider in the circuit, we can generate a rich assortment of related frequencies and, since there's no telling what kind of peripherals are going to be controlled by our circuit, there's also no telling what kind of clock is going to be needed to drive them.

Frequency division is one of the first circuit exercises people get into when they get introduced to digital design. It's also such a basic part of any designer's repertoire that there's a wide assortment of ICs to choose from when the need arises.

There are two basic kinds of dividers available—synchronous and ripple counters. The difference between them defines the way they can be used. Synchronous counters have outputs that always change state in phase with the clock they're dividing. That means there's always a valid count on their outputs since they all change state at the same time.

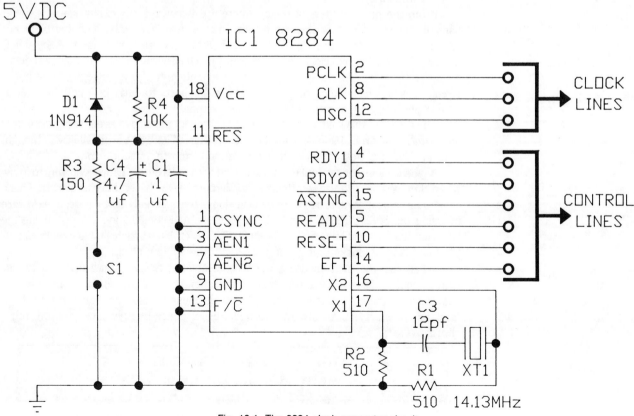

Fig. 10-1. The 8284 clock generator circuit.

136

Ripple counters have one synchronous output—the first, or least significant one—since that's the only one that's driven by the input clock. All the other outputs in the chain use the preceding output as a clock. As a result, there's no way you can be sure you're getting a valid count at the outputs. This should be clear if you take time to go through an example.

The outputs of a synchronous counter will go directly from a count of seven to a count of eight, but ripple counters will output several different counts between the two numbers.

```
Count of seven - 0 1 1 1
Invalid output - 0 1 1 0
Invalid output - 0 1 0 0
Count of eight - 1 0 0 0
```

The invalid counts don't stay on the bus for any length of time. As a matter of fact, they last considerably less than one cycle of the input clock but even so, they do appear at the outputs. If you want to use a divider for things like high speed address decoding you're letting yourself in for considerable brain damage by using a ripple counter since the circuit decoding the address will undoubtedly see some of the invalid counts as the address they're looking for. The main use for ripple counters is either straight frequency division or keeping track of how many events occur over a period of time. Since all we want to do is frequency division, we can use either a synchronous or ripple counter.

BUILDING THE CIRCUIT

It doesn't take much in the way of circuit design to do the job we have in mind—the whole thing is done with two chips. The first one divides down the input frequencies, and the second buffers them before they get sent out to the big bad world. Buffering isn't strictly a necessity but it can save a lot of potential brain damage. Remember that there's no telling what a peripheral device will do. The old fifty sixth Law of Life and Design:

REAL WORLD STUFF DOESN'T ALWAYS FOLLOW THE RULES

is a constant reminder that peripherals have a nasty habit of feeding incredible nastiness back to the controlling circuit. Most of the time you'll see the signals you planned on getting but, when you're least expecting it, other things will show up at the bus. I'm talking about the three evil S's—shorts, spikes, and surges.

Since the damage these things do can be minimized by buffering the board level signals you might as well promote the idea of buffering from an afterthought to an essential part of the design. Think of them as electronic crash helmets—they only have to work once to be worth the extra time needed to put them on the board.

PARTS
1 - 74LS393 Dual Binary Counter
1 - 74LS244 Octal Buffer
2 - .1 μF capacitors

MINIMUM EQUIPMENT
Logic Probe
Multimeter

The frequency division we need can be done by a 74LS393. This is a dual binary ripple counter—two counters in the same package. Since there are two available master frequencies generated by the 8284, we can divide each of them down using the two halves of the 393. The buffer we'll use, a standard 74LS244, can take care of 8 signals so, unless we use another 244, we won't be able to buffer all the clocks we're generating.

The choice of which ones to buffer is up to you. The ones I picked can be seen in the schematic of Fig. 10-3. If you're not sure which would be the most useful for your applications, you can wire the 244 inputs through jumpers which let you select the frequencies or, if you want them all available all the time, just add another 244.

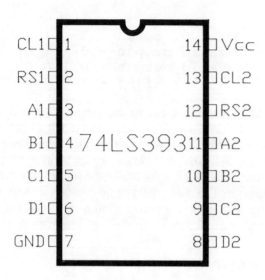

Fig. 10-2. The pinouts of the 74LS393.

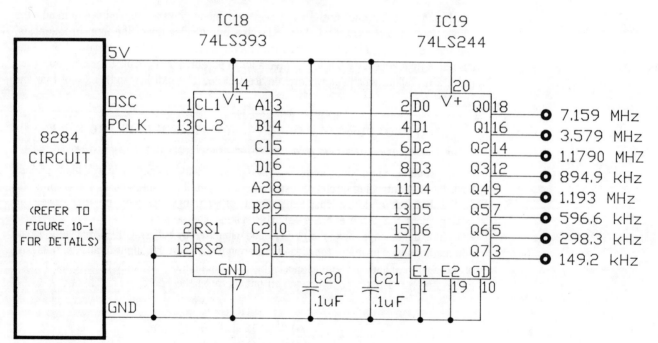

Fig. 10-3. The frequency division circuit.

In order to get the circuit working, put the chips on the board as shown in the placement diagram of Fig. 10-4 and carefully make the connections indicated in Tables 10-1 and 10-2.

Add the two capacitors to the circuit and check the legs of the power supply for a short. After you've done that, you can power-up the circuit with any of the programs we've already discussed. There won't be any noticeable difference in the behavior of the circuit, but you should find a bunch of new clocks at the outputs of the 244.

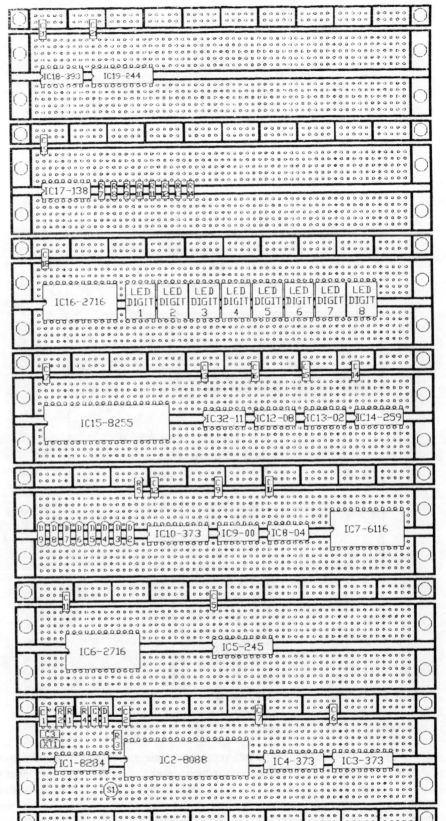

Fig. 10-4. Placement diagram for the frequency division circuit.

ALL BUS STRIPS ARE TIED IN PARALLEL
AND CARRY ONLY POWER AND GROUND

CONNECTIONS TO IC18 (74LS393)	
Pin #	Connect to
1	8284 pin #2 (PCLK)
2	Ground
3	IC19 pin #8
4	IC19 pin #6
5	IC19 pin #4
6	IC19 pin #2
7	Ground
8	IC19 pin #17
9	IC19 pin #15
10	IC19 pin #13
11	IC19 pin #11
12	Ground
13	8284 pin #12 (OSC)
14	5 Volts

Table 10-1. Connections Made to the 74LS393 (IC18).

CONNECTIONS TO IC19 (74LS244)	
Pin #	Connect to
1	Ground
2	IC18 pin #6
3	No Connection
4	IC18 pin #5
5	No Connection
6	IC18 pin #4
7	No Connection
8	IC18 pin #3
9	No Connection
10	Ground
11	IC18 pin #11
12	No Connection
13	IC18 pin #10
14	No Connection
15	IC18 pin #9
16	No Connection
17	IC18 pin #8
18	No Connection
19	Ground
20	5 Volts

Table 10-2. Connections Made to the 74LS244 (IC19).

If you've got an audible logic probe, you'll hear different tones for the different frequencies, but the only way to be sure everything is working, is to use either a frequency counter or a scope. We're way past the point where it's sufficient just to know that something is happening on the lines—the circuit can only be completely checked out by knowing exactly what's going on. As circuit complexity increases, so does the equipment needed to troubleshoot it.

Now that we have some usable synchronous clocks, there are some additional necessities we can add to the circuit. The most important of all of them is a keyboard for data entry. And that's exactly what we're going to turn to next.

11

Adding a Keyboard

EVEN THOUGH THE SYSTEM WE'RE BUILDING IS DESIGNED TO BE CONTROLLED BY FIRM-ware stored in an EPROM, there are times when you'll have to talk to it directly. There are lots of reasons why you might have to do this such as putting in variables, entering quick instructions, or as more likely to be the case, debugging software. In any event, every application you might have for the circuit, sooner or later you'll find a need to use the keyboard.

One of the most useful jobs a circuit like ours can do is to help you learn about controllers in general and the 8088 in particular. Being able to assemble the hardware is only the first step in getting familiar with the 8088. We saw early on that putting together the circuit is only half the battle. Once everything is wired up and working, you still have to take off your hat, bow from the waist, and enter the temple of the great god Software. Frankenstein couldn't control his creation either.

DESIGN CONSIDERATIONS

There are three main areas to think about when you're working out the design for a keyboard intended to be used with a microprocessor-based circuit.

1. How to decode the individual keys.
2. How to communicate with the main circuit.
3. How to handle the keyboard data.

The first of these is a hardware problem, the last one is a software problem, and the second one is a combination of the two. Since we can't do anything about the last two without first taking care of the hardware, let's go through that part of it first.

A keyboard is just a collection of switches along with some way of having each keypress generate a unique code. No matter how many keys you have on the keyboard, they're always wired together in one of two ways—in an XY matrix or with one common leg. Larger keyboards are usually wired in a matrix since fewer connections are needed. Smaller keyboards can be done either way—the choice of going one way or the other, is usually made because of other considerations such as what control signals are available and the unique needs of the particular circuit.

Since we don't need a lot of keys, we can use either approach in designing our keyboard. I'm using a common leg design because a lot of the needed parts for this type of design are already on the board, and this type of circuit is perfectly suited to the system we've been building. It also doesn't need much in the way of new parts which is kind

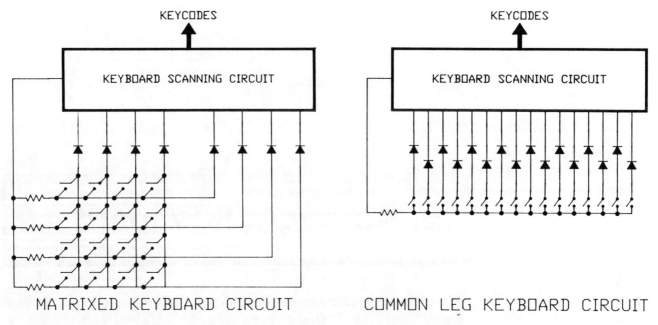

KEYCODES

KEYBOARD SCANNING CIRCUIT

MATRIXED KEYBOARD CIRCUIT

KEYCODES

KEYBOARD SCANNING CIRCUIT

COMMON LEG KEYBOARD CIRCUIT

Fig. 11-1. The basic layout of matrixed and common leg keyboard designs.

of nice since it's always a good idea to keep the parts count as low as possible. Remember the fifth Law of Life and Design:

**THE FEWER PARTS YOU HAVE TO ADD,
THE FEWER PARTS YOU HAVE TO REPLACE**

and we haven't even started to talk about the brain damage that comes from designing a PC Board.

The heart of our keyboard is a 4514. This one of sixteen decoder is a good choice for keyboard encoding since it's fairly simple to use and is a CMOS part to boot. The latter is really important because keyboards are one of the few integral parts of our circuit that uses mechanical parts and whenever you deal with these, you want to make the circuit as noise immune as possible.

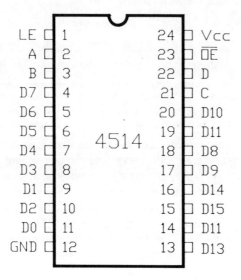

	4514	
LE ☐ 1		24 ☐ Vcc
A ☐ 2		23 ☐ $\overline{OE}$
B ☐ 3		22 ☐ D
D7 ☐ 4		21 ☐ C
D6 ☐ 5		20 ☐ D10
D5 ☐ 6		19 ☐ D11
D4 ☐ 7		18 ☐ D8
D3 ☐ 8		17 ☐ D9
D1 ☐ 9		16 ☐ D14
D2 ☐ 10		15 ☐ D15
D0 ☐ 11		14 ☐ D11
GND ☐ 12		13 ☐ D13

Fig. 11-2. The pinouts of the 4514.

CMOS parts have the ability to swallow noise and the types of circuit glitches that make TTL based circuitry go bananas. The main reason for this is that CMOS transistors change state at just about halfway up the supply rail. Unless you're really unlucky, most of the noise you have running around your circuit is in the millivolt range with an occasional excursion to a volt or so. You should reread the discussion we had in Chapter 7 about circuit noise and actually make the measurements I suggested back then.

Since the CMOS transition point is so far from either end of the supply, CMOS parts usually aren't even aware of the low-level noise in the circuit. They're also a lot quieter when they change state and don't generate the kind of spikes that are forcing us to include one capacitor for each IC we've put in the circuit so far. If you've been having a lot of noise problems on your board, one definite way to get rid of them is to replace the standard TTL parts in our system with their CMOS equivalents. There are some limitations, however.

The frequencies we're dealing with aren't up there with radar and microwave ovens, but they're a lot higher than can be handled by a standard 4000 series CMOS part operating at 5 volts. If you do want to substitute CMOS parts for some of the latches and gates we have in the circuit, make sure and use either 74HC or 74HCT parts. These are pin for pin CMOS equivalents of the TTL parts and they're fast enough to be used in our circuit. Most mail order houses carry a good range of them and they're only a bit more expensive than the regular TTL parts they're replacing. But let's get back to the keyboard.

The 4514 is one of sixteen, active high decoder that's driven by four binary weighted inputs. The basic idea behind our keyboard is to have a binary counter sequence through all the sixteen outputs of the 4514. Each of the keyboard switches have one leg on a 4514 output and the other leg on a common, "any key pressed" line. The common line is held low by a resistor and will only go high when a key is pressed and the output connected to the key is selected by the four address inputs.

A high on the "any key pressed line" is the signal for the keyboard circuit to latch the data on the keyboard address bus. Each keypress will generate a unique four-bit code which can be read from the latch under the control of software since we'll connect the latch to one of the ports on the 8255. We can easily increase the number of codes generated by the keyboard beyond sixteen by using an eight-bit latch for storage. The extra four bits can be hardwired to another four switches and used in conjunction with the switches connected to the 4514's outputs. This will give us the ability to set or clear any combination of the upper four bits being fed to the keyboard I/O port and allows our simple keyboard to generate 256 unique keycodes—more than enough for our system.

The final design we've worked out for the keyboard therefore, will have twenty one keys. Sixteen keys are encoded by the counter, four keys are hardwired as shift keys, and the last key, (just in case you don't remember), is the reset key connected to the 8284. The actual layout of the circuit, shown in Fig. 11-3, is very close to being the complete circuit. I said *"almost"* because even though the circuit will generate keycodes and latch them in the 373, we haven't worked out any way for the circuit to talk to the 8088.

The diodes between the keys and the 4514 output are there as a safeguard for people who can't type. The unselected state of the 4514 outputs is low and the selected state is high. This means that if two encoded keys are pressed at the same time, you're going to see a short on the common switch line. Science says that this is a bad thing.

With the diodes in the circuit, the 4514 outputs are OR'ed together and isolated from each other. Pressing two keys may give you an incorrect character but it won't do any damage to the circuit. By grounding the 4514's $\overline{\text{Output Enable}}$ input (pin #23) and tying the Latch Enable input (pin #1) high, the chip will constantly follow the state of its four select inputs.

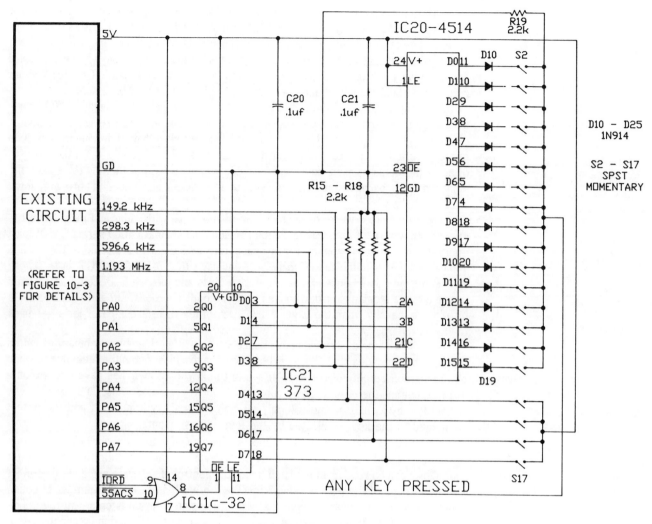

Fig. 11-3. The keyboard circuit.

BUILDING THE CIRCUIT

It only takes two chips to build the circuit but there are also a host of passive components needed to make it work. Keep a careful eye on the polarity of the diodes since it's often hard to see the band on a small signal glass diode like the ones we're using.

PARTS
1 - 4514 One of Sixteen Decoder
1 - 74LS373 Octal Latch
16 - 1N914 Switching Diodes
5 - 2.2k Resistors
20 - SPST Momentary Switches
1 - .1 μF Capacitor

MINIMUM EQUIPMENT
Logic Probe

By the time you've gotten this far, you should all be Olympic Gold Medalists at adding new parts to the board. But the large number of components needed for the keyboard make it easy to screw up so keep a special eye on things as you wire up the keyboard. Put the parts on the board as shown in the placement diagram of Fig. 11-4 and connect them according to Tables 11-1 and 11-2.

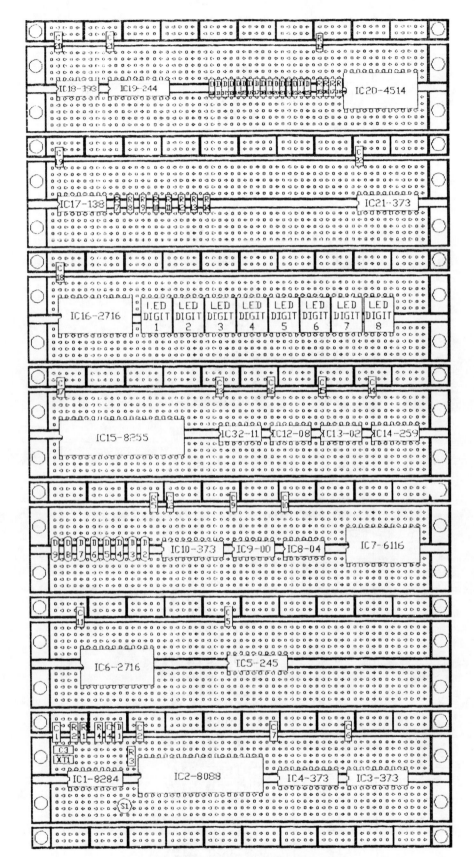

Fig. 11-4. Placement diagram for the keyboard circuit.

ALL BUS STRIPS ARE TIED IN PARALLEL
AND CARRY ONLY POWER AND GROUND

145

CONNECTIONS TO IC20 (4514)	
Pin #	Connect to
1	5 Volts
2	IC18 pin #3
3	IC18 pin #4
4	Anode DO-7
5	Anode DO-6
6	Anode DO-5
7	Anode DO-4
8	Anode DO-3
9	Anode DO-1
10	Anode DO-2
11	Anode DO-0
12	Ground
13	Anode DO-13
14	Anode DO-12
15	Anode DO-15
16	Anode DO-14
17	Anode DO-9
18	Anode DO-8
19	Anode DO-11
20	Anode DO-10
21	IC18 pin #5
22	IC18 pin #6
23	Ground
24	5 Volts

Table 11-1. Connections Made to the 4514 (IC20).

CONNECTIONS TO IC21 (74LS373)	
Pin #	Connect to
1	No Connection
2	8255 Pin #4 (PA0)
3	IC18 Pin #3
4	IC18 pin #4
5	8255 pin #3 (PA1)
6	8255 pin #2 (PA2)
7	IC18 pin #5
8	IC18 pin #6
9	8255 pin #1 (PA3)
10	Ground
11	Any Key Pressed Line
12	8255 pin #40 (PA4)
13	Switch S16
14	Switch S17
15	8255 pin #39
16	8255 pin #38
17	Switch S18
18	Switch S19
19	8255 pin #37
20	5 Volts

Table 11-2. Connections Made to the 74LS373 (IC21).

The connections for the resistors, diodes, and switches are shown in the keyboard schematic of Fig. 11-3. You can connect the switches either directly to the 4514 outputs or to the cathodes of the diodes, whichever is more convenient for you. It's only important that the 4514 outputs be isolated from each other. All the resistors in the circuit have the same job—as pull down resistors to keep the lines from floating when no key is being pressed.

The keyboard switches can be arranged in a square, row, or just about any geometric pattern that suits your fancy. You can mount them on the breadboard or use a separate board and connect them to the main board with ribbon cable. Since there are 22 connections, you can use a 24-pin header on the breadboard and ribbon cable with a standard 24-pin connector. We're not dealing with high frequencies here—the low bit of the 4514 is being fed with a 1.2 MHz clock and the keyboard is being scanned at one sixteenth that rate (75 kHz) so you can use plain ribbon cable.

We haven't finished with the keyboard so there's not much point in snooping around the circuit. If you just can't resist it, connect the $\overline{\text{Output Enable}}$ pin of the 373, (pin #1), to ground since we've left it floating and power-up the circuit. If you put a logic probe on any of the 4514 outputs you should be able to detect the 75 kHz pulses as the clock scans across the outputs. The circuit is simple and the only things that could cause problems are the same ones that always cause problems. I'm talking about incorrect connections, putting parts in backwards (you were careful about the diodes, weren't you?), or even leaving out some connections altogether.

COMMUNICATING WITH THE MAIN CIRCUIT

The outputs of the latch are connected to one of the ports on the 8255, so it's no surprise that the keyboard is going to be dealt with as an I/O device. This is a standard method for handling this, but there are others as well. Some systems reserve one or more memory locations for keyboard data—this is nice because it dumps the keyboard data right into the 8088's memory map making it immediately accessible to the system. The down side of this arrangement is that you need a lot of decoders to select the keyboard location. By having the keyboard talk to the 8088 through an I/O port, it may take a bit longer to get the data but the circuitry is simpler and that's always a prime goal in a small system like ours.

If you study the keyboard schematic of Fig. 11-3, you'll see that the keyboard doesn't really do anything if your fingers are busy doing something else. There's no direct connection to the system since the keyboard data bus is connected to the latch, not the 8255. When a key is pressed, the high on the "any key pressed" line will strobe the 373 and the keycode will be stored in the latch. While that takes care of getting the keycode, we still need some way for it to be transferred to the 8255. This means deciding how we're going to control the latch output—we need a KBDRD signal.

Working out the solution to this is done the same way we dealt with the other decoding problems we were faced with earlier. We have to figure out what lines are active when we want to get the keyboard data into the 8255 and then combine them to enable the output of the 373. Since reading the keyboard means doing a read of the 8255, we already have the signals we need to do the job—IORD and 55ACS, (the Chip Select line for the 8255). Go back to Fig. 8-4 in Chapter 8 to see exactly how these signals are derived.

Both of these are low signals and we want a low generated only when they're active—and that means we have to OR them together. As it happens, we have a couple of spare OR gates on the board.

We can take care of the keyboard latch control with signals and parts we already have on the board, so cut three new pieces of hookup wire and make the connections shown in the following table. The only connections you have to actually make are the ones shown for pin #8, pin #9, and pin #10 since the others were done in Chapter 8 when we were connecting the 8255 to the circuit.

CONNECTIONS TO IC11 (74LS32)	
Pin #	Connect to
1	8088 pin #32 (RD)
2	IC8 pin #12
3	8255 pin #5 (IORD)
4	8088 pin #29 (WR)
5	IC8 pin #12
6	8255 pin #36 (IOWR)
7	Ground
8	IC21 pin #1 (KBDRD)
9	IC11 pin #3 (IORD)
10	IC12 pin #3 (55ACS)
11	No Connection
12	Ground
13	Ground
14	5 Volts

Table 11-3. Connections Made to the 74LS32 (IC11).

Since one of the signals we're using is $\overline{IORD}$, and that signal is being generated by one of the gates in IC11, you only need a small piece of wire to connect pin #3 $\overline{(IORD)}$ to the input of the new gate we're using to generate KBDRD. This is a particularly nice way to handle the keyboard strobe since it will happen automatically every time we read the keyboard.

Even though we haven't completed the circuit, we've gotten to the point where software can be used to have the 8088 test as much of the keyboard as we have at the moment. The listing shown in Fig. 11-5 is a simple loop that will read the keyboard port and transfer the data to one digit of the display. You shouldn't have any trouble following the flow of the program since it's similar to the ones we've already used. Unfortunately, it's also much too big to fit inside the diode ROM we used before.

```
;           ************************************************
;           *                                              *
;           *    A TEST PROGRAM FOR THE KEYBOARD CIRCUIT    *
;           *                                              *
;           ************************************************
;
;
            TITLE    Read The Keyboard Port
;*****************************************************************************
;*          Set variables, segments, equates, and location                 *
;*****************************************************************************
BOB         SEGMENT                      ;Define the Code Segment.
            ASSUME  CS:BOB,DS:BOB,SS:BOB  ;Set all segment registers to
                                          ;the same location.
;
;*****************************************************************************
;*                 The beginning of executable code                        *
;*****************************************************************************
;This is a short program that will set up the 8255 and then run a loop to get
;a key from the keyboard and transfer it to digit #1 on the display.
;----------------------------------------------------------------------------
            ORG      100h                 ;This will be 000h in the EPROM
                                          ;but the assembler needs this.
START:      MOV      AL,90h               ;Load the 8255 setup value.
            OUT      03h,AL               ;Send it to the command port.
```

Fig. 11-5. KBTEST1.ASM—A diagnostic program for the keyboard.

```
KBDREAD:            IN      AL,00h                  ;Get data from the keyboard.
                    OUT     01h,AL                  ;Send it to digit #1.
                    JMP     KBDREAD                 ;Do it all over again.
;---------------------------------------------------------------------------
;The only way out of this program is to disconnect the power from the board.
;
;*******************************************************************************
;*                      The Boot Code
;*******************************************************************************
                    ORG     8F0h                    ;The power-up Location
                    JMP     START                   ;Go to the main code.
;
;*******************************************************************************
;*                   The end of the program                                  *
;*******************************************************************************
;
BOB                 ENDS                            ;Tell assembler this is the end
                                                    ;of code for this segment.
                    END     START                   ;Tell assembler this is the end
                                                    ;of the program.
```

<u>Hex Dump of KBTEST1.ASM</u>

```
0000 - 00 00 00 00 00 00 00 00 00 00 00 00 00 00 00 00
0010 - 00 00 00 00 00 00 00 00 00 00 00 00 00 00 00 00

0020 - 07CF are filled with zeros

07D0 - 00 00 00 00 00 00 00 00 00 00 00 00 00 00 00 00
07E0 - 00 00 00 00 00 00 00 00 00 00 00 00 00 00 00 00
07F0 - B0 90 E6 03 E4 00 E6 01 EB FA 00 00 00 00 00 00
```

Fig. 11-5. (continued)

I've been constantly threatening to dump the idea of using the 4051 but I keep remembering how frustrating it is to build hardware and not have any way of testing it with software. So, once again, if you're still without a way to burn EPROMs, you can use the short program shown in Fig. 11-6 with the diode ROM—but, at the risk of repeating myself, let me tell you that the only way you're going to get real use from the circuit we're building, is by having a way to burn EPROMs.

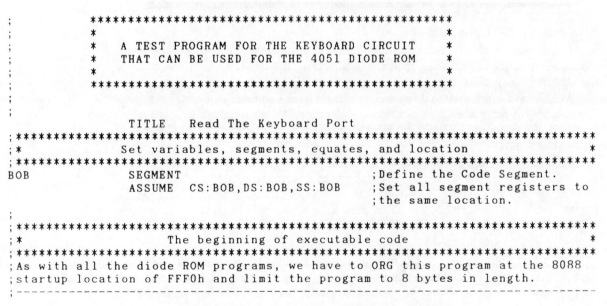

```
;       ***************************************************
;       *                                                 *
;       *    A TEST PROGRAM FOR THE KEYBOARD CIRCUIT      *
;       *    THAT CAN BE USED FOR THE 4051 DIODE ROM      *
;       *                                                 *
;       ***************************************************
;
;
            TITLE   Read The Keyboard Port
;*******************************************************************************
;*            Set variables, segments, equates, and location                 *
;*******************************************************************************
BOB                 SEGMENT                         ;Define the Code Segment.
                    ASSUME  CS:BOB,DS:BOB,SS:BOB    ;Set all segment registers to
                                                    ;the same location.
;
;*******************************************************************************
;*                   The beginning of executable code                        *
;*******************************************************************************
;As with all the diode ROM programs, we have to ORG this program at the 8088
;startup location of FFF0h and limit the program to 8 bytes in length.
;---------------------------------------------------------------------------
```

Fig. 11-6. KBTEST2.ASM—A 4051 program for the keyboard.

```
              ORG     7F0h                    ;The 2716 location for the 8088
                                              ;powerup instruction of FFFF0h
START:        MOV     AL,90h                  ;Load the 8255 setup value.
              OUT     03h,AL                  ;Send it to the command port.
              IN      AL,00h                  ;Get data from the keyboard.
              OUT     01h,AL                  ;Send it to digit #1.
;-------------------------------------------------------------------------------
;The 4051 will keep executing this program over and over since it only looks
;at the three least significant address lines.  The 6116 has to be disabled
;or removed as described in Chapter #8 or bus contention will result.
;********************************************************************************
;*                        The end of the program                              *
;********************************************************************************
;
BOB           ENDS                            ;Tell assembler this is the end
                                              ;of code for this segment.
              END     START                   ;Tell assembler this is the end
                                              ;of the program.
```

<u>Hex Dump of KBTEST2.ASM</u>

```
0000 - 00 00 00 00 00 00 00 00 00 00 00 00 00 00 00 00
0010 - 00 00 00 00 00 00 00 00 00 00 00 00 00 00 00 00

0020 - 07CF are filled with zeros

07D0 - 00 00 00 00 00 00 00 00 00 00 00 00 00 00 00 00
07E0 - 00 00 00 00 00 00 00 00 00 00 00 00 00 00 00 00
07F0 - B0 90 E6 03 E4 00 E6 01 00 00 00 00 00 00 00 00
```

Fig. 11-6. (continued)

If you're going to wire the program up with diodes you'll have to disable the RAM. Reread the discussion at the end of Chapter 8 just in case you don't remember this. Reread it anyway since leaving the RAM in the circuit will cause bus contention when the 8088's program counter clears the A7 address line—keep in mind the eighty eighth Law of Life and Design:

BIOLOGICAL MEMORY IS NOT PERMANENT MEMORY

Brain cells are RAM, not ROM.

The following table is a list of the diode connections to transfer a short version of the Fig. 11-6 listing to the 4051 circuit you used before. But this is it. After this one, the 4051 is history. Seriously.

We still have some work to do before we actually have a working keyboard circuit. Remember that there are three separate things needed to put together a complete keyboard. We've done two of them but there's one more left to work out—how to handle the keyboard data.

Even though we can produce unique codes and have them read into the 8255 with an "IN" instruction we still need some way to let the system know that a key has been pressed and we also need some standard way to handle the data produced by the keyboard. Storing keyboard data is no problem since all we have to do is set aside a memory location as the place to receive the keycode. If that's not enough, a block of memory locations can be used as a buffer.

The point to note here is that there's no way of telling what use you're going to have for a keyboard. To take this even further, since the keyboard is set up as a standard I/O port, there's no reason why the whole circuit can't be finally built as a plug

4051 DIODE CONNECTIONS - ANODE TO 4051									
4051 PINS	**4051 OUTPUT**	**D 0**	**D 1**	**D 2**	**D 3**	**D 4**	**D 5**	**D 6**	**D 7**
13	0					X	X		X
14	1					X			X
15	2		X	X			X	X	X
12	3	X	X						
1	4			X			X	X	X
5	5								
2	6		X	X			X	X	X
4	7	X							

Table 11-4. Diode Connections for the 4051 Keyboard Test Program.

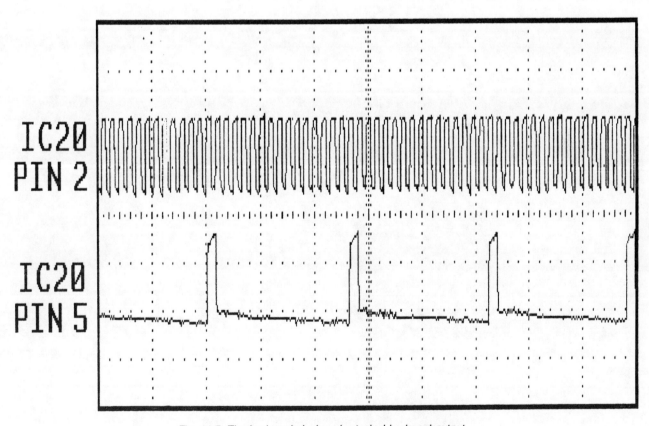

Fig. 11-7. The keyboard clock and a typical keyboard output.

in unit that can be replaced by something else that produces data. As always, it pays to keep things as flexible as possible.

What we're looking for is a general purpose way of responding to an active signal on the "any key pressed" line since this signal is just a way of notifying the main circuit that some peripheral event has occurred. You could probably do this with some creative gating scheme to set a hardware flag that can be checked by the 8088, but it's a lot smarter and easier to get the job done by making use of the powerful interrupt structure of the 8088. Let's do it.

12

Understanding Interrupts

THERE'S ALWAYS MORE THAN ONE WAY TO GET A JOB DONE. SOME WAYS ARE EASIER, some are faster, some are even cheaper but, as you explore your options, you'll usually find that one is better. This is generally true when you're designing electronics and particularly true when you're working with microprocessors.

Although a system like ours can be used for just about anything you have in mind, most of the applications dreamed up for it are going to involve external events—controlling them, monitoring them, or some combination of both these things. There's no reason why you have to be limited to dealing with only one peripheral at a time. There's more than enough power in our system to control several devices at the same time. But there's a catch.

The 8088 may be a heavy duty performer in a small board system, but like most other microprocessors, it can only do one thing at a time. This isn't usually a problem since, as we've seen, it does things very quickly but when you're dealing with real world control, it's usually true that external devices don't want to wait around when the time comes to service them.

The standard way of dealing with the control of multiple devices has been to build a software loop that constantly monitors the signal lines from the external devices and takes the appropriate action when one of the lines is activated. This approach to solving the problem is called ''polling'' and anyone who has some programming experience under their belt, even elementary stuff in BASIC, will have done this at one time or another. In the simplest case, it would look something like this:

```
10    REM GET A YES OR NO
20    INPUT A$
30    IF A$ = "Y" THEN GOTO 1000
40    IF A$ = "N" THEN GOTO 2000
50    GOTO 20
```

Once the program reaches this point, it will stay there forever until either a ''Y'' or ''N'' is pressed. Admittedly, this is a really simple case because only one device, the keyboard, is being tested but the principle is exactly the same, no matter how many devices are put inside the loop.

It doesn't take much time to make each trip through this loop but you can see that if you start adding more and more steps inside the loop, each device is going to be tested less and less frequently. A program like the above example probably won't suffer much if there's a lag in responding to ''Y'' or ''N'', but even reading the keyboard can be time critical. If a keyboard is being used to blast aliens on a home computer the alien survival rate is going to be directly proportional to how often the program reads the keyboard. If you're doing the same thing on an arcade machine, you'll run through a lot of quarters.

Response time isn't the only disadvantage you'll come up against if you use a polling technique to keep an electronic eye on peripheral devices. Remember that the microprocessor can only do one thing at a time so when it's running the loop it's not running anything else. If you're controlling a device that needs servicing every second or so, a lot of valuable CPU time is being wasted since the microprocessor's basic clock deals in microseconds.

You can set up a timer in your program that causes the CPU to test the external signal line every so often but the fifty seventh Law of Life and Design clearly states that:

IMPORTANT THINGS ONLY HAPPEN WHEN YOU'RE NOT WATCHING THEM

and you can bet your favorite pair of designer underwear that the more important the event, the further away you'll be when it happens.

In the best of all possible worlds the control of external events would be handled very differently. The microprocessor should be free to do whatever it wants and be automatically switched to the routines that handle the external events whenever they indicate that they have to be serviced. And that's exactly what interrupts do for you.

INTERRUPTS IN GENERAL

If you're into controlling stuff, (and that's probably the main use you'll find for the circuit we're building), interrupts are just what the doctor ordered. By using them properly, it almost seems as if a system is doing more than one thing at a time—don't go demanding all your money back for this book, remember I said "almost".

Interrupts are the most intelligent way to handle the usual kind of external devices— but there are limitations. If you're controlling something that has to be constantly watched, you're as well off using a standard software loop since constant watching means the circuit has only one main job anyway. But for everything else, interrupts are the way to go.

We've already taken a brief look at the interrupt structure of the 8088 but that was all theory and as the sixty seventh Law of Life and Design states:

THEORY AND PRACTICE ARE ONLY THEORETICALLY RELATED

since knowing that something exists and making it work are two very different things.

To save you the trouble of going back through the book, let's take a little time to review the basics of interrupts on the 8088.

On its most fundamental level, an interrupt is an automatic jump to a routine in software. The jump can be caused by either software or hardware because the internal architecture of the 8088, as well as the other members of the Intel CPU family, have an extensive repertoire of instructions devoted to interrupt handling. To make interrupt use as flexible as possible, there are three different kinds of interrupts built into the 8088 and while they have things in common, in order to get the most from them, you have to understand the differences between them.

The 8088 can handle a total of 256 different interrupts. Some are generated automatically by the CPU, (such as a "Divide by Zero" or an "Interrupt on Overflow"), some are done only in software, (by use of the "INT" instruction), and some are generated by hardware, (by using either the 8088's INTR or NMI pin). Each of these three classes of interrupt have their own unique characteristics but when it comes right down to it, they all result in a jump to a handling routine in memory.

The starting address of all the interrupt handling routines is in a table located at the bottom of the memory map—00000h to 003FFh to be exact. If you've been following this you'll be wondering why you need 1024 (003FFh) bytes of storage space to handle 256 interrupts. The reason is that each interrupt address is four bytes long. The first two bytes are the offset of the address and the second two bytes are the segment address. You should remember from the discussions we had when we first got into the 8088 that the CPU's segmented addressing scheme combines the segment and offset to produce an absolute twenty-bit address. If you're not clear about this, reread the earlier section on the 8088's architecture.

Every interrupt in the 8088 scheme of things has a unique number from 0 to 255. When an interrupt is generated—by either hardware or software—the 8088 looks up the corresponding address in the table and immediately jumps to the routine stored at that address. Since the table is located in RAM, it has to be built by the programmer and, if you plan on using interrupts, the first job your software has to do is build the table for the interrupt numbers, (called *"types"*), that you intend to use.

If you've got some assembler experience under your belt, think of the interrupt vector table as a jump table—a convenient way to get to basic routines that are repeatedly used in your software. If you never dealt with assembler code in your life . . . well, at least you haven't developed any bad habits. 8088 interrupt stuff isn't hard to under-

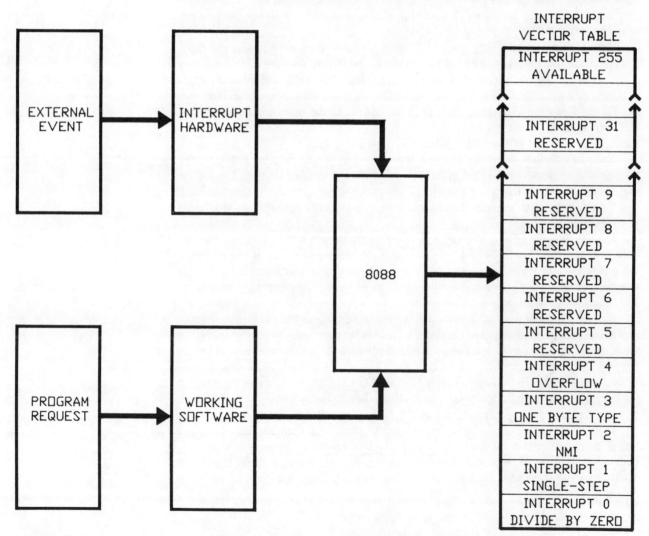

Fig. 12-1. The interrupt vector table to be accessed by the 8088 through software or externally by hardware.

stand and, if you've made it this far in the book, I personally guarantee that you won't have any trouble. Trust me.

We went through the theoretical side of interrupts earlier so I'm not going to spend a lot of time rehashing old material. If you want to bone up on the basics, reread the earlier chapters and look through the data sheets. I'll be assuming you've already got a handle on the fundamental workings of interrupts since what we're going to do here is concentrate on the more practical side of things. It's great to know the theory but putting it to work is, as we've seen over and over, a whole different ball of wax.

ASSIGNING INTERRUPTS

The keystone of all interrupts is the vector table at the bottom of RAM but even though it's built by software, interrupts themselves are triggerable by either software or hardware. Using interrupts through software is, as you can imagine, a lot less involved than a hardware generated interrupt. After all, the table has to be built in both cases and all you have to do to use a software interrupt is include an INT instruction in your program.

Hardware interrupts are more complex because . . . well, they take hardware. The problem is further complicated by the fact that there's only one interrupt input, (pin #18, INTR), on the 8088. It doesn't take much imagination to realize that you'll need more than a simple signal on INTR to let the 8088 know which interrupt you want to use. Just as the 8255 made it easier to hang I/O on the system, there's an equivalent piece of hardware, the 8259, designed for interrupts.

Before we get into the nitty gritty of circuit details and take a close look at the 8259, it's important to note that you're not free to use all the interrupts—the 8088 itself uses some of them. These are located at the very beginning of the table and, should certain things happen while the 8088 is working, the CPU will automatically generate an interrupt. Should this happen, the system will look at the bottom of the table and expect to find the address of the handling routine there. And who do you think has the responsibility for building that part of the table? Why, you do—of course.

Even though the generation of these few interrupts is built into the 8088, you're the one who has to put the address in the table and write the handling routine. The routine can be nothing more than a one byte IRET (Return From Interrupt) instruction but if you forget to create it, you run the risk of having the system zipping off into the wilds of hyperspace.

Even though the first 32 interrupts, (0 to 31), have been reserved by Intel, they've only assigned the first 5, (0 to 4), to particular jobs. Since the rest of the reserved interrupts are still unused, you can use them for anything you want but if Intel decides to come out with a peripheral or chip that's hardwired to use one of them, you're going to be faced with problems.

Keep in mind that there's room for 256 entries in the table so you can be sure there's more than enough room left over for you. The only reason for using the reserved vector locations would be if you've got a system with limited RAM. In this case, it would make sense to use the reserved table locations since it would be a much more efficient use of system memory. But no matter what kind of RAM shortage you're facing, there's no way you can use the bottom five locations since they're hardwired into the 8088 and, short of microsurgery, you can't change the CPU's microinstructions.

If you find yourself in a situation where you're faced with memory limitations and still plan to implement a number of interrupts, the best course to follow is to start your interrupt table above 31 and use the locations reserved for interrupts 5 to 31 for scratchpad RAM. Every system needs space to store temporary variables and it's a lot easier to relocate them than it is to move interrupts.

INTERRUPT HARDWARE

The 8088 only has two interrupt inputs, (NMI and INTR), so it takes some work on your part to be able to have several hardware interrupts available. I'm only talking about using the INTR pin since you can only have one NMI at a time in a system. The 8088's INTR pin is the entryway to it's entire interrupt system and it takes some specialized hardware to make it work. Of course I'm talking about the 8259.

The 8259 is a smart interrupt controller that's been designed to work with Intel CPU's. Although it takes a bit of brain stretching to use it, the advantages far outweigh the disadvantages and making it the core of our interrupt system is what is referred to in most of the technical journals as "good decision". Remember the forty fourth Law of Life and Design:

> ## AVOID BRAIN DAMAGE

so while it may initially seem easier to use a gates only brute force type of solution for creating a multiple hardware interrupt setup, it works out much better to use the 8259. The hardware is simpler, the PC board is simpler, and the whole system is much more flexible.

The 8259 is a close cousin of the 8255 we now have working on the board. Just as we saw that the 8255 gave us the power to dynamically reconfigure the I/O ports, the 8259 does the same sort of thing for interrupts. Before we actually put one to work, let's take a look at the chip itself.

THE 8259 PINOUTS

In a nutshell, the 8259 is an interrupt manager that can watch eight input lines and decide which are the more important. Intel refers to this chip as "Programmable Interrupt Controller" or PIC. The first word in the name should give you a clue as to what it takes to use this chip. Calling it "programmable" means that the system using it has to initialize it before it can be used. This shouldn't send you out of the room screaming since it's the same thing we ran across with the 8255. The 8259 has to be programmed and the way that's done is to send a series of command words defining the operating characteristics we want. This is exactly what we did with the 8255. Even though the 8259 is a much more complex piece of silicon than the 8255, setting it up is only more involved, not really more difficult. So let's take a look at the chip.

Fig. 12-2. The pinouts of the 8259.

As with any complex controller IC, the pins fall into four basic classifications—power, control, data, and addressing.

Pin #14 and pin #28 are the ground and V+ pins respectively. These are the same as the similar ones on every chip we've been using so far and, as we've been doing all along, we'll put a small bypass cap on the V+ pin to help eliminate transition spikes.

There are nine separate control pins on the 8259. Five of them are used by the 8088 and the remaining four are used by the 8259.

The INT and INTA control lines (pin #17 and pin #26) are connected directly to the 8088. We've already seen, (when we were dissecting the 8088), that the basic CPU interrupt sequence is to let the 8088 know that an interrupt is being done, (a low signal on the 8088 INTR pin), and then wait for the CPU to signal that it's ready to process lines on the 8259 are designed to match the 8088 lines in signal level and timing so all you've got to do to make them work is wire them up.

The 8259 is a programmable device that lives on the system busses and the CS, WR, and RD lines, (pin #1, pin #2, and pin #3), perform the same functions the equivalent lines did on the 8255. Whenever the system wants to talk to the 8259, a low has to be put on the CS pin and then, depending on what you want to do, either the RD or WR can be activated.

The remaining four control lines are used if you want to have more than one 8259 in the system. Each chip can handle eight different interrupts but some systems might require more than that. The CAS0, CAS1, and CAS2 lines, (pin #12, pin #13, and pin #15), are used to build a private interrupt bus when two or more 8259s are used. If you put together a system like this, one 8259 is designated as the master with the CAS pins as outputs and the other ones are set up as slaves with the CAS pins as inputs. Since each 8259 master can control up to eight slaves, it's possible to build a system with as many as 64 levels of hardware interrupts.

The SP/EN line, (pin #16), is used in a multiple 8259 system to indicate whether the chip is set up as a master (SP/EN tied high) or a slave (SP/EN tied low). If you're only using one 8259, (as we'll be doing), this line can be used as an Enable Output to control a buffer placed between the 8259 and the system data bus. When you program the 8259 to operate in the "buffered mode", it will put an active low on SP/EN whenever it sends information on its data pins.

There are two separate data busses on the 8259. External devices talk to the 8259 on the Interrupt Request bus, (pins #18 through #25), and whenever they want servicing they put a high on the pin they're connected to. The big difference between this bus and all the others we've been dealing with is that only one line can be activated at a time—it's strictly first come first serve. You can tell the 8259 that some lines are more important than others so that one interrupt can "interrupt" another while it's being ser-

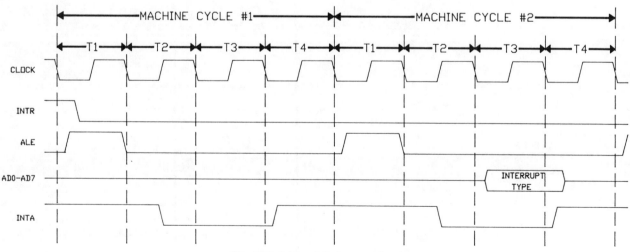

Fig. 12-3. Interrupt timing waveforms.

viced. This is why the 8259 is often referred to as a *"priority controller"*. The chip can be programmed to give more weight to one interrupt over another and it will automatically service the most important ones should a conflict arise.

Although the chip can be reprogrammed at any time, you'll have more success in using it if you've got your application clear in your mind ahead of time. Writing software for a single board system like ours is far from being a trivial task and keeping the programs as simple and straightforward as possible is a good way to avoid an unnecessary trip to the funny farm. If it's at all possible, a chip like the 8259 should really be a "set it and forget it" type of deal.

The second data bus on the 8259 is the eight-pin bidirectional one that it uses to transfer data back and forth to the 8088. This is the one that connects directly to the system data bus and is used along with the 8259's $\overline{CS}$, $\overline{RD}$, and $\overline{WR}$ lines. Programming data travels here as well as the vectoring information produced when the 8259 services an interrupt request.

The 8259's address line is only one bit wide. The A0, (pin #27), is usually connected directly to the A0 line on the system address bus. When the chip is being programmed, some of the command words have to be sent with this line high, and some have to be sent with this line low. If this sounds a bit confusing, it's because A0 isn't really an address line at all. It's really a cross between an address and a data line.

A good way to understand what's going on is to think of the 8259 as having two command registers. This isn't strictly true but you can get more information from the data sheet and, in any event, knowing exactly what's going on isn't nearly as important as understanding how the chip is used. In order to talk to the 8259 registers and program them for a particular mode of operation, the chip is usually set up to communicate over two sequential I/O ports. That lets us use standard IN and OUT commands to set the chip up for the system.

Some of the command words are loaded into register 0 (A0 low) and some have to be sent to register 1 (A0 high). This is the best way to keep it all straight in your mind and it also makes things nice and clear when you're looking at assembler listings to program the chip. Once we get the hardware set up in our system and look at how the chip is programmed, you'll see exactly what I mean.

The best way to learn to use this chip is to stick it on the board and put it to work. Before we do that, however, lets take a minute to see what's involved in programming it.

PROGRAMMING THE 8259

No matter what use you find for the system we're building, you'll be writing software for the 8088 and letting it run. The more time the CPU has to devote to following your instructions, the faster things will happen. Conversely, the more time the CPU has to spend massaging peripheral devices, the less time it's going to have for you.

This somewhat trivial observation is what led to the development of smart peripheral controllers. In a certain sense this is really what gave rise to the idea of microprocessors in the first place. A smart chip like the 8259 is really a small microprocessor since it can be programmed to operate in several different modes. The 8255 also has this qualification but the 8259 is considerably smarter and, as you would expect, programming it is more complex, not more difficult.

There are two kinds of instructions that have to be sent to the 8259. The first are *"Initialization Command Words"*—ICW's. These have to be sent to the 8259 before the chip can begin processing any interrupt requests. Once the chip has been initialized by them, it can accept *"Operational Command Words"*—OCW's. These tell the 8259 how to prioritize interrupt requests, whether to ignore some interrupt requests completely, to put its current register status on the system data bus, and so on.

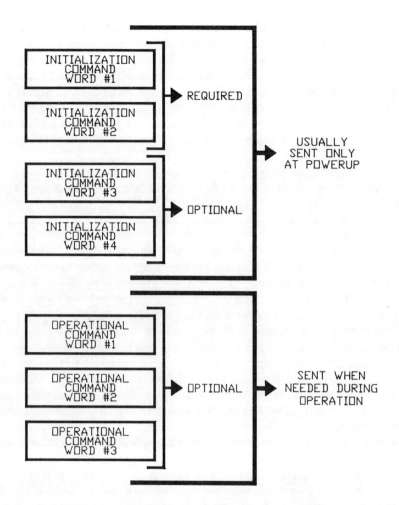

INITIALIZATION COMMAND WORD #1

INITIALIZATION COMMAND WORD #2

REQUIRED

INITIALIZATION COMMAND WORD #3

INITIALIZATION COMMAND WORD #4

OPTIONAL

USUALLY SENT ONLY AT POWERUP

OPERATIONAL COMMAND WORD #1

OPERATIONAL COMMAND WORD #2

OPTIONAL

OPERATIONAL COMMAND WORD #3

SENT WHEN NEEDED DURING OPERATION

Fig. 12-4. Programming parameters for the 8259.

It takes up to four ICW's to define the basic operating parameters for the 8259 and once they've been sent to the chip, (usually right at the onset of the program), you generally never deal with them again as long as you keep the circuit powered up. Since ICW's are the software equivalent of building control circuitry, it's important to make sure you're setting the chip up properly. Mistakes in the ICW's are harder to track down than hardware errors because there's no way you can put a meter on them. And even though the setup is done in software, an ICW screw up is harder to find than a program bug since there's no way to set breakpoints.

Each of the four ICW's sets different parameters so a typical setup may not only use different configurations of each ICW but may also use different numbers of ICW's as well. Where one system may complete its setup with ICW1 and ICW2, another may need ICW1, ICW2, and ICW4. This may seem complicated but it's really not a lot different than the sort of stuff we talked about when we were looking at the 8255.

You can get a complete description of the 8259's gory details from the data sheet but the best way to get an initial understanding of the ICW's, (and OCW's), is to look at them one at a time.

It will come as no surprise to you to learn that the first ICW that gets sent to the 8259 is ICW1. As with all the instructions that are sent to the 8259, ICW1 is composed of eight data bits. We saw before that there's some confusion as to what to think of the A0 line. Since some 8259 instructions require A0 to be low and others want it to be high, it clarifies the issue to think of the chip with two command registers. Now that we're actually looking at the instructions, you can see that the setup is really a bit different.

Intel has the 8259 look at the A0 line in much the same way as the data lines—sort of a ninth bit. When you're writing the software to program the 8259, instructions that have A0 low will be sent to the even numbered port and instructions that want A0 high will go to the odd numbered port. The 8259's odd use of the A0 line is why you need two I/O ports to talk to it.

Whenever the 8259 sees an instruction with A0 low and D4 high, it regards it as ICW1. Each of the bits in the ICW sets a particular parameter for the chip. This means that the byte you send out is built up a bit at a time the same way we worked out the bit patterns for the character generator. In that case, a high would light one of the LED segments, while in this case a high is the same as throwing a switch. All the other ICW's, (ICW2 through ICW4), have to be sent with A0 high.

The low order bit in ICW1 is used to indicate which ICW's you'll be sending to the 8259. Making D0 high lets the chip know that you'll be sending ICW4. This is *not* the same as telling it you'll be sending four ICW's!! Each of the ICW's carries very specific information so ICW4 is the name of an ICW, not just the fourth one you send.

D1 is also a flag that's used to let the 8259 know what ICW's to expect. You set it high if you're only using one 8259 in the system and low if there are more than one. When more than one 8259 is in the system, (more than 8 levels of hardware interrupt), the slave 8259's have to be programmed as well and that's the job of ICW3.

It takes a minimum of two ICW's, (ICW1 and ICW2), to program the 8259. The chip will only expect the remaining two if you tell it to expect it and, as we've seen, this information is carried in the first two bits of the first ICW, ICW1.

The 8259 was designed to be used with both the 8088 and the 8085. Since each of these microprocessors handles interrupts differently, the 8259 has to know who it's talking to. One of the main differences between the two CPU's is their addressing scheme. We already know all about the 8088's segmented addressing—each twenty-bit address is the result of combining a sixteen-bit segment address with a sixteen-bit offset. The 8085 deals with interrupts differently—vectoring and other things are much cruder—and as many as eight bytes are needed to jump to an interrupt routine.

The 8088 makes it much easier for designers since all its built in logic means that the only piece of information the 8259 has to send on the bus is the number of the requested interrupt—everything else can be handled internally in the 8088. Because of this, several bits in the ICW's are disregarded when the 8259 is told that it's going to be talking to an 8088. That's precisely the case with D2, the next bit in ICW1.

The practical effect of the 8259's handling of a hardware interrupt is to put an interrupt vector on the bus. The 8259 has to know what increment to use for successive address vectors. If D2 in ICW1 is set low, the 8259 will allow eight bytes for each address, (needed in some schemes on the 8085), and if D2 is set high, it will use a spacing of four bytes. The 8259 will disregard this bit and set itself to use a four byte interval if it's told, (in ICW4), that it's connected to an 8088.

The next bit in ICW1, D3, allows a certain amount of flexibility in the design of the hardware that signals the interrupt. If D3 is set high, the 8259 will be triggered by a high level on any one of its interrupt request pins. A low in D3 tells the 8259 to be triggered by a low to high transition on an interrupt request line—this is "edge triggering". Each of these settings has advantages and disadvantages but the preferred method is to use edge triggering since it's much less sensitive to timing and it's also easy to have external hardware convert a high level to a positive going pulse. Level triggering can be tricky since a level that remains high longer than the time needed to run the service routine may trigger a second interrupt. The next bit is D4 and, as we've already learned, it has to be set high in ICW1.

The last three bits of ICW1 and all the bits in ICW2 are used to define the address of the interrupt vectoring for the CPU. If the 8259 is connected to an 8085, bits D5, D6, and D7 of ICW1 correspond to address bits A5 through A7 and the bits in ICW2, (D0 through D7), correspond to address bits A8 through A15. The lower five bits of the address are generated by the 8259 and depend on which one of the eight interrupts was activated. If the microprocessor is an 8088, however, the setup is much simpler.

The 8088 fixes its interrupt vector table at the bottom of RAM so there's no need for the 8259 to generate the entire address. If you tell the 8259 that it's talking to an 8088, it only cares about the upper address lines A11 through A15 and ignores A5 through A10. When an interrupt occurs, the 8259 sends A11 through A15 as the upper five bits of the interrupt vector address and the bottom three bits are set in accordance with the number of the interrupt request.

The third Initialization Command Word, ICW3, is only sent when more than one 8259 is used in the circuit. As such, the only time the 8259 will expect to see one is if D1 in ICW1 is low. The bits in ICW3 are used to identify each slave in the system. This lets the master 8259 communicate with the slave 8259's on the private cascade bus and allows a unique vector to be associated with each interrupt request line in the circuit.

The last ICW is ICW4 and it's here that you can let the 8259 know that it will be talking to an 8088. Setting bit D0 high tells the 8259 that it's working with an 8088 and setting it low indicates that it will be connected to an 8085. Remember that setting this bit high will cause the 8259 to disregard several of the settings in earlier ICW's.

The second bit in ICW4, D1, determines whether the 8259 will end an interrupt sequence automatically or expect to get an *End of Interrupt* command from the microprocessor. Ending an interrupt automatically means that the command will be generated internally right after the trailing edge of the last $\overline{\text{INTA}}$ pulse from the microprocessor. Unless you have a special reason for wanting to keep control, it's a lot simpler to let the 8259 do the work for you since the requirement to send the End of Interrupt command to the 8259 puts an extra burden on your software. In any event, it doesn't make a lot of sense to create extra work for yourself while you're still working the kinks out of a breadboard system.

The next two bits in ICW4 are used to tell the 8259 whether or not to operate in the "Buffered Mode". Making this active will cause the 8259 to put an enabling signal on its SP/EN line, (pin #16), whenever it wants to send an interrupt request to the microprocessor. A low in D4 will disable the buffered mode and a high will enable it. Since a master and slave 8259 have different requirements, bit D3 is used to set the chip for one or the other—D3 is set low for a slave and high for a master.

The last bit that has to be programmed is D4. The setting of this bit determines whether or not the 8259 will be in the *"Special Fully Nested Mode"* or not. This mouthful of words is an absolutely classic example of "Brainless Buzzwordism", sometimes referred to as "Digital Doublespeak".

The normal "Fully Nested Mode" means that the 8259 will assign the highest priority to Interrupt Request #0 and the lowest to Interrupt Request #7. The "Special Fully Nested Mode" is the same sort of thing for systems with multiple 8259's. There are, obviously, a few extra considerations since the hardware setup is more complex, but nothing that warrants such brainbending names. Remember the fifty fourth Law of Life and Design:

NAMES THAT SAY NOTHING MEAN NOTHING

so explanations that don't make sense after the tenth reading aren't sensible explanations. To steal a line from a famous person:

"The fault dear reader, lies not in the reader but the writer."

Assuming that you're the one with the problem just because you can't understand something is a big mistake. Don't underestimate yourself.

Once you've sent the 8259 the ICW's to set it up properly for your application you can start thinking about OCW's. These can be used if you want to alter some of the default operating characteristics of the chip. Although most applications work perfectly well with the default setup, it's occasionally useful to change two of the modes—interrupt enabling and order of priority.

There are three OCW's that can be sent to the chip and all of them are optional. OCW1 masks off interrupt request lines, OCW2 alters the order of interrupt priorities, and OCW3 is used to read and write to the 8259's internal registers. The mechanics of using OCW's is in the data sheets and, once the ICW's have been sent, OCW's can be used to dynamically change the behavior of the 8259 as the need arises during the course of the program.

The biggest problem with a general discussion is that things only get discussed in general. It's hard, if not impossible, to understand what's important and what can be ignored. This is particularly true with interrupts since it's a basic part of 8088 design and there's a lot of possible permutations and combinations—after all, the whole idea behind interrupts is to allow design flexibility.

We could spend hours talking about the theoretical aspects of using interrupts and, if you're lucky, some of it might even stand out in your mind. It's much better to follow the dictates of the forty sixth Law of Life and Design:

A WORD IS ONLY WORTH A THOUSANDTH OF A PICTURE

and move on to a practical example. And what better example to use than our own circuit? That's right, people . . . it's time to get our hands dirty again.

13

Adding Interrupt Hardware

THINGS SOMETIMES AREN'T WHAT THEY SEEM TO BE. ABOUT TWELVE MILLION YEARS ago my father took me to the circus—it was my first time and I was so excited I had a hard time keeping my pants dry. There were acrobats, animals, and all the usual stuff but what really stuck in my mind was seeing twenty clowns come out of a really tiny car.

The next day I got a bunch of friends together and we all went over to my neighbor's Volkswagon. There must have been fifteen of us or so and I figured if the clowns could get twenty into their car, getting fifteen of us in the VW bug was a piece of cake. So we opened the car doors and started piling in. People didn't have to lock their cars then.

We managed to get everyone in and then it was my turn. No matter how hard I tried, there was no way I was going to be able to get in the car—and I tried . . . I really tried. I didn't get myself in but I did manage to get myself stuck halfway out. And there we were . . . nothing to do but scream for help.

After my father and neighbor finally managed to get all of us out of the car, we stood there looking at the mess we had made out of the VW interior. I looked at my father and said, ''But what about all the clowns?''

''Things,'' he said, ''are not always what they seem.'' And the same is true of interrupts.

Now that you've plowed your way through the last chapter, there's no doubt that you're thinking of the interrupt hardware and software as a sure route to brain damage. Well, things are not always what they seem.

When it comes right down to it, the 8088 is offering you a really good deal if you take advantage of interrupts. We already know all of the benefits we can get with interrupts but having only a theoretical understanding of what has to be done to make it all work can give the impression that it's all just not worth it. It really is. The best way to get a real understanding of interrupts is to begin using them, so . . . onwards.

INTERRUPT MAPPING

If you're brain has really been soaking up everything we've been doing to get our system up and running, it shouldn't come as any surprise to you that the key to working through an electronic design is to break everything down into steps. Complex circuits are collections of much smaller ones and adding peripherals is a snap if you look at a circuit problem the same way. The first thing that has to be done to add hardware interrupts to our circuit is deciding where they're going to live. This is really a lot like the decisions we had to make when we were adding I/O ports to the system. With interrupts, however, there are some considerations that make the problem a bit more complicated.

Since Intel has reserved a bunch of locations in the vector table we have to be careful how we map our own interrupts into the system. This isn't such a big problem because there's room for 255 separate interrupts (0000h to 03FFh) but, no matter how free we are to choose locations in the table, we still have to plan things before we start laying out our hardware and software.

You're free of course, to use any arrangement you want, but if this is the first time you've ever dealt with interrupts, set your system up as I describe. Once you've got everything working, screwing around with the mapping and hardware will be a good learning experience. I'm going to assume that you've been through the previous chapter and some of the earlier ones in which we talked about interrupts. What we'll be dealing with here is the practical side of things and a lot of it won't make any sense if you don't have a handle on the theory. With that out of the way, let's work out our interrupt map.

We're adding eight hardware interrupts to the system and there's no reason why we can't take the first available space for them. Although Intel has reserved the bottom 31 for themselves, only the first five are used for anything in particular—the rest have been reserved just in case Intel decides to introduce new ICs. Since nothing at the moment uses them, we could use all of those locations ourselves, but there's no particular advantage in doing this—only the possibility of a disadvantage later on. Since we've seen many times over that cutting options is a bad thing, if Intel wants to keep them empty, it would seem like a good thing to accommodate them.

Having said all that, what we're going to do is what you do a lot of in life—compromise. Intel may want the room at the bottom of the table but you can't always get everything you want. The system we're putting together is short of RAM at the moment, (only 2K), and holding the entire bottom of the RAM map open just in case Intel wants to use the space, is a gesture of generosity we just can't afford.

If we were to play by Intel's rules, we would have to forget about memory locations 00h to 7Fh (31 interrupts at 4 bytes per interrupt) but, just to be nice about things, we'll reserve three interrupts for Intel anyway. This means we have to set aside room for eight reserved interrupts—the first five are predefined and the next three are the ones we just agreed to reserve.

Our initial interrupt vector table, therefore, starts at the first location in RAM (0000h) and also includes enough space for the eight 8259 generated hardware interrupts we're adding to the system. Notice that I said our "initial" vector table. Remember that interrupts can be generated by software as well as hardware. Even though these two types are produced differently, the 8088 handles them in exactly the same fashion.

Once the 8088 has received an interrupt request, it doesn't care if it was produced in hardware via the INTR pin or by software via an INT instruction—the results are the same in both cases. The routines we assign to our eight hardware interrupts can be called by software as well. If we have some peripheral device connected to the 8259 that generates a type seven interrupt, the 8088 will run the routine whose starting address is located at 001Ch in RAM. We could run the same routine by having the software do an INT 7.

Interrupts are usually referred to by type numbers. This isn't a new concept, only a matter of a new name. The type number is just a way of referring to where the interrupt's vector address is located in the table. A type four interrupt is called that because its starting address is the fifth one in the table (at location 0010h). Remember that the first location in the table is for a type zero interrupt. But let's get back to our system.

We're going to have eight reserved interrupts, type zero to type seven. That means the 8259's first interrupt is going to be assigned as a type eight and its vector will be stored at location 0020h in the table. Since each interrupt vector is four bytes long, we'll be using the next 32 consecutive bytes in the table. The interrupts generated by the 8259 therefore, are going to be assigned as type 8 to type 15 and will use 0020h through 003F in the vector table.

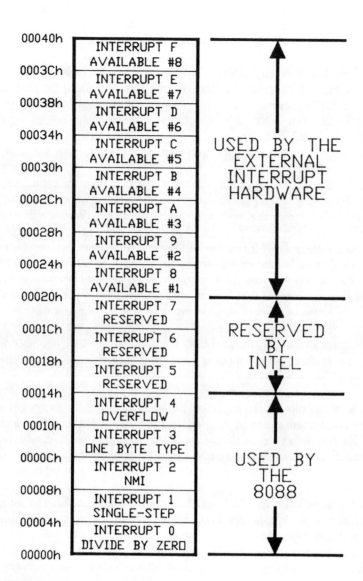

00040h	INTERRUPT F AVAILABLE #8	
0003Ch	INTERRUPT E AVAILABLE #7	
00038h	INTERRUPT D AVAILABLE #6	
00034h	INTERRUPT C AVAILABLE #5	USED BY THE EXTERNAL INTERRUPT HARDWARE
00030h	INTERRUPT B AVAILABLE #4	
0002Ch	INTERRUPT A AVAILABLE #3	
00028h	INTERRUPT 9 AVAILABLE #2	
00024h	INTERRUPT 8 AVAILABLE #1	
00020h	INTERRUPT 7 RESERVED	
0001Ch	INTERRUPT 6 RESERVED	RESERVED BY INTEL
00018h	INTERRUPT 5 RESERVED	
00014h	INTERRUPT 4 OVERFLOW	
00010h	INTERRUPT 3 ONE BYTE TYPE	
0000Ch	INTERRUPT 2 NMI	USED BY THE 8088
00008h	INTERRUPT 1 SINGLE-STEP	
00004h	INTERRUPT 0 DIVIDE BY ZERO	
00000h		

Fig. 13-1. The system interrupt map.

8259 MAPPING

The 8259 is a programmable device so we have to work out some way for the 8088 to talk to it. This is nothing new—the same thing had to be done with the 8255. It's possible to reserve some memory locations for it but that would take a lot of gating and address decoding. A much smarter route to follow, the same one we did with the 8255, is to dedicate two I/O ports to the 8259 and communicate with it by using the 8088's IN and OUT instructions.

Since we're going to use two ports to talk to the 8259, the next logical step is to decide exactly which ports we're going to use. The 8088 can address more than 64,000 of them but all the ones located above port #255 have to be addressed by using the DX register so let's limit our search to the lower ones that can be accessed directly. We put the 8255 ports at the bottom of the I/O map and assigned it to be port #0 through port #3. The circuit is set for a second 8255 and that one is already mapped to be port #4 through port #7. We could take the next two ports for the 8259 but there are a few things we should first consider.

Even though we've been dedicating several of the 8255 ports to be used for essential peripherals such as the display and the keyboard, all the ports are really set up for general purpose I/O. It's not inconceivable that the time would come when you want to use them for something else—we already talked about replacing the keyboard. In the world of

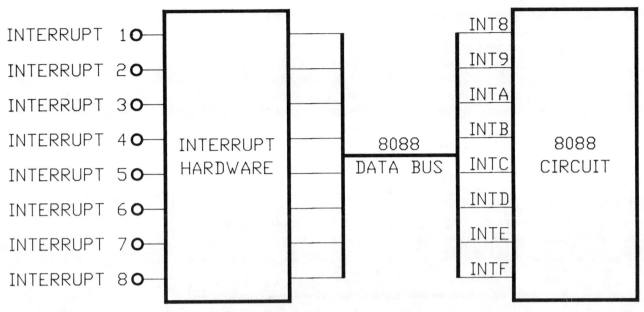

Fig. 13-2. Assigning the hardware interrupts.

microprocessor design, it's really smart to be logical about things and, while it's impossible to design in every possible eventuality, it's a good idea to be as orderly as you can.

There's an essential difference between the ports on the 8255 and those on the 8259—pretty much the same as there is between RAM and ROM. When we were working out the memory map for our circuit we cut it in half—the upper 512K for ROM and the lower 512K for RAM. The 8259 ports are the first hardware dedicated ones we've had to deal with. The 8255 ports can be used for anything we want but the 8259 ports can only be used to control the 8259.

Keeping this in mind, it might turn out to be useful to split the first 255 I/O ports in half—the bottom part for configurable ports and the upper half for dedicated ports. Splitting the I/O map like this is done the same way we split the memory map—we can use the high order address bit, A7, as the chip select toggle.

This is as good a time as any to point out the limitations of the mapping technique we've been using for both memory and I/O. There's nothing wrong with what we've been doing but you might have realized by now that we can only deal with a certain number of ports before an addressing problem arises.

Using the A7 line to toggle between two banks of I/O is adequate as long as we limit the number of I/O ports to those that can be directly addressed by the chips we're using as decoders. This is easier to see if we take a look at IC14, the 259 we're using to decode the 8255. A low on the A7 line will enable the 259 and let it automatically select either of the 8255's whenever we access I/O any of the first eight I/O ports. All this is well and good but let's see what happens if we add more ports at the bottom of the I/O map.

Since the 259 can select two 8255s, we currently have the ability to address port #0 through port #7. Port #0, for example, is selected whenever all the following conditions are satisfied:

1. The 8088 executes an I/O instruction.
2. Address line A7 is low.
3. Address lines A0, A1, and A2 are low.

If we add the next port, (port #8), we're going to have a bus conflict as soon as it's addressed because the same three conditions will be true. The difference is that the A3 line will be high for port #8 and low for port #0. Since the 259 isn't paying any attention to the A3 line, it will enable a port every time the above three conditions are met. The way to fix this is obvious—more address lines have to be decoded to make the port selection more discriminating.

If you add lots of ports, this can become a real decoding nightmare since the chip count will go up very rapidly. This wouldn't be so bad all by itself but it also makes for very complicated PC boards and let me tell you, that can be a real hassle.

Working out system maps—for I/O, memory, or anything else—can be a major design headache since the more you add, the more likely it is you'll overlook something. What you want ideally is some method that can be easily changed as you add to the system. Something that could be done without having to rip stuff off the board. Something like a mapping ROM.

Once we get these interrupts up and running, we'll spend some time looking at ways that the system can be enlarged and one of the things we'll be talking about is using an EPROM to control the decoding of both memory and I/O. It may take a bit more planning but it can make your life a lot easier. Law of Life and Design number sixty-four:

THE EASY WAY IS THE BEST WAY

Believe it.

Now that we've worked out the mapping for the 8259 and have decided how we're going to assign the interrupts, we're ready to begin wiring the parts into the circuit. Once that's done, we'll see exactly how to use software to initialize the interrupts.

ADDING THE HARDWARE

It's funny, but the further along we get with designing our system, the less parts are needed for each additional section. Look back over the work we've done so far and you'll see that while earlier sections required adding eight or nine parts to the board, the parts count gets less and less as we expand the system.

The hardware needed for the interrupts is minimal. One of the main reasons for this is that we've already created a whole host of control signals. What you should realize is that there's no relation at all between the complexity of the job and the complexity of the circuitry needed to get the job done. The entire interrupt system we've spent so much time talking about can be implemented with just two chips—a decoder and the 8259 as shown in the schematic of Fig. 13-3.

Using smart chips like the 8259 is . . . well, smart.

PARTS
1 - 8259 Programmable Interrupt Controller
1 - 74LS138 1 of 8 Decoder
2 - .1 μF capacitors
1 - 68 pF capacitor

MINIMUM EQUIPMENT
Oscilloscope

Put the ICs on the board as indicated in the placement diagram of Fig. 13-4 and make the connections shown in Tables 13-1 through 13-4. Note that most of the connections shown for IC11 and IC12 have already been made. All we're doing there are putting some gates to work that are still free and are available for use. It's a good thing to keep silicon from being wasted.

Once you've made all the IC connections, add the two .1 μF capacitors across power and ground for each chip. The 68pF capacitor should be connected from 8259 pin #26, $\overline{(INTA)}$, to ground. I found there to be an unacceptable amount of noise on that line

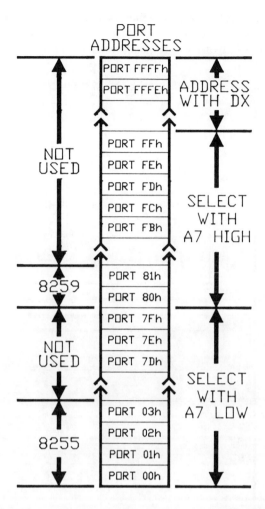

Fig. 13-3. Mapping the 8259 ports into the system.

PORT
ADDRESSES

PORT FFFFh	
PORT FFFEh	ADDRESS WITH DX
PORT FFh	
PORT FEh	
PORT FDh	SELECT WITH A7 HIGH
PORT FCh	
PORT FBh	
PORT 81h	
PORT 80h	
PORT 7Fh	
PORT 7Eh	
PORT 7Dh	SELECT WITH A7 LOW
PORT 03h	
PORT 02h	
PORT 01h	
PORT 00h	

NOT USED

8259

NOT USED

8255

due to both the inherent characteristics of the solderless breadboards and the length of the wire leading to the 8088. This may or may not be true on your board and, unfortunately, there's only one way to see if it's a problem you have to deal with.

If there's too much noise, the operation of the 8259 will be very flakey—sometimes it will work and sometimes it won't. What makes this such a miserable state of affairs is that there's no way to tell if the circuit is screwing up because of noise or whether there's an error in the hardware or software.

When this kind of problem shows up, the only instrument that can tell you if it stems from excessive noise is an oscilloscope. All of the noise glitches on the line are going to be due to oscillations at oddball high frequencies. All of the frequencies running around the board sneak their way into the power lines and it's impossible to tell what frequency and amplitude will show up at IC pins.

What it all boils down to is that if the circuit gives intermittent errors, noise on the control lines is a real possibility. Putting a 68pF capacitor on the lines should solve the problem.

Now that all the parts are on the board, there's a simple check to make which will tell you if everything's connected properly. Measure the resistance from power to ground to make sure you don't have a dead short and then, assuming everything's okay, apply power to the board. If you can run the same software you ran before the interrupt hardware was added to the board, chances are you've done everything correctly. If there are glitches, it's probably an indication that you've wired something together incorrectly.

It would be nice to be able to pinpoint problem areas for you but as the circuit gets more and more complex the possibilities for error are huge. We're cutting it way down by building the circuit piece by piece but there's still no easy way to tell exactly where a problem is coming from by looking at the symptoms. You can get a good idea but there's no getting around the fact that you're going to have to play circuit detective.

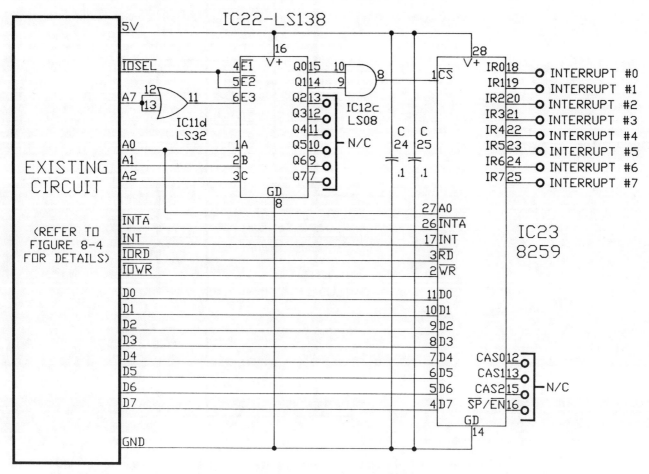

Fig. 13-4. The external interrupt circuit.

CONNECTIONS TO IC11 (74LS32)	
Pin #	Connect to
1	8088 pin #32 (RD)
2	IC8 pin #12
3	8255 pin #5 (IORD)
4	8088 pin #29 (WR)
5	IC8 pin #12
6	8255 pin #36 (IOWR)
7	Ground
8	IC21 pin #1 (KBDRD)
9	IC11 pin #3 (IORD)
10	IC12 pin #3 (55ACS)
11	IC22 pin #6
12	IC3 pin #19 (A7)
13	IC3 pin #19 (A7)
14	5 Volts

Table 13-1. Connections Made to the 74LS32 (IC11).

170

CONNECTIONS TO IC12 (74LS08)	
Pin #	Connect to
1	IC13 pin #1
2	IC13 pin #4
3	8255 pin #6 (55ACS)
4	IC13 pin #10
5	IC13 pin #13
6	No Connection (55BCS)
7	Ground
8	IC23 pin #1 (59ACS)
9	IC22 pin #14
10	IC22 pin #15
11	No Connection
12	Ground
13	Ground
14	5 Volts

Table 13-2. Connections Made to the 74LS08 (IC12).

CONNECTIONS TO IC22 (74LS138)	
Pin #	Connect to
1	IC3 pin #2 (A0)
2	IC3 pin #5 (A1)
3	IC3 pin #6 (A2)
4	IC8 pin #12
5	IC3 pin #12
6	IC11 pin #11
7	No Connection
8	Ground
9	No Connection
10	No Connection
11	No Connection
12	No Connection
13	No Connection
14	IC12 pin #9
15	IC12 pin #10
16	5 Volts

Table 13-3. Connections Made to the 74LS138 (IC22).

The only rule of thumb to follow is that if the problem is constant it's most likely a wiring error. Sporadic problems are probably due to noise and can undoubtedly be solved by a judicious sprinkling of 68pF capacitors.

The 74LS138 will decode the address and data lines in such a way that the 8088 can talk to the 8259 as port #80h and port #81h. Keep in mind the discussion we just had about port and memory mapping since the same considerations apply here. The 8259 will be enabled by any I/O operation that brings A7 high and puts the appropriate levels on A0 and A1. We can put this aside for the moment and just be really careful about how we write our software, but if you have plans to do any I/O expansion, hold off until later on after we've worked our way through a more detailed discussion of what can be done to improve the system mapping. At the moment however, we've got eight levels of hardware interrupt wired up on the board and it's time to see how to use them.

CONNECTIONS TO IC23 (8259)	
Pin #	Connect to
1	IC12 pin #8 (59ACS)
2	IC11 pin #6 (IOWR)
3	IC11 pin #3 (IORD)
4	IC5 pin #11 (D7)
5	IC5 pin #12 (D6)
6	IC5 pin #13 (D5)
7	IC5 pin #14 (D4)
8	IC5 pin #15 (D3)
9	IC5 pin #16 (D2)
10	IC5 pin #17 (D1)
11	IC5 pin #18 (D0)
12	No Connection (CAS0)
13	No Connection (CAS1)
14	Ground
15	No Connection (CAS2)
16	No Connection (SP/EN)
17	8088 pin #18 (INTR)
18	No Connection (IR0)
19	No Connection (IR1)
20	No Connection (IR2)
21	No Connection (IR3)
22	No Connection (IR4)
23	No Connection (IR5)
24	No Connection (IR6)
25	No Connection (IR7)
26	8088 pin #24 (INTA)
27	IC3 pin #2 (A0)
28	5 Volts

Table 13-4. Connections Made to the 8259 (IC23).

USING INTERRUPTS

Putting the interrupt controller to work is simple. What's not simple is deciding what devices should trigger an interrupt since what we're really talking about is how our system is going to be used and that, as you know, is entirely up to you. The only common device that all of our systems will share is the keyboard and that, luckily enough, is a perfect choice for being driven by interrupts.

When we last left the keyboard circuit, it could do everything any keyboard circuit should do except notify the system that a key had been pressed. Now that we have some interrupts available, however, we can use one of them to have the 8088 service the keyboard.

The "any key pressed" line from the keyboard is active high so it's perfectly suited to trigger the interrupt. The only consideration we have to work out is to decide which of the eight interrupt lines we want to use. Since this is the first interrupt we're adding to the circuit, we might as well use the first interrupt on the 8259. All this means from a hardware point of view is that we have to run a wire from the any key pressed line to pin #18 (IR0) of the 8259. Simple stuff.

Interrupts can be used to handle just about any peripheral input you might want to have controlled by the board. There are always sensors available that can be added to a device that will produce a signal capable of triggering an interrupt. All that you really

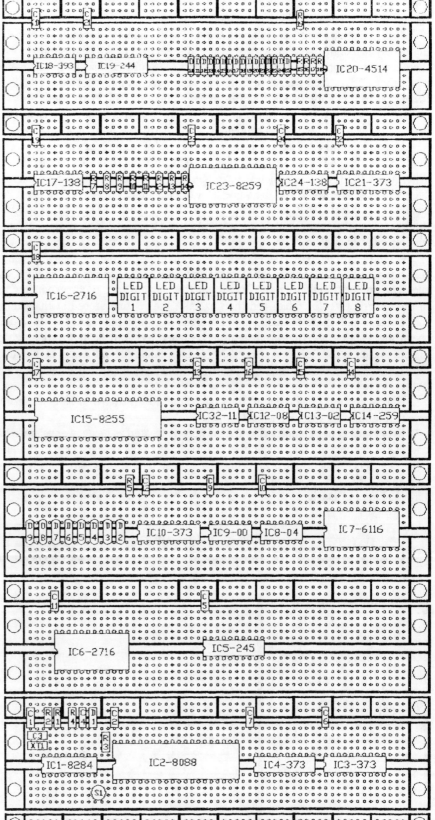

Fig. 13-5. Placement diagram for the external interrupt circuit.

ALL BUS STRIPS ARE TIED IN PARALLEL
AND CARRY ONLY POWER AND GROUND

need to make this happen is a TTL high on any free interrupt request line and the appropriate interrupt handlers in memory.

Although we've been dealing with the hardware side of interrupts, remember that this is only half of the system. As we've already seen, there's a lot of similarity between the unique interrupt structure of the 8088 and the more familiar jump tables common with other CPUs. As a matter of fact, once you have an interrupt vector table built in RAM you can use any of the routines by executing an INT instruction.

Before we leave the hardware side of interrupts, however, let's be clear about the exact sequence of events that happens when a hardware interrupt is requested.

As soon as the 8259 sees a high on any one of its Interrupt Request lines, it lets the 8088 know about it by sending a high from its INT pin to the INTR pin of the 8088. When the CPU receives the interrupt request, it puts out two interrupt acknowledge cycles. These are just about the same as a regular bus cycle but there are two extra clock cycles inserted between them. The 8088 lets the 8259 know that it's received the interrupt request by issuing a low during the T2 and T3 time of the first interrupt acknowledge bus cycle.

On the next bus cycle, the 8088 will issue another low during T2 and T3 and that's the time that the 8259 has to put the interrupt type on the data bus. The 8088 will take the type number, multiply it by four to get the address of the corresponding location in the interrupt vector table, and then execute the routine stored at that address.

There's a lot more to this . . . you can get so completely buried in the details that the whole idea of interrupts will seem to be much too complicated to deal with. Data sheets and most 8088 books spend a lot of time talking about every single nuance of interrupts. This is all well and good, but there's one very important thing that they don't bother to tell you.

Ninety percent of all the stuff they talk about doesn't have to be considered when you're putting together a practical circuit.

Every aspect of a complex chip like the 8259 is treated as being of equal importance—and that's just not the way it is in the real world of circuit design. One of the elements of doing a successful design is knowing how to read data sheets—knowing how to separate things that are important from things that are only interesting. The twenty fourth Law of Life and Design,

THE ONLY IMPORTANT FACTS ARE THE FACTS YOU NEED

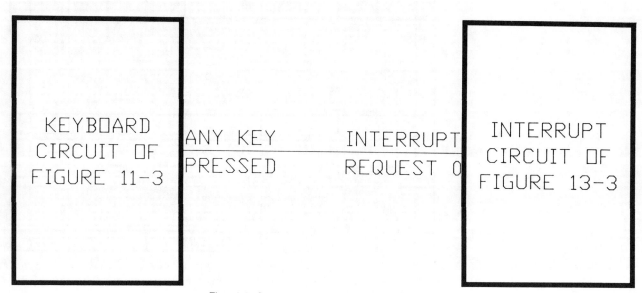

Fig. 13-6. Connecting the keyboard to the 8259.

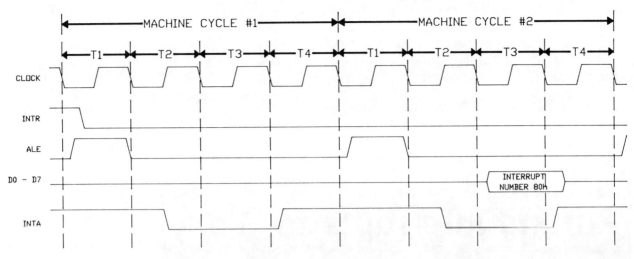

Fig. 13-7. Interrupt timing.

says it all. Reference books may tell you everything there is to know but the only things that are important are the ones you're looking for. What's "important" depends on your point of view.

Dealing with interrupts may seem to be a bit brainbending. We've spent a lot of time talking about them and, believe it or not, we're not finished yet. We've got all our hardware in place so the time has come to deal with the other half of interrupts—software.

14

Putting Interrupts to Work

EVERYTHING'S READY. WE'VE DUG OUR WAY THROUGH A TON OF THEORY ABOUT INTER-rupts and spent the last batch of pages getting the hardware in place. All that's left to start using them is to let the 8088 know that we've done all this work. So zip into the nearest telephone booth, rip off your shirt, and drop your outer guise of mild mannered Hardware Hacker, and assume your other identity—Software Man.

Oh, excuse me . . . I mean Software Person.

There's an awful lot more to tell about the theoretical side of the 8259—just glance through the data sheet if you don't believe me. At this point, however, we know more than enough to understand what has to be done to make the whole interrupt system work on our board. And you'll pick up most of the things we haven't talked about as we work our way through the mechanics of setting up an interrupt.

THE BASIC ELEMENTS

Most people who are just getting into interrupts find things confusing because setting them up isn't a one-step procedure. You might have seen that in the last chapter as we put all the hardware on the board since there was more to consider than just wiring parts together. If you want to avoid spending endless hours working undetectable bugs out of the system, it pays to be extremely methodical when you're building an interrupt system—especially the first time around.

Once you're familiar with how to set up interrupts, you can be just as adventurous as you want in dealing with the software requirements but it's really self destructive to be anything other than extremely conservative when you're still feeling your way around. We've talked about this before but it's important enough to mention again.

Designing microprocessor-based circuits from the ground up is one of the most difficult things you can do in electronics. And it has nothing to do with the amount of experience you've had. Even if you regularly build gee-whiz type stuff starting only with earth, air, fire, and water, it's a real job to get the software and hardware all working correctly.

In our case, we have to be even more careful. We're handicapped by a lack of equipment and, depending on your background, a lack of real experience as well. Veteran designers, particularly those working in well equipped labs, have access to instruments that make it easier to get a board up and operating. I've already mentioned oscilloscopes, but there are other things that can take even more of the pain out of troubleshooting. Instruments such as in circuit emulators or logic analyzers can shotgun a circuit and zoom in on problems in less than a hundredth the time it takes with the minimum bench setup we have. And some potential problems can't be solved at all without them.

Unfortunately, there's the eighty seventh Law of Life and Design:

CONVENIENCE COSTS

so the more useful the instrument, the more expensive it is.

I've carefully worked out the development procedures so we can put our system together with a minimum of equipment but that means we have to be even more anal about following the rules and taking everything a step at a time. And that's especially true right now because programming interrupts is a fairly complex business. It can be really easy to make a mistake and really hard to find it.

But enough lecturing.

There are four basic considerations when you're designing hardware based interrupts and each one has to be handled successfully if the whole thing is going to work.

1. The 8259 ports have to be mapped into the 8088 address space.
2. The 8259 interrupts have to be mapped into the vector table.
3. The interrupt routine starting address has to put in the table.
4. The interrupt routine itself has to be loaded into memory.

We've already taken care of the first two items on this list but let's briefly review the second one.

One of the things that are programmed with ICW's is the interrupt vector address. It's important to understand the difference between the interrupt vector address sent by the 8259 and the interrupt starting address stored by the 8088. They're not the same and the reason it can be confusing is due entirely to an unfortunate choice of terms by Intel.

When one of the 8259's interrupt request lines is brought high by an external device, the 8259 will put the interrupt vector address on the data bus. If you think it's strange to talk about putting an address on the data bus, you're not the only one. The 8259 data sheet sometimes refers to the vector address but most system designers refer to it as the interrupt vector type—including Intel's own 8088 data sheet.

Since the data bus is eight bits wide, the 8259 can send up to 255 different vector types to the 8088. The five most significant lines of the vector type are programmed by the ICWs but the last three bits are automatically handled by the 8259 and are determined by which of the interrupt request lines are brought high. If IR0 (pin #18) is signaled, the 8259 will put 000h on the lower three bits of the data bus, if IR1 is made high a 001h will be on the three least significant data lines, and so on down the line. The 8259 has eight interrupt request pins and therefore can send any sequential group of eight vector types to the 8088.

But these vector types aren't addresses—they're really more like pointers since the 8088 doesn't look at them as an absolute address of any kind. The key to building

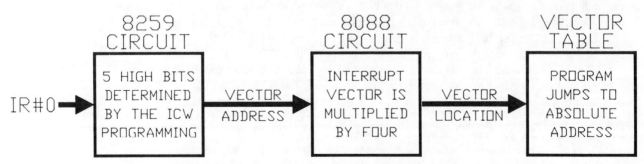

Fig. 14-1. The structure of the interrupt vector table entries.

177

an interrupt table is to make sure you understand exactly what the 8088 does with the information it gets from the 8259.

When the 8088 gets the vector type from the 8259, it multiplies the number by four and uses the product as the location of the interrupt routine's starting address in the vector table. You'll remember that the addresses are stored in increments of four because the 8088 needs four bytes to uniquely identify any absolute address in it's one meg memory space. The first two bytes are the offset and the second two bytes are the Code Segment.

PROGRAMMING THE 8259

Setting up the 8259 is one of the first things any software we use has to do and since we're talking to the 8259 as a set of I/O ports, we'll be dealing with it the same way we did with the 8255—as a series of OUT instructions. There are some differences since we only had to send one word to the 8255 to set it up while the 8259, as we saw in the last chapter, is going to take at least two words. The particular bytes we send depend on how we want the 8259 to operate, what vector types we're going to assign, and how we want to assign the interrupt priorities.

We've already seen that there are two kinds of commands we can send to the 8259, Initialization Command Words, (ICWs), and Operational Command Words, (OCWs). It takes a minimum of two ICWs to get the 8259 working, but most configurations will require at least three to be sent in order to have the 8259 set up. You'll remember that ICW's establish the basic operating conditions of the chip.

Once the fundamental characteristics of the 8259 have been set, you may want to send up to three OCWs. These are used to modify variable parameters such as interrupt request masking and response priority. A system that wants to read the 8259's registers would also have to use an OCW.

But the best way to understand this is to work out the commands for our own system, so let's go through all of them and see exactly what considerations there are and how each one of the individual bytes are constructed.

INITIALIZATION COMMAND WORDS (ICWs)

We've already established that we'll be using ports #80 and #81 to talk to the 8259 and that the interrupts it sends will be assigned as vector types 8 through 15 (08h through 0Fh). Before we can work out the ICWs, however, we still have a few decisions to make and the best way to go through them is to take them in the same order they show up in the ICWs.

Bit 0 of ICW1 is used to let the 8259 know whether to expect ICW4. This is important because if the 8259 isn't sent one of the optional ICWs (ICW3 and ICW4) it assumes the default condition equal to making ICW3 and ICW4 equal to 00h. If you can accept the defaults, it's not necessary to change them but, as we'll see when we get there, some of them aren't right for our system. Bit 0 of ICW1, therefore, has to be set to a one.

Bit 1 of ICW1 indicates whether there's more than one 8259 in the circuit. We're only using one of them so bit 1 will also be set to one. This also tells the 8259 not to expect ICW3 since that word only has to be sent if there are multiple 8259s on the board.

Bit 2 of ICW1 sets the interval between interrupt vectors put on the data bus. This can be set to be either four or eight bytes and, as we already know, the 8088 uses a four byte interval so bit 2 has to be set to a 1. It's not really necessary to deal with this bit since telling the 8259, (in ICW4), that it's talking to an 8088 will cause it to use a four byte interval regardless of how this bit is set.

Bit 3 of ICW1 determines whether the 8259 interrupt request inputs will be edge or level triggered. We discussed this in the previous chapter and you'll find that most applications are best handled by making the 8259 edge sensitive. Level triggering can cause timing problems if the interrupts occur frequently since the 8259 will be triggered twice if the handling routine ends before the level drops back to a low. Edge triggering is better for a first attempt at an interrupt system so we'll make bit 3 of ICW1 a zero.

Bit 4 of ICW1 has to be set to a one since doing this, (along with having A0 as a zero), identifies the byte as ICW1.

Bits 5 through 7 of ICW1 are only needed when the 8259 is used with an 8080 or 8085.

The first three bits in ICW2 are address bits needed by the 8080 and 8085 and aren't used when the 8259 talks to the 8088.

The last five bits in ICW2 correspond to the five high order bits of the interrupt type the 8259 will send to the 8088. The lower three bits depend, as we've seen, on which of the eight interrupt request lines was activated. Since we've decided to assign these interrupts as type 08h through type 0Fh we have to set the five bits as 00001b. This makes the 8259 report all interrupts as 00001XXXb with the exact setting of the last three bits contingent on which interrupt request line was triggered. ICW3 won't be sent since we only have one 8259 in the circuit.

Bit 0 of ICW4 tells the 8259 which microprocessor it's talking to and, consequently, is set to a 1. This also causes the 8259 to ignore the settings of some of the bits in the earlier ICWs.

The setting of bit 1 of ICW4 determines how the 8259 knows when an interrupt is finished. Setting this to a one will cause the 8259 to be ready to recognize another interrupt request as soon as it sees the trailing of the second (final) $\overline{\text{INTA}}$ pulse from the 8088. If we make this a zero, the software interrupt handling routine will have to send a specific "End Of Interrupt" command to the 8259 to tell it that it's okay to accept another interrupt request.

There's no preferred way of doing this since everything depends on the application. For the moment, however, it's smarter to have the 8259 do as much of the work as possible so we want it to generate an automatic End Of Interrupt. Bit 1 of ICW4, therefore, will be a one.

Bits 2 and 3 of ICW4 are used to control whether or not the 8259 will issue a buffer enable signal on pin #16 when it's reporting an interrupt. Even if we never take advantage of this signal, there's absolutely no reason for preventing it. By setting each of these bits to a one, we'll be telling the 8259 that it's the master 8259 in the system and we want it to bring pin #16 low whenever it sends a vector to the 8088.

Bit 4 of ICW4 determines whether or not the 8259 will operate in the "Special Fully Nested Mode". We went through this together in the last chapter and, since this mode only becomes important when there are multiple 8259s in the circuit, it's not something we need. Bit 4 of ICW4, therefore, will be a zero.

The last three bits in ICW4 have to be left as zeros since, (along with A0), they're part of the ICW4 signature.

Before we take a look at the OCW's, let's get everything we've done so far with ICWs into a usable form. I've explained how each bit has to be set and what was considered in making each decision but the results are a lot clearer when they're put into Table 14-1.

Table 14-1. The ICWs Used to Program the 8259.

REVIEW OF INITIALIZATION COMMAND WORDS FOR THE 8259									
WORD	A0	D7	D6	D5	D4	D3	D2	D1	D0	HEX
ICW1	0	0*	0*	0*	1	0	1*	1	1	17h
ICW2	1	0	0	0	0	1	0*	0*	0*	08h
ICW4	1	0	0	0	0	1	1	1	1	0Fh

* = Not needed if the 8259 is in the 8088/86 mode.

The "HEX" column contains the actual bytes we'll be sending to the 8259 and the "A0" column indicates which port (80h or 81h) we have to address when we send them.

OPERATIONAL COMMAND WORDS (OCWS)

Once the ICWs have been sent to the 8259, the chip is ready to start watching the interrupt request lines—OCWs aren't needed to make the chip operational. ICWs are required commands—the chip won't do anything until they're sent—while OCWs are optional commands that either modify some of the chip's characteristics or allow the 8088 to read the 8259's internal registers. And since they're optional, most applications that use them will send them to the 8259 on an as needed basis while the circuit is operating.

Most applications using the 8259 send a stream of ICWs to set up the chip and then forget about it entirely. We could easily do the same thing since, at least to start with, we don't have any real need to change the defaults. But, since you can't change anything without understanding it first, let's go through the OCWs and see if anything there has to be altered.

All the bits in OCW1 are used as enabling flags for the interrupt request lines—the eight bits in the byte directly correspond to the eight interrupt pins of the 8259. The default value for each of them is zero which means that the lines are enabled. By setting a bit to a one, you'll be telling the 8259 to mask off that line—not to pay any attention to an interrupt request on that pin.

If you're not using all eight of the interrupts, it's a good idea to mask the pin off since that means you won't have to worry about an interrupt being generated by noise or circuit accidents.

The initial stages of the circuit we're building don't have any real need for the options available with OCWs but, just to show you the mechanics of using them, we can use OCW1. Since we're only using one interrupt at the moment, (for the keyboard), it makes sense to mask off all the other ones. We'll assign the keyboard to interrupt request line #0, (pin #18), and mask off all the other ones. This means that bit 0 of OCW1 will be zero, (the default), and the other seven bits will be set to a one.

The first three bits of OCW2 are used to establish the interrupt priority order. The default setting of 000 gives the highest priority to interrupt request #0 and the lowest priority to request #7. This order can be changed by using these three bits to set the request you want to receive the lowest priority. If you were to set them to 010, for example, request line #2 would have lowest priority and line #3 would have the top priority. The settings in these three bits only take effect if bit 6 of OCW3 is set to a one.

Bits 3 and 4 are ID bits for OCW2 and, therefore, have to be set to zero.

Bit 5 of OCW2 controls the 8259 handling of "End Of Interrupt" commands. If it's a zero, (the default), the 8259 will ignore any End Of Interrupt commands it receives. This is the way we set up the 8259 with bit 1 of ICW4. Setting this bit to a one will cause the 8259 to take action when it gets an End Of Interrupt but the specifics depend on the state of bits 7 and 8.

Bit 6 of OCW3 is really a flag with two jobs. It tells the 8259 whether or not to pay attention to the first three bits to set the interrupt request priorities and also indicates whether the 8259 has to follow the settings of bits 5 and 7 in the handling of End of Interrupt commands (bit 5) and how interrupt priorities will be rotated (bit 7). Setting bit 6 to a one will make the 8259 look at the settings of all these other bits. If it's a zero they'll all be ignored.

The last bit in OCW2, (bit 7), is used with several of the other bits in this word to determine what happens to interrupt priorities when the 8259 receives and executes an End Of Interrupt command. The exact action taken depends on the combination of bits that have been set and ranges from a reordering of priorities to no change at all. If this bit is a zero, the default setup will remain in effect.

180

The last word is OCW3 and this is one you turn to when you want to read the 8259's status or set special interrupt masking.

Bits 0 and 1 of OCW3 determine which of the 8259's internal registers will be read. You can find out which interrupt is being honored right at the moment by reading the In Service Register (ISR) or which interrupts are currently waiting for service by reading the Interrupt Request Register (IRR). The register to be read is selected by the combination of bits that are set.

Bit 2 of OCW3 is used to put the 8259 in "polling" mode and this deserves an explanation since we spent some time in the last chapter talking about why using the interrupt structure of the 8088 was much better than the traditional polling method for handling peripherals.

There's no getting around the fact that interrupts are a lot better than polling. But even though they're faster, more efficient, and a lot more versatile, there comes a time in the life of every circuit when "better" isn't the best way of doing things. For the life of me, I can't think of a single application where polling is preferable, but you must have seen the fifty eighth Law of Life and Design:

> ## YOU CAN'T THINK OF EVERYTHING

so I'm sure that there's something out there that works better with a polling algorithm. Besides, people have a tendency to stick to what they know and that brings up the fifteenth Law of Life and Design:

> ## THE WAY YOU KNOW BEST MAY NOT BE THE BEST WAY

but America is a democracy and one of the guarantees that was left out of the Bill of Rights due to an ink shortage was the right of everyone to screw themselves up.

When you set bit 3 of OCW3, you're telling the 8259 that you'll do polling instead of using interrupts. Every time you do a read of the 8259, the chip will respond almost as if it had received an $\overline{INTA}$. I said "almost" because instead of putting a vector on the data bus, it will put out a special byte called the "polling word". This is an eight-bit word but only the first three (D0, D1, and D2) and last (D7) carry data.

If interrupt requests are being made, bit 7 is set to a one and the number of the interrupt with the highest priority can be found in bits 0 through 3. If no interrupt request lines have been activated, bit 7 will be a zero. When you're doing polling on the 8259, therefore, you set bit 3 of OCW3, do a read of the chip, and then have your software look at bit 7. If it's a one, you know an interrupt request is pending and you would use the interrupt number as some sort of an index into a jump table.

As you can see, therefore, a polling setup means that you can take advantage of the 8259's power without building an interrupt vector in memory. And this is really the only advantage the polling method has over interrupts—it saves memory because you don't have to use RAM space for the vector table. But it's still only a limited advantage because your software will again have the responsibility of reading the 8259 status to find out when something's happened—all the nice automatic interrupt vectoring is out the window. Bits 3 and 4 of OCW3 are signature bits and have to be set to a one and zero respectively.

Bits 5 and 6 of OCW3 deal with what Intel decided to refer to as the *"Special Mask Mode"*. The reason for it is that when the 8259 recognizes an interrupt, it normally disables all interrupts of lower priority until it sees an End Of Interrupt (either automatic or sent by the CPU). Occasions might arise in which the system might have a need to recognize a lower priority interrupt while it's still in the midst of an interrupt handling routine.

When the Special Mask Mode is set, it lets the 8259 respond to all interrupt levels, lower and higher, except the one being handled and any that have been disabled by OCW1. Setting bit 6 to a one will enable the Special Mask Mode and setting bit 7 to a one will tell the 8259 whether to pay any attention to bit 6.

It's not really necessary, or even important, to remember all the details of the bytes that can be sent to program the 8259. Most of the applications you'll be running will treat the 8259 on a "set it and forget it" basis. All you have to do is keep a general awareness of the possibilities in your mind and a data book on your desk. These are the kind of things that you look up, not recall from memory.

The only change we're going to make to the default settings of the 8259 OCWs is in OCW1 to mask off all the interrupts except IR0. And even this is only for the purpose of checking out the system. Once again, Table 14-2 shows exactly what we're going to do.

Table 14-2. The OCWs Used to Program the 8259.

REVIEW OF OPERATIONAL COMMAND WORDS FOR THE 8259										
WORD	A0	D7	D6	D5	D4	D3	D2	D1	D0	HEX
OCW1	1	1	1	1	1	1	1	1	0	FEh

Now that we've gone through all the programming possibilities for the 8259, it turns out that we'll be sending a total of four bytes to set up the chip. What's more important than the particular bytes is the process we went through to decide what those bytes should be. It goes without saying that the reason the 8259 is so flexible is to make it easy to use it in a wide variety of applications.

When you finish this book you'll have a versatile 8088 based system that can be used for just about any application you have in mind, but you're not going to get anywhere at all if you don't have an intuitive feeling for the system's capabilities. The bytes we're sending to the 8259 are only the ones that best suit the needs of the software and hardware we're handling at the moment. You can be sure that it won't be the best suited for other stuff we do with the circuit. Remember the ninety fourth Law of Life and Design:

SOFTWARE IS NOT WRITTEN IN STONE

it's written here in assembler and if you want to really learn how to put this circuit to work, it's a good idea to follow along with the instructions given here and then—immediately—start changing the diagnostic software to see what happens. Don't worry, nothing you can do by changing the software will damage the hardware.

Once you know the system is working, start screwing around with the code. Change small things at first, but things that can be noticed when the program is run. Good examples of this kind of thing are the delay constants and counting sequences since the changes will be very obvious as soon as you turn the system on. And immediately noticeable changes are great confidence builders. Great programs from small changes grow—or something like that.

And don't stop there. Keep making any changes that seem logical to you until the program crashes. And when that happens, figure out what you did wrong and fix it.

Contrary to popular belief, you don't learn anything at all from your mistakes—but you do learn a whole lot of stuff from correcting your mistakes.

SOFTWARE SETUP

All the pieces of the interrupt puzzle are coming together. We know where the hardware interrupts are going to live in the I/O space and have worked out a mapping scheme for the interrupt vector table. All that's left for us to do is see how to make them fit into application software. This is the easy part . . . really.

Since all the hardware and mapping has already been decided, we can almost forget that we're dealing with interrupts and start thinking of the software side of things as a traditional jump table setup. This is because once the hardware is in place, interrupt operation becomes totally automatic.

Imagine what happens. You've got interrupts set up to monitor the current draw in a circuit you're testing, while the main part of your software does something totally unrelated. So there you are, in the middle of your program—the software is running along in cruisamatic busily executing some kind of mathematics—when all of a sudden the current exceeds the limit and triggers an interrupt.

The 8088 drops everything and jumps into the interrupt routine. It sounds alarms, decreases the current draw in the test circuit, and goes back to the math routine—all on autopilot. It's all over even before you were aware it happened.

Magic. But only if you set it up properly.

THE INTERRUPT VECTOR

The first thing to take care of when you're setting up an interrupt is to put the routine's address in the vector table at the bottom of your system RAM. The exact location on the table depends on how you've set up the 8259 programming and how you've laid out the interrupt map.

We've already done both of these. I'll save you some page turning and go through it again. We're setting up the 8259 so that whenever it reports an interrupt, the upper five bits it puts on the data bus will be 00001b. Since the 8259 can report any of eight interrupts, all the vectors will be of the form 00001XXXb. The last three bits will depend on which interrupt was triggered.

We also decided to connect the keyboard, (the only interrupt we'll be using at the moment), to the 8259's IR0 pin. This means that the keyboard interrupt will cause the 8259 to put a 00001000b (08h) on the system data bus. The 8088 will take this vector, (or interrupt type), and multiply it by four to get the appropriate location in the vector table and that location, (32d or 20h), is exactly where we have to put the address of the routine to read the keyboard.

We've also talked about the format of the address that goes in the vector table, but let's review it once more. The 8259 has been set up to deal in four byte increments because the segmented 8088 addressing scheme requires four bytes to uniquely specify an address in the one meg address space. The interrupt handling procedures built into the microcode of the 8088 want the first two bytes in the table location to be the offset and the last two bytes to be the segment. Each pair of bytes have to be stored backwards—low order byte before the high order byte—for reasons that are neither important or interesting. It's a carryover from the days of microprocessor prehistory and is just one of those things you have to live with.

Now that we have all of this information at our mental fingertips, we can make the very final decision about the keyboard vector—what address to put in the table.

INTERRUPT ROUTINE MAPPING

We've already done this kind of thing several times. All of our I/O, memory, and hardware interrupts had to be logically organized before we work out the hardware and software elements that relate to them. The same thing will be true here since the 8088 supports 255 separate interrupts.

It's really unlikely that you'll ever need 255 interrupts, but it is true that memory space has to be allocated for the routines that take care of the interrupts you do use. There's one aspect of interrupt routines that makes working out the map for them a bit different than any of the other mapping we've done before. That, if you haven't been able to guess, is that it's impossible to know how much room to leave since there's no restriction on the length. After all, "interrupt service routine" is just a fancy name for what is really just a plain vanilla subroutine in a piece of software.

To give you an idea of how variable this is, consider a situation in which the only job the circuit has is to handle interrupt driven peripherals while displaying a real time clock. This isn't so far fetched —think of a digital alarm clock.

In this case, the mainstream code—the part that runs when there are no interrupts to service—would be very small and the interrupt routines would be much larger. In other words, the service routines would take up the bulk of memory. It's important to keep this in mind because there's a tendency to think of interrupt routines as little pieces of software that get tucked away in whatever memory holes are found available. The exact opposite could very well be true.

In our system, as in any other one, any decision about where to locate interrupt routines is going to revolve around the main memory map and the amount of memory on the board. We're using 2716s as the system ROM at the moment, so working out the locations for interrupt routines really means deciding how we want to allocate the 2K bytes of available ROM.

The software we've been using so far has been located to start at the bottom of the 2716 and work its way north. The only other places we've been using are some bytes at the top of ROM for a power-up jump to the start of the program. Since there's no way of telling just how much room we're going to need for interrupts, (or program space for that matter), we're free to do whatever we want.

For no reason other than that the numbers work out more evenly, we can state that the segment we'll use for interrupts is FFE0h and since the keyboard is set up as INT 20h, we might as well use that very same number as the offset—it will help keep things straight in our minds and that's not a bad thing since this is the first time we're playing around with interrupts.

There's nothing magic about any of these numbers. The segment and offset could just as easily have been something else. In some really large systems that are used as

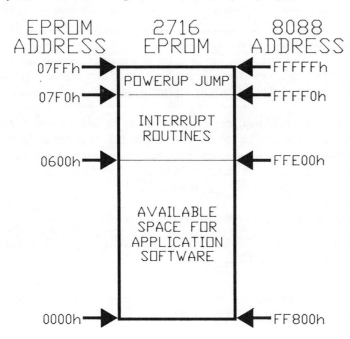

Fig. 14-2. Mapping the interrupt routines in the EPROM.

dedicated controllers, you'll find that several 64K segments are often reserved for interrupt routines and there are ROMs on the board that contain nothing except the interrupt routines. We're not quite that far yet.

DOING THE DEED

There's no sense in putting it off any longer. We've spent so much time getting to this point that waiting any longer would be what the U. S. Constitution refers to as "cruel and unusual punishment". Let's make it happen.

We've worked out all the details that have to be considered to use an interrupt for the keyboard and all that's left is to actually write the routine. This is what you'll find in KYBD-1.ASM, a program that's similar to the others we've used. The code that's been added there is all related to handling the 8259 in general and the keyboard interrupt in particular.

```
;
;    ****************************************************************
;    *                                                              *
;    *    A TEST PROGRAM FOR THE 8088 CIRCUIT USING PORT #0         *
;    *    OF THE 8255 FOR KEYBOARD DATA AND 8259 INT #0 FOR         *
;    *    LETTING THE 8088 KNOW THAT A KEY HAS BEEN PRESSED         *
;    *                                                              *
;    ****************************************************************
;
;-------------------------------------------------------------------
;This program will use the first 8255 port, (port #0), as a keyboard input port
;for a scanning keyboard.  The keyboard has 16 scanned keys on the lower 4 bits
;and 4 hardwired keys on the high bits for a maximum keyboard size of 256 keys.
;
;                        8255      Connection
;                        ============================
;                        PA-0      Keyboard - D0
;                        PA-1      Keyboard - D1
;                        PA-2      Keyboard - D2
;                        PA-3      Keyboard - D3
;                        PA-4      Keyboard - D4
;                        PA-5      Keyboard - D5
;                        PA-6      Keyboard - D6
;                        PA-7      Keyboard - D7
;
;The keyboard is connected to the 8255 through a 373 latch.  The 'KEY PRESSED'
;line, (common to all the keys), latches the keypress data and generates an
;INT 0 on the 8259 so the 8088 will look at absolute address 00020h to get the
;address of the keyboard interrupt servicing routine.  The four bytes there are
;the displacement (00020h - 00021h) and the Code Segment (00022h - 00023h).
;-------------------------------------------------------------------
;
TITLE    Test Keyboard Interrupt
;
;*******************************************************************************
;*                          SYSTEM EQUATES                                    *
;*******************************************************************************
FIXED                    SEGMENT AT 0000h        ;All the variable storage will
                         ASSUME  DS:FIXED        ;be at the bottom of RAM.
         KBDAT           EQU     DS:[0088h]       ;Keyboard data.
         KBINT           EQU     DS:[0020h]       ;Address of Keyboard Vector.
         DELAY           EQU     DS:[0100h]       ;Address of the delay constant.
         WAITCNT         EQU     0036h            ;The time delay constant.
         DISPLAY1        EQU     DS:[0080h]       ;Digit #1.
         DISPLAY2        EQU     DS:[0081h]       ;Digit #2.
         DISPLAY3        EQU     DS:[0082h]       ;Digit #3.
```

Fig. 14-3. KEYBOARD.ASM—A diagnostic program for the 8259.

185

```
                DISPLAY4           EQU         DS:[0083h]            ;Digit #4.
                DISPLAY5           EQU         DS:[0084h]            ;Digit #5.
                DISPLAY6           EQU         DS:[0085h]            ;Digit #6.
                DISPLAY7           EQU         DS:[0086h]            ;Digit #7.
                DISPLAY8           EQU         DS:[0087h]            ;Digit #8.
                KEYBOARD           EQU         00000h                ;8255 #1 Port #0 (Keyboard).
                DISPLED            EQU         00001h                ;8255 #1 Port #1 (Display).
                CONTROL1           EQU         00002h                ;8255 #1 Port #2 (General).
                IOCMD1             EQU         00003h                ;8255 #1 Port #3 (Command).
                INTPORT0           EQU         00080h                ;8259 #1 Port #0.
                INTPORT1           EQU         00081h                ;8259 #1 Port #1.
FIXED                              ENDS                              ;No more variables.
;
;***************************************************************************************
;*                           SET THE 8088 SEGMENTS                                     *
;***************************************************************************************
BOB                SEGMENT                                          ;Define initial segments.
                   ASSUME   CS:BOB,DS:BOB,CS:BOB                    ;Set all segment registers to
                                                                    ;the same location.
                   ORG 100h                                         ;Set program start location.
;
;***************************************************************************************
;*      INITIALIZE THE 8255, THE 8259, THE STACK, AND THE DATA SEGMENT                 *
;***************************************************************************************
;                            SETUP FOR THE 8255
;--------------------------------------------------------------------------------------
START:             CLI                                              ;Disable interrupts for setup.
                   MOV      AL,90h                                  ;This sets the 8255 to operate
                                                                    ;in Mode 0 (basic input output)
                                                                    ;with port 0 as an input and
                   OUT      IOCMD1,AL                               ;ports 1 and 2 as outputs.
;--------------------------------------------------------------------------------------
;                            SETUP FOR THE 8259
;--------------------------------------------------------------------------------------
;The 8259 set up is done by sending three ICW's (Initialization Command Words)
;and one OCW (Operational Command Word) to program the 8259 as follows:
;
;        WORD    A0     D7    D6    D5    D4    D3    D2    D1    D0      HEX
;       -----------------------------------------------------------------------
;        ICW1    0      0*    0*    0*    1     0     1*    1     1       17h
;        ICW2    1      0     0     0     0     1     0*    0*    0*      08h
;        ICW4    1      0     0     0     0     1     1     1     1       0Fh
;        OCW1    1      1     1     1     1     1     1     1     0       FEh
;
;       -----------------------------------------------------------------------
;           * = Not needed if the 8259 is in the 8088/86 mode.
;--------------------------------------------------------------------------------------
                   MOV      AL,17h                                  ;Load ICW1.
                   OUT      INTPORT0,AL                             ;Send it to the 8259.
                   MOV      AL,08h                                  ;Load ICW2.
                   OUT      INTPORT1,AL                             ;Send it to the 8259.
                   MOV      AL,0Fh                                  ;Load ICW4
                   OUT      INTPORT1,AL                             ;Send it to the 8259.
                   MOV      AL,0FEh                                 ;Load OCW1
                   OUT      INTPORT1,AL                             ;Send it to the 8259.
;--------------------------------------------------------------------------------------
;                            SETUP FOR THE SEGMENTS
;--------------------------------------------------------------------------------------
                   MOV      AX,0070h                                ;Set the location of the stack
                   MOV      SS,AX                                   ;bottom at 00700h and set the
                   MOV      SP,00F0h                                ;top of the stack at 000F0h.
                   MOV      AX,0000h                                ;Tell the 8088 that the data
                   MOV      DS,AX                                   ;segment is at 00000h.
```

Fig. 14-3. (continued)

```
;
;*********************************************************************************
;*            ZERO OUT THE DISPLAY AND LOAD THE KEYBOARD VECTOR              *
;*********************************************************************************
BLANK:         MOV     AL,00h                    ;Now load the value that will
                                                 ;cause the character generator
                                                 ;to send zeros to each segment.
               MOV     BYTE PTR DISPLAY1,AL      ;Store the number '0' character
               MOV     BYTE PTR DISPLAY2,AL      ;in each of the locations that
               MOV     BYTE PTR DISPLAY3,AL      ;are reserved for the numbers
               MOV     BYTE PTR DISPLAY4,AL      ;to be displayed in each of the
               MOV     BYTE PTR DISPLAY5,AL      ;displays.
               MOV     BYTE PTR DISPLAY6,AL      ;Once all the eight locations
               MOV     BYTE PTR DISPLAY7,AL      ;have been loaded, the display
               MOV     BYTE PTR DISPLAY8,AL      ;can be set to zeros by calling
               CALL    SCAN                      ;the digit scanning routine.
;--------------------------------------------------------------------------------
;                     LOAD THE KEYBOARD VECTOR
;--------------------------------------------------------------------------------
               MOV     WORD PTR KBINT,0020h      ;Offset for keyboard routine.
               MOV     WORD PTR KBINT+2,0FFE0h   ;Segment for interrupts.
               STI                               ;All done so enable interrupts.
               JMP     GO                        ;It's SHOWTIME folks.
;
;*********************************************************************************
;*                     DIGIT MULTIPLEXING ROUTINE                            *
;*********************************************************************************
SCAN:          PUSH    AX                        ;Save the current accumulator.
               PUSHF                             ;Save the current flags.
;--------------------------------------------------------------------------------
;The next several instructions will sequentially load AL with the current value
;of the numbers from the page zero variables and output the current value to
;each of the corresponding digits at port 1.
;--------------------------------------------------------------------------------
               MOV     AL,DISPLAY1               ;Get the current digit 1 value.
               OUT     DISPLED,AL                ;Send it to the display.
               MOV     AL,DISPLAY2               ;Get the current digit 2 value.
               ADD     AL,20h                    ;Set the high bits for digit 2.
               OUT     DISPLED,AL                ;Send it to the display.
               MOV     AL,DISPLAY3               ;Get the current digit 3 value.
               ADD     AL,40h                    ;Set the high bits for digit 3.
               OUT     DISPLED,AL                ;Send it to the display.
               MOV     AL,DISPLAY4               ;Get the current digit 4 value.
               ADD     AL,60h                    ;Set the high bits for digit 4.
               OUT     DISPLED,AL                ;Send it to the display.
               MOV     AL,DISPLAY5               ;Get the current digit 5 value.
               ADD     AL,80h                    ;Set the high bits for digit 5.
               OUT     DISPLED,AL                ;Send it to the display.
               MOV     AL,DISPLAY6               ;Get the current digit 6 value.
               ADD     AL,0A0h                   ;Set the high bits for digit 6.
               OUT     DISPLED,AL                ;Send it to the display.
               MOV     AL,DISPLAY7               ;Get the current digit 7 value.
               ADD     AL,0C0h                   ;Set the high bits for digit 7.
               OUT     DISPLED,AL                ;Send it to the display.
               MOV     AL,DISPLAY8               ;Get the current digit 8 value.
               ADD     AL,0E0h                   ;Set the high bits for digit 8.
               OUT     DISPLED,AL                ;Send it to the display.
;--------------------------------------------------------------------------------
               POPF                              ;Restore the previous flags.
               POP     AX                        ;Restore the previous AX.
               RET
;
;*********************************************************************************
;*                     MAIN BODY OF THE CODE                                 *
;*********************************************************************************
;The only thing the code is doing is a constant refreshing of the display by
```

Fig. 14-3. (continued)

```
;calling the SCAN routine.  Since SCAN gets the values for the digits from the
;RAM locations, any new value entered from the keyboard will be displayed.
;---------------------------------------------------------------------------
GO:             CALL    SCAN                    ;Update the display.
                JMP     GO                      ;Not very exciting, is it?


;
;*******************************************************************************
;*                   THE KEYBOARD INTERRUPT ROUTINE                           *
;*******************************************************************************
;The segment for all interrupt routines is FFE0h.  Since the 2716 is mapped in
;at FF800 - FFFFF this leaves 512 bytes (FFFFFh - FFE00h) of room for interrupt
;routine code.  The segment address FFE0h in the 8088 address range translates
;to 600h in the 2716 range of 0000h - 07FFh.  The assembler is ORG'ing the code
;at 0100h so the location of the keyboard routine is at 100h + 600h + 20h (this
;is the offset) or an absolute address of 720h.
;---------------------------------------------------------------------------
                ORG     0720h
GETKEY:         PUSH    AX                      ;Save the current accumulator.
                IN      AL,KEYBOARD             ;Get the key in the accumulator
                MOV     BYTE PTR KBDAT,AL       ;Store the key in the buffer.
                MOV     BYTE PTR DISPLAY8,AL    ;and display it on digit #8
                POP     AX                      ;Put the accumulator back.
                IRET

;
;*******************************************************************************
;*                     T H E   B O O T   C O D E                              *
;*******************************************************************************
;The 8088 power up location of FFFF0h is actually 07F0h in the 2716.  The boot
;instruction has to be ORG'ed at 08F0h since the assembler wants to ORG the
;above main code at 0100.  The result is that the 2716 will have the main code
;at 0000h and the boot code at 07F0h.
;---------------------------------------------------------------------------
                ORG     08F0h                   ;The 2716 location for the 8088
                                                ;power-up instruction allowing
                                                ;for the assembler's ORG 100
                                                ;requirement for the main code.
                JMP START                       ;Go to the main code located at
                                                ;0000h in the 2716.
                DB      00,00,00,00,00,00,00    ;Nul bytes to fill the 2716
                DB      00,00,00,00,00,00        ;with 00's after the power up
                                                ; jump described above.

;
;*******************************************************************************
;*                     THE END OF THE PROGRAM                                 *
;*******************************************************************************
BOB             ENDS                            ;Tell assembler this is the end
                                                ;of code for this segment.
                END     START                   ;Tell assembler this is the end
                                                ;of the program as well.
```

Hex Dump of KEYBOARD.ASM

```
0000 - FA B0 90 E6 03 B0 17 E6 80 B0 08 E6 81 B0 0F E6
0010 - 81 B0 FE E6 81 B8 70 00 8E D0 BC F0 00 B8 00 00
0020 - 8E D8 B0 00 A2 80 00 A2 81 00 A2 82 00 A2 83 00
0030 - A2 84 00 A2 85 00 A2 86 00 A2 87 00 E8 10 00 C7
0040 - 06 20 00 20 00 C7 06 22 00 E0 FF FB EB 3C 90 50
0050 - 9C A0 80 00 E6 01 A0 81 00 04 20 E6 01 A0 82 00
0060 - 04 40 E6 01 A0 83 00 04 60 E6 01 A0 84 00 04 80
0070 - E6 01 A0 85 00 04 A0 E6 01 A0 86 00 04 C0 E6 01
0080 - A0 87 00 04 E0 E6 01 9D 58 C3 E8 C2 FF EB FB 00
0090 - 00 00 00 00 00 00 00 00 00 00 00 00 00 00 00 00
00A0 - 00 00 00 00 00 00 00 00 00 00 00 00 00 00 00 00
```

Fig. 14-3. (continued)

```
00B0 - 05FF are filled with zeros

0600 - 00 00 00 00 00 00 00 00 00 00 00 00 00 00 00 00
0610 - 00 00 00 00 00 00 00 00 00 00 00 00 00 00 00 00
0620 - 50 E4 00 A2 88 00 A2 87 00 58 CF 00 00 00 00 00
0630 - 00 00 00 00 00 00 00 00 00 00 00 00 00 00 00 00
0640 - 00 00 00 00 00 00 00 00 00 00 00 00 00 00 00 00

0650 - 07CF are filled with zeros

07D0 - 00 00 00 00 00 00 00 00 00 00 00 00 00 00 00 00
07E0 - 00 00 00 00 00 00 00 00 00 00 00 00 00 00 00 00
07F0 - E9 0D F8 00 00 00 00 00 00 00 00 00 00 00 00 00
```

Fig. 14-3. (continued)

As with all the programs we've worked with, you'll find the listing is completely commented and is (or should be) self explanatory. There may be a way to write something that would be small enough to fit in the diode ROM I've been threatening to do away with, but (and I really mean it this time) I'm officially putting that behind us. The diode ROM is history.

If you want to continue on this journey through 8088 land, you're going to have to do something about burning EPROMs. They're just as necessary to the circuit as gas is for your car. Even if you own the world's most terrific car, you can only get so far by rolling it down hill —sooner or later you've got to put gas in the tank. It may cost a few bucks but hey, that's the way it is.

The keyboard program will program the 8259 just as we've described in this chapter using the I/O ports we decided on. The routine that handles the interrupt is located in memory at the address we worked out and will be called every time a key is pressed. There are a few things to notice in the listing.

Whenever a key is pressed, the keyboard port (8255 port #0) will be read and the value will be put in a one byte buffer (KBDAT) located at 88h. Once that's done, the same value will be stored in the location reserved for digit #8. The next time the display is refreshed, the keyboard value will be read from the display buffer and sent out the display port to finally show up on the LEDs.

While the interrupt routine is similar to a standard subroutine, it does have its differences. The most important one shows up at the end of the routine where an IRET instruction is used instead of an RET. A complete explanation for this can be found in the data sheet but, in a nutshell, it revolves around all the stuff the 8088 has to do before it can honor an interrupt request. This includes things like saving the program counter, disabling maskable interrupts, and so on. It's important to have a good understanding of just what the 8088 has to do to run an interrupt routine and, when you get comfortable with using them, it's worth your time to get into it.

When you're just getting started, however, it just doesn't make any sense to fill your head with the theoretical side of things. You're much better off concentrating on getting a handle on all the practical details. Theory's not worth much if you don't have any idea of how to make it do something.

To give you an idea of just how much work the 8088 has to do before getting to your routine, I'll tell you that the 8088 uses up 62 clock cycles taking care of the necessary housekeeping. It's a bit less for a software generated interrupt but it shows you that the reason it can seem so easy to use interrupts is the power of the handling routines built into the 8088. It's doing most of the donkey work for you—and doing it transparently as well.

If you're having trouble getting the routine to work, the problem has to be in the way you've wired up the 8259. We've been really very careful to add software and hardware in a step by step fashion and you should only have gotten to this point by having everything up to it work correctly. Since we've hardware and software tested every one of the subsystems on the board—including the keyboard hardware—the only place an error can have been made is in the way the 8259 is set up on the board.

Go back to the last chapter and check your connections against the hookup tables. It only takes one mistake to transform the whole board from a working piece of electronics that can do anything in general to an interesting piece of art that can do nothing in particular.

By this time, you should be impressed with the powerful things you can do by using the solitary INTR pin of the 8088. But that's not the only interrupt input we have to work with since the NMI input is only two tenths of an inch away.

Having an interrupt that's not maskable can be really handy and it makes good sense to use it for something that has as broad a range of circuit appeal as possible. I've got some ideas and I expect you do as well. So let's tackle that next.

15

Building a System

EVERY MICROPROCESSOR-BASED CIRCUIT EVER MADE, AND PROBABLY EVERY ONE THAT
will ever be made in the future, (now that's what they call a really "sweeping
statement"), always has two basically different kinds of software available at the same
time. This may sound like a strange thing to say but if you think about it for a second,
you'll be able to figure out what I'm going to say before you read any further.

No matter what kind of job you want CPU circuitry to do, there's a sharp division
between the software that manages the application and the software that manages the
circuit. The former takes care of the job and the latter takes care of the microprocessor.

Consider this. If you're using a computer to run a word processor, the application
program (the word processor) lets you write, but it has to rely on the computer's built
in firmware (software in a ROM) to handle all of the circuit hardware. This would include
things like the video, keyboard, disk drive, printer, and so on. All these things are
contained in a program that's sometimes referred to as the *Basic Input Output System*,
or BIOS. That's not all there is to it—there's more.

One of the things you've unconsciously picked up in going through this book is that
the 8088 by itself can't do anything. We've already seen that it takes a lot of extra
hardware to put together a working circuit, but even if you connected the CPU pins
to an acre of silicon real estate you'd still only have something suitable for framing, not
for using.

When you turn on a microprocessor-based circuit like ours nothing much is going
to happen unless there's software available to tell the CPU what to do. We've been
running diagnostic programs to test the various pieces of hardware we've been adding
to the circuit but we're at a point now where the programs are getting more and more
complex and the software needed to test them is getting more complex as well. What
we have to do is start looking at the system we've built and see what essential elements
will always be needed.

The list of functions we'll put together will compromise the basic overhead of the
system and all these should be permanently available in the firmware at known locations.
By doing this, any application software you use can call them when they're needed.

The two basic kinds of software in any system, therefore, are the primitive routines
that talk to the hardware in the circuit and the application programs that use them. The
former are permanent parts of the circuit and the latter are only loaded when they're
needed.

We've spent all our time so far giving the circuit the muscle it has to have to do
any kind of meaningful work. What we're going to do now is give the circuit some brains.
We want our system to wake up smart.

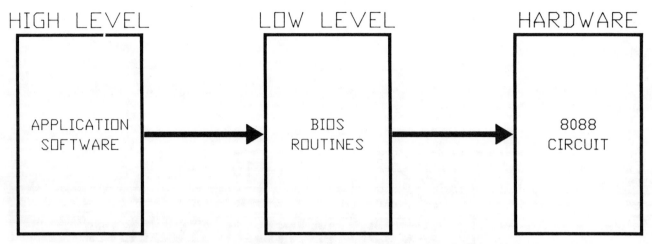

HIGH LEVEL	LOW LEVEL	HARDWARE
APPLICATION SOFTWARE	BIOS ROUTINES	8088 CIRCUIT

Fig. 15-1. The relationship between the BIOS, the system, and application software.

WORKING OUT THE DETAILS

It may seem as if we spend more time getting ready to do things than actually doing them, but that's the way it is when you design general purpose circuits like this. Since you want to be able to use it for everything in general it has to be as flexible as possible. Not only that, but mistakes get harder and harder to correct as you move down the development cycle from idea to breadboard to PC board.

What we're talking about doing now is creating a list of routines that will be of most use to the software we plan on writing for the circuit. Of course, there's no way to predict what kind of software we'll be writing. The classic "chicken and egg problem".

There are, however, some things that are so basic we can be sure that every application will need them. An initial list would contain things such as:

1. Update the display.
2. Provide an accurate clock.
3. Read a key from the keyboard.
4. Write to the display.
5. Show the contents of memory.
6. Read from an I/O port.
7. Write to an I/O port.
8. Test memory.

and I'm sure you can think of many, many more.

Whatever you put on the list, there will be some things you want to be available when you need them, and some things you want to have happen all the time, no matter what the circuit is doing.

The first two things on the list are examples of things you want to happen automatically. It wastes program space, development time, and the chances of writing error free programs if the responsibility for updating the display is left to the application software. That isn't to say that you shouldn't be able to influence or change it easily in your program—that would make the system less flexible. And that's a no-no.

The same is true of providing an accurate clock. We've got lots of frequencies running around the circuit but it would be really useful to have some place for application software to look to get an accurate count of the passage of time—lots of control applications need this to monitor external events.

While these two things should be controllable by software, most of the time they should happen with no thought whatsoever—they should be transparent to the running software, totally automatic. Let's see how that can be done.

PREDEFINED INTERRUPTS

Now that we know everything that's important about interrupts, (we have one working, remember?), it's very easy to understand what's so special about an NMI. In the simplest terms, the 8088 looks at the NMI input as the "End Of The World" interrupt. You can't tell the CPU to disregard it and it takes precedence over everything else. When the NMI talks, the CPU listens—always.

Aside from that, it's no different than any of the other interrupts we've described earlier. Most systems use NMI to report catastrophic errors such as power loss and other system failures. The IBM PC uses NMI to report a parity error in memory. If you remember what we found when we were looking at the parity flag, you'll understand that this isn't so terrific. NMI is too powerful a tool to waste on something as error prone as parity checking.

As a starting point we'll use NMI to handle display updating and maintaining an accurate clock. The software side of this is fairly simple since the procedure for setting it up is exactly the same as the keyboard interrupt we just finished. And as soon as we get there, you'll see that the hardware side is a piece of cake. Really.

Of all the locations Intel has reserved in the vector table, only the first five have actually been used. This means that the 8088 is microcoded to look at those locations when any one of the associated interrupts are generated. Let's take a look at them.

Interrupt 0 is triggered automatically if the result of a division is bigger than the 8088 can handle. Imagine trying to solve for the value of PI (3.1415 ad nauseum). The 8088 can be instructed to deal with 32 bit division but, while that's room for lots of significant figures, any division that produces a larger quotient will cause an INT 0 to be automatically generated.

When you're developing software, Interrupt 1, the *Single Step*, is your best friend. By setting the Trap Flag in the Flag Register, you can force the 8088 to generate an INT 1 right after each instruction is executed. This can only be done in a round about fashion since the 8088 doesn't have a single instruction for it. To set the Trap Flag, you have to PUSH the flags onto the stack, set the Trap Flag, and then POP the byte back to the register. Once this is done, the 8088 will run your handling routine after each instruction is executed. This could be a diagnostic routine, a memory location check, or anything that cuts the brain damage that's unfortunately an inescapable part of any software development. Get to know this interrupt since the sixty eighth Law of Life and Design clearly states:

> **NEVER SAY NO TO THINGS THAT HELP**

Fig. 15-2. The reserved interrupt vector table locations.

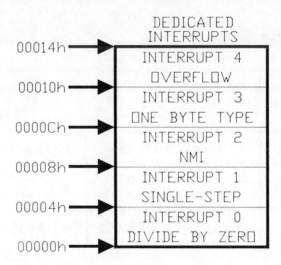

We'll be using Interrupt 2 in a bit—the fabulous *Non-Maskable Interrupt*. Remember that even though it has its own input pin on the CPU and the 8088 gives it the highest priority, it's still just an interrupt like all the others.

Intel has assigned Interrupt 3 as the *"One Byte Interrupt"*. This is similar to Interrupt 1, the single step, in that it's a great aid in debugging software. The coding for this instruction is only one byte long—INT—so it can replace any instruction in the entire 8088 set. If there's a hitch in some software you're working on and you have a good idea where it is, you can systematically replace each of the suspected instructions with an INT until you manage to pinpoint the problem. Should the routine you want to debug be in the middle of the program, (and it usually is), it's a lot more efficient to use the INT than setting the Trap Flag and having the program break after each instruction.

The last predefined interrupt is type 4, *Interrupt On Overflow*, and it will be generated if the overflow flag is set to a one in the flag register and an INTO instruction has been executed.

You may decide not to use any of these interrupts but that doesn't mean you can ignore them since most of them can't be turned off with software. Trying to develop software without taking into account the possibility of any of these interrupts is like riding in a car without wearing a safety belt—in other words, it's just a stupid thing to do. Several of these interrupts are generated automatically and if you haven't worked out a handling routine for them you're going to have problems.

Imagine what happens. Your program is running along in cruisamatic and everything's working just the way you planned. Along comes some sort of unforeseen circumstance— and believe me, they do have a way of coming along—it causes a type 0 interrupt to be generated, and all of a sudden your program is in hyperspace. A system crash. A bad thing.

Even if you don't plan on using any of the predefined interrupts, you still have to provide a handler for them. This is no big deal—a handler is just a fancy name for a subroutine. You can keep the total overhead for all the interrupts you don't want to use down to one byte, a single IRET instruction. As a matter of fact, it's possible to cut it down to zero overhead if you've got an IRET instruction available. All you have to do is stuff the proper locations in the vector table with the absolute address of the IRET and you've finished taking care of handling unexpected interrupts. Piece of cake.

It's very important to keep these predefined interrupts in mind as you're working out the details of your BIOS because they have to be handled in some manner or another. Since nothing helps more than a systematic presentation, Table 15-1 sums up every important fact about these interrupts.

Now that we've got all this stuff straight, we can start figuring out how to design our BIOS. The first thing we'll be doing is working out the details of the screen refreshing and maintaining an accurate clock.

GENERAL CONSIDERATIONS

At the moment we only have two jobs we want handled automatically by the NMI line, but that's no guarantee there won't be other things we want done the same way.

Table 15-1. Reserved Interrupt Details.

Interrupt	Vector Address	Maskable	Definition
Type #0	00000h to 00003h	No	Divide By Zero
Type #1	00004h to 00007h	Yes	Single Step
Type #2	00008h to 0000Bh	No	Hardware NMI *
Type #3	0000Ch to 0000Fh	No	One Byte (INT)
Type #4	00010h to 00013h	No	Overflow (INTO)

Just as with everything else we've done so far, we have to plan how our interrupt routines are going to be mapped into memory.

This may sound tedious since we've been doing the same thing for all the hardware and software that's been added to the system, but you have to get used to doing things this way. There's no getting around the truth of the forty eighth Law of Life and Design.

> ## LOGICAL CIRCUITS TAKE LOGICAL THOUGHT

since circuits put together without thought will always be thoughtless circuits.

We've reached the part of our design where there's no "right way" to do the job. Software is written to do a particular job and there's as many ways to write it as there are jobs to be done. The emphasis in the routines we'll be creating will be on ease of understanding. I have no doubt that anyone of you with a programming background can do a lot better—and I hope you do.

It's more important to understand the process than the product and once you have a handle on how things fit together you can arrange all the details to suit yourself. At the moment, however, we'll create a set of routines that are as intuitive as possible and that can be done by basing them on the work we've already done.

Before we get to the design of the software we still have to take care of the hardware side of things. Remember that NMI is a separate line on the 8088 and we need some circuitry to trigger it.

The 8088 NMI pin is an edge triggered input that wants a positive going pulse and any hardware we design to feed this pin has to meet this minimum qualification. The only other requirement we have for the NMI circuitry comes from the fact that we want to use it as the basis of an accurate real world clock.

There are several ways to do this. Intel makes the 8253 timer, a programmable chip with three timer/counters that can be set up with software in much the same way as the 8255 and 8259 we've already put on the board. If you find yourself with a need for several accurate counters, this is a good choice but for our immediate purposes, we can handle the NMI line with something a lot simpler.

If you examine everything we've done to our circuit so far, you'll realize that we've got a whole bunch of accurate clocks already sitting on the board. The problem is that none of them produce time intervals that are easy to use as the basis for real world timing. All of our buffered clocks meet the test of accuracy but it's hard to build any meaningful time intervals from something like 298.3 kHz. What we need is a derived frequency with an easy to use value.

And, as it turns out, that's simple to do.

NMI HARDWARE

When digital clocks first started to show up on the market, they all got their timing accuracy from the standard 60 Hz frequency available from the local utility company. Battery powered clocks soon became popular and even though they initially worked off a 32 kHz crystal, it didn't take long for someone to realize that there was a more popular crystal in everyday use—the 3.579545 MHz colorburst crystal that's used in every TV set. The result of this was the appearance of the 5369AA, a 17 stage CMOS divider from National Semiconductor that could take colorburst in at one end and put out 60 Hz at the other end.

This was a terrific thing but that's not the end of it—the 5369 was designed to be even more flexible than that because it was set up as mask programmable. That may not be much help to people working in the field but it did give National Semiconductor the ability to get different frequencies by building the chip with different masks.

One of the standard versions of the chip is the 5369EST. The mask is set up in this case to take 3.579545 MHz at the input and divide it down to 100 Hz at the output.

That's exactly the kind of thing we need since we have a 3.579545 MHz signal already being generated on the board. Way back when we decided to produce a set of usable clocks because the hardware needed was only minimal and there could turn out to be times when they would be useful.

Well, this is one of those times.

PARTS
1 - 5369EST Oscillator/Divider

MINIMUM EQUIPMENT
Frequency Counter

As a special gift for everyone in recognition of all the brain damage you undoubtedly went through in getting this far, this addition to the circuit is the simplest one we've ever done. All we're adding to the board is a single IC—and it's an 8-pin minidip as well.

Keep in mind that this is a mask programmable chip and there are a few standard versions of it floating around. The only way to tell one from another is by the part number suffix. The 5369AA produces 60 Hz, the 5369EYR produces 50 Hz, and the 5269EST produces 100 Hz. Any one of these chips will work in the circuit but the software we're going to write is going to assume that NMIs are being generated at a 100 Hz rate. Most parts suppliers have this version of the chip available but if you find you have to use the more popular 5369AA, you'll have to make adjustments to the software. Put the

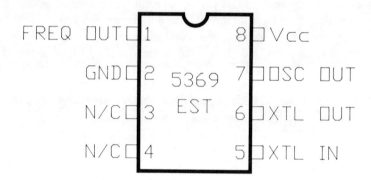

Fig. 15-3. The pinouts of the 5369EST.

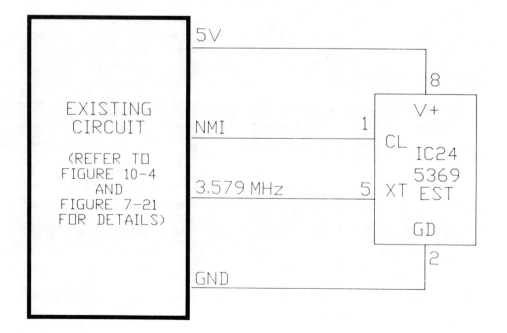

Fig. 15-4. The NMI generation circuit.

chip on the board as shown in the placement diagram of Fig. 15-5 and make the connections indicated in Table 15-2. You'll notice that we're not putting our usual small bypass capacitor on the board since the IC is a CMOS part and doesn't cause the same sort of problems as TTL.

Once you've made these connections, all the software we've used so far is obsolete. Having an NMI generated once every hundredth of a second means that we need the NMI handler to get the circuit working. It also means that there's no way to immediately test the hardware to see if everything is hooked up properly. Since we haven't really done all that much, it's rather hard to make a mistake, but if you're the kind of person who likes to be sure about each and every step, you'll have to leave the 8088's NMI pin grounded and run any of the software we've written so far.

It doesn't matter which of the programs you run since all we want to do is look at the output of the 5369EST. When you have the board operating, put the frequency counter probe on pin #1 of the 5369EST and you should see a 100 Hz clock that's an ideal shape for using with NMI since the waveform only has short duration positive spikes and the risetime is typical of the type you get with CMOS—extremely steep, sharp shoulders, and just about noise free.

If you don't see the 100 Hz signal on the pin, the only conclusion is that the chip is undoubtedly bad since we've tried every other part of the circuit before this.

Table 15-2. Connections Made to the 5369EST (IC24).

CONNECTIONS TO IC24 (5369EST)	
Pin #	Connect to
1	8088 pin #17 (NMI)
2	Ground
3	No Connection
4	No Connection
5	IC18 pin #10
6	No Connection
7	No Connection
8	5 Volts

NMI SOFTWARE

Before we get into this, be aware that even though there are several hardware and timing differences between standard 8088 interrupts and Non-Maskable Interrupts, they all mean nothing whatsoever once the CPU reaches the point of looking in the vector table. Some applications have to know whether they're handling an NMI or a standard hardware interrupt because there are slight differences in the way the 8088 will deal with them. For our purposes however, the differences are totally unimportant. We'll let the 8088 do its thing, and then we'll do ours.

DISPLAY REFRESHING

We've already got most of the display refresh routine we need for the NMI interrupt handler. We've done it in earlier software and all we really have to do is modify the code to make it suitable. This is no big deal since the changes are minor.

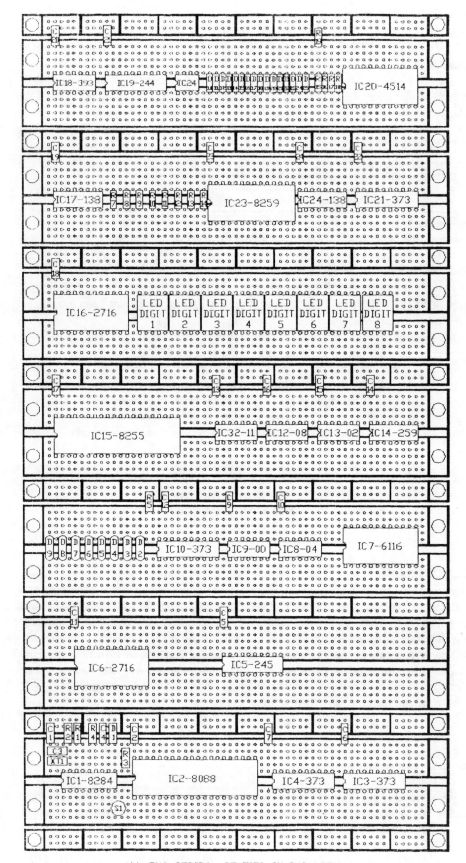

Fig. 15-5. Placement diagram for the NMI generation circuit.

ALL BUS STRIPS ARE TIED IN PARALLEL
AND CARRY ONLY POWER AND GROUND

Here's the listing for the code we've been using.

```
;****************************************************************
;*                  DIGIT MULTIPLEXING ROUTINE                 *
;****************************************************************
SCAN:       PUSH    AX                  ;Save the current accumulator.
            PUSHF                       ;Save the current flags.
;---------------------------------------------------------------
            MOV     AL,DISPLAY1         ;Get the current digit 1 value.
            OUT     DISPLED,AL          ;Send it to the display.
            MOV     AL,DISPLAY2         ;Get the current digit 2 value.
            ADD     AL,20h              ;Set the high byte for digit 2.
            OUT     DISPLED,AL          ;Send it to the display.
            MOV     AL,DISPLAY3         ;Get the current digit 3 value.
            ADD     AL,40h              ;Set the high byte for digit 3.
            OUT     DISPLED,AL          ;Send it to the display.
            MOV     AL,DISPLAY4         ;Get the current digit 4 value.
            ADD     AL,60h              ;Set the high byte for digit 4.
            OUT     DISPLED,AL          ;Send it to the display.
            MOV     AL,DISPLAY5         ;Get the current digit 5 value.
            ADD     AL,80h              ;Set the high byte for digit 5.
            OUT     DISPLED,AL          ;Send it to the display.
            MOV     AL,DISPLAY6         ;Get the current digit 6 value.
            ADD     AL,0A0h             ;Set the high byte for digit 6.
            OUT     DISPLED,AL          ;Send it to the display.
            MOV     AL,DISPLAY7         ;Get the current digit 7 value.
            ADD     AL,0C0h             ;Set the high byte for digit 7.
            OUT     DISPLED,AL          ;Send it to the display.
            MOV     AL,DISPLAY8         ;Get the current digit 8 value.
            ADD     AL,0E0h             ;Set the high byte for digit 8.
            OUT     DISPLED,AL          ;Send it to the display.
;---------------------------------------------------------------
            POPF                        ;Restore the previous flags.
            POP     AX                  ;Restore the previous AX.
            RET
```

The first change we're going to have to make is due to the fact that this routine, (or something very close to it), is going to be run at least every hundredth of a second. As a result, there's no way to tell what the application software is going to be doing when the NMI is generated. This includes the registers as well. So we've come to the first rule for writing interrupt routines:

PRESERVE YOUR ENVIRONMENT

If you have programming experience, you already recognize this since it's also a necessity for any type of subroutine.

We're not making heavy use of the registers in the routines we'll be writing for NMI, but there's no telling what might be added to them later on. It's a good idea to start things out on the right foot by making register saves and restores a basic part of all NMI routines.

Translated into real terms, this means that all the registers have to be saved before the routine is done. The last thing the routine has to do before it returns control to the application is restore all the registers.

You can see that we've already done some of that in the original listing. We didn't bother saving all the registers since the program was very short and we knew exactly which registers were in use. This is a luxury we won't have in a BIOS since there's no way of knowing what the application is doing.

The practical change to the listing, therefore, will be to make use of the stack to save and restore the registers. The actual code will be this.

```
        PUSH    AX                      ;Save the accumulator.
        PUSH    BX                      ;Save the BX register.
        PUSH    CX                      ;Save the CX register.
        PUSH    DX                      ;Save the DX register.
        PUSH    DS                      ;Save the data segment.
;-------------------------------------------------------------------
;       CALL    ROUTINE TO UPDATE THE DISPLAY
;-------------------------------------------------------------------
DONE:   POP     DS                      ;Restore the data segment.
        POP     DX                      ;Restore the DX register.
        POP     CX                      ;Restore the CX register.
        POP     BX                      ;Restore the BX register.
        POP     AX                      ;Restore the accumulator.
        IRET                            ;Return to the application.
```

Notice that we've saved the current data segment (DS) and haven't bothered saving the flags or current code segment.

Whenever the 8088 runs an interrupt routine, it automatically saves the flags and code segment and puts the original ones back when the interrupt routine is finished. We're saving the data segment, however, since our display data is located in a particular data segment and we can't be sure what segment the application is using.

This leads directly to the second modification we have to make to the routine—setting the data segment correctly. The two lines of code we need to do this should look familiar to you since we used them near the head of the last program we wrote for the system.

```
MOV     AX,0000h        ;Tell the 8088 that the data
MOV     DS,AX           ;segment is now at 0000h.
```

We don't have to do anything similar to put things back since the POP at the end of the routine will take care of that for us.

CLOCK MAINTENANCE

There wasn't much brain damage in writing the first half of the NMI routine since we could adapt a lot of the code we already had. The clock, however, is something entirely new and is going to require a bit more thought. Before we write the clock code, we have to decide exactly what the clock is going to do and how we're going to set it up in software.

Since the clock is going to be driven by an NMI, the maximum timing accuracy we'll be able to get is a hundredth of a second. The most basic issue for us is to decide whether the clock is going to be used for timing or whether it's going to keep time. The two of these are not the same.

For reasons buried deep in the past and shrouded in mystery, clocks don't work on a base 10 or base 16 system. As a matter of fact, they don't work on any system at all—60 seconds to the minute, 60 minutes to an hour, 24 hours to a day, and so on and so forth. If you think about it, the numbers are really strange. Maybe there is something to the metric system after all.

The problem with using the NMI interval to keep time is that the routine has to be much more complex. It has to increment succeeding digits on overflow counts of 60 and 24. The 8088 won't do this all by itself—there's no handy dandy type instruction called CLK or TIME that you can use to get the job done. If you want to use NMI to maintain a real time clock, you've got to write the routine yourself.

If you just want to use NMI for accurate timing, things are a lot simpler. Basically, you just need a counter that's incremented by an accurate clock. Since a counter can be nothing more than a few memory locations and an accurate clock is provided by the NMI interval, we already have all the pieces we need. It would seem to make a lot more sense to just count NMIs and let the application software take care of converting the count to real time.

After all, we're into saving BIOS space and all we really should provide there are primitive routines that can be called by application software. Not using ROM space to write the routines that convert the hundredths of a second count to a real time count of seconds, minutes, hours, and days seems like a smart idea since, intuitively at least, it would take a lot less space.

Let's take a more detailed look and actually try it before we make a hard decision about which way is the best for a small system like the one we're building.

If all we want to do is keep track of the number of seconds and we have four locations reserved in RAM for the clock, a typical routine to do the job would be something like this.

```
NMITIME:    INC     BYTE PTR HUNDS        ;Add to the hundredths count.
            CMP     BYTE PTR HUNDS,64h    ;Have we reached 100?
            JNZ     ENDNMI               ;If not, we're done.
            MOV     BYTE PTR HUNDS,00h    ;Zero out the hundredths.
            INC     BYTE PTR SECS1        ;Add to seconds count #1.
            CMP     BYTE PTR SECS1,00h    ;Has it counted through 255?
            JNZ     ENDNMI               ;If not, we're done.
            INC     BYTE PTR SECS2        ;Add to seconds count #2.
            CMP     BYTE PTR SECS2,00h    ;Has it counted through 255?
            JNZ     ENDNMI               ;If not, we're done.
            INC     BYTE PTR SECS3        ;Add to seconds count #3.
            CMP     BYTE PTR SECS3,00h    ;Has it counted through 255?
            JZ      NMITIME              ;At the maximum so start again.
ENDNMI:                                  ;The rest of the NMI Routine.
```

You can see that when location SECS3 reaches 00h, the whole thing will start all over again—the count will reset to zero. The maximum amount of time you could store in a system like this would be FFFFFFh seconds— equivalent to 16,777,215 seconds or a little bit less than 195 days. If you wanted to keep track of tenths of a second, SECS1 would store the tenths and the last two digits would be the only ones that stored full seconds. The maximum count in that case would be up to FFFFh or 65,535 seconds— about 18.5 hours.

Now let's suppose you wanted to keep track of real time—seconds, minutes, hours, and days—in the same four byte space. The routine would be modified to look like this:

```
NMITIME:    INC     BYTE PTR HUNDS        ;Add to the hundredths count.
            CMP     BYTE PTR HUNDS,64h    ;Have we reached 100?
            JNZ     ENDNMI               ;If not, we're done.
            MOV     BYTE PTR HUNDS,00h    ;Zero out the hundredths.
            INC     BYTE PTR SECS1        ;Add to the seconds counter.
            CMP     BYTE PTR SECS1,3Ch    ;Has it counted 60 seconds?
            JNZ     ENDNMI               ;If not, we're done.
            MOV     BYTE PTR SECS1,00h    ;Zero out the seconds counter.
            INC     BYTE PTR SECS2        ;Add to the minutes counter.
            CMP     BYTE PTR SECS2,3Ch    ;Has it counted 60 minutes?
            JNZ     ENDNMI               ;If not, we're done.
            MOV     BYTE PTR SECS2,00h    ;Zero out the minutes counter.
            INC     BYTE PTR SECS3        ;Add to the hours counter.
```

```
        CMP     BYTE PTR SECS3,18h  ;Has it counted 24 hours?
        JZ      NMITIME             ;At the maximum so start again.
ENDNMI:                             ;The rest of the NMI Routine.
```

We needed a few more instructions to reset the counters at the right time but, other than that, it's really not much different, is it?

The routine is essentially the same one we used when we were just counting seconds but the payback we get for the same memory space is considerably less—instead of a maximum count of 195 days, the system will reset after one day. And if we stored tenths of a second, we'd only have room to count minutes and it would all zero out after just one hour.

This is one of those deals where intuition can lead you astray and it's a classic example of why you have to be really methodical when you're in the planning stages of either hardware or software. Systems like ours are most often used for controlling things and there's no telling how long the operation has to last. In some circumstances it may be more convenient to have real time available but we've seen that the price you have to pay for that is really steep.

There are no rules for BIOS routines. You can do whatever you want in the ROM—after all, this is America. If you want to set up a real time clock—hey, you're the one that's shelling out the bucks for the parts.

For my money, the loss of all that time is just too much of a price to pay for a real time clock so I'm going to set up a seconds counter rather than a clock. Anyway, I already have a wristwatch.

Now that we've gone through all the considerations and decided what the clock should do, all that's left before we actually start to write the routine is to decide on the maximum duration. We've seen that a four byte count gives us a maximum time of about 195 days. That's if we don't devote a separate byte to tenths of a second—but, consider it for a second, we don't really need it since we can pick the tenths of a second count from the byte that's counting hundredths. I mean, it doesn't take an advanced degree in mathematics to figure out that seventy five hundredths is the same as seven and a half tenths.

So there we are. We've decided on the format of the timer and the duration of the count—all that's left is to write the code. The broad outline of the NMI handler, therefore, is this:

```
        PUSH    AX                  ;Save the accumulator.
        PUSH    BX                  ;Save the BX register.
        PUSH    CX                  ;Save the CX register.
        PUSH    DX                  ;Save the DX register.
        PUSH    DS                  ;Save the data segment.
        MOV     AX,0000h            ;Tell the 8088 that the data
        MOV     DS,AX               ;segment is now at 0000h.
;       ------------------------------------------------------------
;                   ROUTINE FOR CLOCK MAINTENANCE
;       ------------------------------------------------------------
;                   ROUTINE TO UPDATE THE DISPLAY
;       ------------------------------------------------------------
DONE:   POP     DS                  ;Restore the data segment.
        POP     DX                  ;Restore the DX register.
        POP     CX                  ;Restore the CX register.
        POP     BX                  ;Restore the BX register.
        POP     AX                  ;Restore the accumulator.
        IRET                        ;Return to the application.
```

We've been putting our system variables at RAM location 80h and up. In the last piece of software we used, ten variables were defined but only nine of them were used since the variable DELAY was a carryover from an earlier piece of software. Now that we're starting to write actual system software, there's no reason to keep DELAY around.

Not only that, but it would be smart to spend a moment to work out a more definitive variable map.

The last one we had was in the final piece of software we ran to test the keyboard interrupt in the last chapter.

```
;****************************************************************
;*                      SYSTEM EQUATES                        *
;****************************************************************
FIXED           SEGMENT AT 0000h        ;All the variable storage will
                ASSUME  DS:FIXED        ;be at the bottom of RAM.
    KBDAT       EQU     DS:[0088h]      ;Keyboard data.
    KBINT       EQU     DS:[0020h]      ;Keyboard Vector Address.
    DELAY       EQU     DS:[0100h]      ;Delay Constant Address.
    WAITCNT     EQU     0036h           ;The time delay constant.
    DISPLAY1    EQU     DS:[0080h]      ;Digit #1.
    DISPLAY2    EQU     DS:[0081h]      ;Digit #2.
    DISPLAY3    EQU     DS:[0082h]      ;Digit #3.
    DISPLAY4    EQU     DS:[0083h]      ;Digit #4.
    DISPLAY5    EQU     DS:[0084h]      ;Digit #5.
    DISPLAY6    EQU     DS:[0085h]      ;Digit #6.
    DISPLAY7    EQU     DS:[0086h]      ;Digit #7.
    DISPLAY8    EQU     DS:[0087h]      ;Digit #8.
    KEYBOARD    EQU     00000h          ;8255 #1 Port #0 (Keyboard).
    DISPLED     EQU     00001h          ;8255 #1 Port #1 (Display).
    GENERAL1    EQU     00002h          ;8255 #1 Port #2 (General).
    IOCMD1      EQU     00003h          ;8255 #1 Port #3 (Command).
    INTPORT0    EQU     00080h          ;8259 #1 Port #0.
    INTPORT1    EQU     00081h          ;8259 #1 Port #1.
FIXED           ENDS                    ;No more variables.
;----------------------------------------------------------------
```

We can lose DELAY and WAITCNT since we're not using them any more and doing that puts KBDAT at the top of the variable space. This is as good a time as any to make a decision about the keyboard. At the moment, we only have one byte of reserved space for keyboard data, but it's a good idea to leave space for a small buffer. That would allow multicharacter commands to be easily entered from the keyboard. You can reserve as much room as you want but an eight-byte buffer is more than adequate for most purposes. This means we're devoting bytes 88h through 8Fh as the keyboard buffer.

We can put the four bytes for the clock right above the keyboard so we're going to declare 90h through 93h as the system timer. The first byte (90h) will be the hundredths counter and the following bytes will be used to keep track of the seconds. Our new variable map will be like this.

```
;****************************************************************
;*                      SYSTEM EQUATES                        *
;****************************************************************
FIXED           SEGMENT AT 0000h        ;All the variable storage will
                ASSUME  DS:FIXED        ;be at the bottom of RAM.
    KEYBOARD    EQU     00000h          ;8255 #1 Port #0 (Keyboard).
    DISPLED     EQU     00001h          ;8255 #1 Port #1 (Display).
    GENERAL1    EQU     00002h          ;8255 #1 Port #2 (General).
    IOCMD1      EQU     00003h          ;8255 #1 Port #3 (Command).
    INTPORT0    EQU     00080h          ;8259 #1 Port #0.
    INTPORT1    EQU     00081h          ;8259 #1 Port #1.
    ZERODIV     EQU     DS:[0000h]      ;Zero Division Vector Address.
    ONESTEP     EQU     DS:[0004h]      ;Single Step Vector Address.
    NMIVEC      EQU     DS:[0008h]      ;NMI Vector Address.
    ONEBYTE     EQU     DS:[000Ch]      ;One Byte Vector Address.
```

```
OVERFLOW    EQU         DS:[0010h]              ;Overflow Vector Address.
KBINT       EQU         DS:[0020h]              ;Keyboard Vector Address.
DISPLAY1    EQU         DS:[0080h]              ;Digit #1.
DISPLAY2    EQU         DS:[0081h]              ;Digit #2.
DISPLAY3    EQU         DS:[0082h]              ;Digit #3.
DISPLAY4    EQU         DS:[0083h]              ;Digit #4.
DISPLAY5    EQU         DS:[0084h]              ;Digit #5.
DISPLAY6    EQU         DS:[0085h]              ;Digit #6.
DISPLAY7    EQU         DS:[0086h]              ;Digit #7.
DISPLAY8    EQU         DS:[0087h]              ;Digit #8.
KBDAT1      EQU         DS:[0088h]              ;Keyboard Data Address #1.
KBDAT2      EQU         DS:[0089h]              ;Keyboard Data Address #2.
KBDAT3      EQU         DS:[008Ah]              ;Keyboard Data Address #3.
KBDAT4      EQU         DS:[008Bh]              ;Keyboard Data Address #4.
KBDAT5      EQU         DS:[008Ch]              ;Keyboard Data Address #5.
KBDAT6      EQU         DS:[008Dh]              ;Keyboard Data Address #6.
KBDAT7      EQU         DS:[008Eh]              ;Keyboard Data Address #7.
KBDAT8      EQU         DS:[008Fh]              ;Keyboard Data Address #8.
HUNDS       EQU         DS:[0090h]              ;Hundredths of a Second.
SECS1       EQU         DS:[0091h]              ;Seconds Counter #1.
SECS2       EQU         DS:[0092h]              ;Seconds Counter #2.
SECS3       EQU         DS:[0093h]              ;Seconds Counter #3.
FIXED       ENDS                                ;No more variables.
; ----------------------------------------------------------------------
```

We now have all the stuff needed to write the NMI routine so we can take the outline
we had before and fill in all the blanks. Doing that will produce a listing that looks like this.

```
; **********************************************************************
; *            NON-MASKABLE INTERRUPT HANDLING ROUTINE               *
; **********************************************************************
            PUSH  AX              ;Save the accumulator.
            PUSH  BX              ;Save the BX register.
            PUSH  CX              ;Save the CX register.
            PUSH  DX              ;Save the DX register.
            PUSH  DS              ;Save the data segment.
            MOV   AX,0000h        ;Tell the 8088 that the data
            MOV   DS,AX           ;segment is now at 0000h.
; ----------------------------------------------------------------------
;                   ROUTINE FOR CLOCK MAINTENANCE
; ----------------------------------------------------------------------
NMITIME:    INC   BYTE PTR HUNDS      ;Add to the hundredths count.
            CMP   BYTE PTR HUNDS,64h  ;Have we reached 100?
            JNZ   ENDNMI              ;If not, we're done.
            MOV   BYTE PTR HUNDS,00h  ;Zero out the hundredths.
            INC   BYTE PTR SECS1      ;Add to seconds count #1.
            CMP   BYTE PTR SECS1,00h  ;Has it counted through 255?
            JNZ   ENDNMI              ;If not, we're done.
            INC   BYTE PTR SECS2      ;Add to seconds count #2.
            CMP   BYTE PTR SECS2,00h  ;Has it counted through 255?
            JNZ   ENDNMI              ;If not, we're done.
            INC   BYTE PTR SECS3      ;Add to seconds count #3.
            CMP   BYTE PTR SECS3,00h  ;Has it counted through 255?
            JZ    NMITIME             ;At the maximum so start again.
; ----------------------------------------------------------------------
;                   ROUTINE TO UPDATE THE DISPLAY
; ----------------------------------------------------------------------
```

```
ENDNMI:        MOV    AL,DISPLAY1      ;Get the current digit 1 value.
               OUT    DISPLED,AL       ;Send it to the display.
               MOV    AL,DISPLAY2      ;Get the current digit 2 value.
               ADD    AL,20h           ;Set the high byte for digit 2.
               OUT    DISPLED,AL       ;Send it to the display.
               MOV    AL,DISPLAY3      ;Get the current digit 3 value.
               ADD    AL,40h           ;Set the high byte for digit 3.
               OUT    DISPLED,AL       ;Send it to the display.
               MOV    AL,DISPLAY4      ;Get the current digit 4 value.
               ADD    AL,60h           ;Set the high byte for digit 4.
               OUT    DISPLED,AL       ;Send it to the display.
               MOV    AL,DISPLAY5      ;Get the current digit 5 value.
               ADD    AL,80h           ;Set the high byte for digit 5.
               OUT    DISPLED,AL       ;Send it to the display.
               MOV    AL,DISPLAY6      ;Get the current digit 6 value.
               ADD    AL,0A0h          ;Set the high byte for digit 6.
               OUT    DISPLED,AL       ;Send it to the display.
               MOV    AL,DISPLAY7      ;Get the current digit 7 value.
               ADD    AL,0C0h          ;Set the high byte for digit 7.
               OUT    DISPLED,AL       ;Send it to the display.
               MOV    AL,DISPLAY8      ;Get the current digit 8 value.
               ADD    AL,0E0h          ;Set the high byte for digit 8.
               OUT    DISPLED,AL       ;Send it to the display.
; ------------------------------------------------------------------------
               POP    DS               ;Restore the data segment.
               POP    DX               ;Restore the DX register.
               POP    CX               ;Restore the CX register.
               POP    BX               ;Restore the BX register.
               POP    AX               ;Restore the accumulator.
               IRET                    ;Return to the application.
```

Fig. 15-5. (continued)

Notice that we've eliminated the label "DONE" that used to be near the end of the NMI routine. There wasn't any need to keep it around since the actual exit routine itself comes immediately after we've finished updating the display.

Now that we're done with all this work, let's see what we can do with it. The listing called CLOCK1 has all our new BIOS routines in it and the main part of the code will make our system function as a digital clock. The initial time will be 00:00:00:00 and the clock will advance in the format HH:MM:SS:SS where the last two digits are counting hundredths of a second.

```
;
;    ***********************************************************
;    *                                                         *
;    *    THE  FIRST  PROGRAM  FOR  THE  8088  CIRCUIT  THAT  USES   *
;    *    NMI  FOR  DISPLAY  REFRESHING  AND  CLOCK  MAINTENANCE     *
;    *                                                         *
;    ***********************************************************
;
; ------------------------------------------------------------------------
;This program will use an NMI routine to keep track of real time and and have
;the display show a real time clock as HH:MM:SS:SS where the last two digits
;are counting the hundredths of a second - the basic rate of the NMI interrupt.
; ------------------------------------------------------------------------
;
TITLE   CLOCK1 - Display Real Time
;
```

Fig. 15-6. CLOCK.ASM—An NMI driven digital clock program.

```
;**************************************************************************
;*                          SYSTEM EQUATES                                *
;**************************************************************************
FIXED                   SEGMENT AT 0000h        ;All the variable storage will
                        ASSUME  DS:FIXED         ;be at the bottom of RAM.
        KEYBOARD        EQU     00000h          ;8255 #1 Port #0 (Keyboard).
        DISPLED         EQU     00001h          ;8255 #1 Port #1 (Display).
        GENERAL1        EQU     00002h          ;8255 #1 Port #2 (General).
        IOCMD1          EQU     00003h          ;8255 #1 Port #3 (Command).
        INTPORT0        EQU     00080h          ;8259 #1 Port #0.
        INTPORT1        EQU     00081h          ;8259 #1 Port #1.
        ZERODIV         EQU     DS:[0000h]      ;Zero Division Vector Address.
        ONESTEP         EQU     DS:[0004h]      ;Single Step Vector Address.
        NMIVEC          EQU     DS:[0008h]      ;Non Maskable Vector Address.
        ONEBYTE         EQU     DS:[000Ch]      ;One Byte Vector Address.
        OVRFLOW         EQU     DS:[0010h]      ;Overflow Vector Address.
        KBINT           EQU     DS:[0020h]      ;Address of Keyboard Vector.
        DISPLAY1        EQU     DS:[0080h]      ;Digit #1.
        DISPLAY2        EQU     DS:[0081h]      ;Digit #2.
        DISPLAY3        EQU     DS:[0082h]      ;Digit #3.
        DISPLAY4        EQU     DS:[0083h]      ;Digit #4.
        DISPLAY5        EQU     DS:[0084h]      ;Digit #5.
        DISPLAY6        EQU     DS:[0085h]      ;Digit #6.
        DISPLAY7        EQU     DS:[0086h]      ;Digit #7.
        DISPLAY8        EQU     DS:[0087h]      ;Digit #8.
        KBDAT1          EQU     DS:[0088h]      ;Keyboard Data Address #1.
        KBDAT2          EQU     DS:[0089h]      ;Keyboard Data Address #2.
        KBDAT3          EQU     DS:[008Ah]      ;Keyboard Data Address #3.
        KBDAT4          EQU     DS:[008Bh]      ;Keyboard Data Address #4.
        KBDAT5          EQU     DS:[008Ch]      ;Keyboard Data Address #5.
        KBDAT6          EQU     DS:[008Dh]      ;Keyboard Data Address #6.
        KBDAT7          EQU     DS:[008Eh]      ;Keyboard Data Address #7.
        KBDAT8          EQU     DS:[008Fh]      ;Keyboard Data Address #8.
        HUNDS           EQU     DS:[0090h]      ;Hundredths of a Second.
        SECS1           EQU     DS:[0091h]      ;Seconds Counter #1.
        SECS2           EQU     DS:[0092h]      ;Seconds Counter #2.
        SECS3           EQU     DS:[0093h]      ;Seconds Counter #3.
FIXED                   ENDS                    ;No more variables.
;
;**************************************************************************
;*                      SET THE 8088 SEGMENTS                             *
;**************************************************************************
BOB                     SEGMENT                 ;Define initial segments.
                        ASSUME  CS:BOB,DS:BOB,CS:BOB  ;Set all segment registers to
                                                ;the same location.
                        ORG 100h                ;Set program start location.
;
;**************************************************************************
;*    INITIALIZE THE 8255, THE 8259, THE STACK, AND THE DATA SEGMENT      *
;**************************************************************************
;                       SETUP FOR THE 8255
;------------------------------------------------------------------------
START:          CLI                             ;Disable interrupts for setup.
                MOV     AL,90h                  ;This sets the 8255 to operate
                                                ;in Mode 0 (basic input output)
                                                ;with port 0 as an input and
                OUT     IOCMD1,AL               ;ports 1 and 2 as outputs.
;
;------------------------------------------------------------------------
;                       SETUP FOR THE 8259
;------------------------------------------------------------------------
;The 8259 set up is done by sending three ICW's (Initialization Command Words)
;and one OCW (Operational Command Word) to program the 8259 as follows:
;
```

Fig. 15-6. (continued)

206

```
;          WORD   A0    D7  D6  D5  D4  D3  D2  D1  D0      HEX
;          ----------------------------------------------------------------
;          ICW1    0    0*  0*  0*   1   0  1*   1   1      17h
;          ICW2    1    0   0   0    0   1  0*  0*  0*      08h
;          ICW4    1    0   0   0    0   1   1   1   1      0Fh
;          OCW1    1    1   1   1    1   1   1   1   0      FEh
;
;          ----------------------------------------------------------------
;          * = Not needed if the 8259 is in the 8088/86 mode.
;
;--------------------------------------------------------------------------
           MOV    AL,17h                       ;Load ICW1.
           OUT    INTPORT0,AL                  ;Send it to the 8259.
           MOV    AL,08h                       ;Load ICW2.
           OUT    INTPORT1,AL                  ;Send it to the 8259.
           MOV    AL,0Fh                       ;Load ICW4
           OUT    INTPORT1,AL                  ;Send it to the 8259.
           MOV    AL,0FEh                      ;Load OCW1
           OUT    INTPORT1,AL                  ;Send it to the 8259.
;--------------------------------------------------------------------------
;                        SETUP FOR THE SEGMENTS
;--------------------------------------------------------------------------
           MOV    AX,0070h                     ;Set the location of the stack
           MOV    SS,AX                        ;bottom at 00700h and set the
           MOV    SP,00F0h                     ;top of the stack at 000F0h.
           MOV    AX,0000h                     ;Tell the 8088 that the data
           MOV    DS,AX                        ;segment is at 00000h.
;
;**************************************************************************
;*                    THE INTERRUPT VECTOR ENTRIES                       *
;**************************************************************************
;The interrupt routines build up from absolute address FFE00h.  Since the 2716
;is mapped in at FF800 - FFFFFh the EPROM base location for the interrupt code
;is 600h.  The assembler wants to ORG stuff at 0100h so a 100h offset has to be
;added to have the code wind up at 600h in the 2716.  This means the interrupt
;routines have to be ORG'd at 0700h.  In order to use the assembler's OFFSET
;directive to determine the starting address of each interrupt routine, the
;segment specified in the interrupt vector table has to be 700h less than the
;absolute address of FFE00h - or FF700h.  This means the segment and offset for
;the first interrupt routine will be FF70h (segment) and 0700h (offset).  The
;8088 will combine these to produce an absolute address as follows:
;
;                   Segment Address = FF700h
;                          Offset  =   0700h
;                   --------------------------
;                   Absolute Address = FFE00h
;
;so the vector table entry of each interrupt routine will have the same segment
;and the offset will be the same as the starting address in the listing.
;--------------------------------------------------------------------------
;                       LOAD THE KEYBOARD VECTOR
;--------------------------------------------------------------------------
           MOV    WORD PTR KBINT,OFFSET GETKEY   ;Keyboard routine offset.
           MOV    WORD PTR KBINT+2,0FF70h        ;Segment for interrupts.
;
;--------------------------------------------------------------------------
;                         LOAD THE NMI VECTOR
;--------------------------------------------------------------------------
           MOV    WORD PTR NMIVEC,OFFSET NMI      ;NMI routine offset.
           MOV    WORD PTR NMIVEC+2,0FF70h        ;Interrupt segment.
;
;--------------------------------------------------------------------------
;              LOAD VECTORS FOR UNUSED PREDEFINED INTERRUPTS
;--------------------------------------------------------------------------
           MOV    WORD PTR ZERODIV,OFFSET TEMP    ;Divide by Zero offset.
           MOV    WORD PTR ZERODIV+2,0FF70h       ;Interrupt segment.
```

Fig. 15-6. (continued)

207

```
            MOV     WORD PTR ONESTEP,OFFSET TEMP       ;Single step offset.
            MOV     WORD PTR ONESTEP+2,0FF70h          ;Interrupt Segment.
            MOV     WORD PTR ONEBYTE,OFFSET TEMP       ;One byte offset.
            MOV     WORD PTR ONEBYTE+2,0FF70h          ;Interrupt segment.
            MOV     WORD PTR OVRFLOW,OFFSET TEMP       ;Overflow offset.
            MOV     WORD PTR OVRFLOW+2,0FF70h          ;Interrupt Segment.
;
; ********************************************************************************
; *                    INITIALIZE THE VARIABLES                                 *
; ********************************************************************************
;                     ZERO OUT THE DISPLAY
;---------------------------------------------------------------------------------
BLANK:      MOV     AL,00h                             ;Now load the value that will
                                                       ;cause the character generator
                                                       ;to send zeros to each segment.
            MOV     BYTE PTR DISPLAY1,AL               ;Store the number '0' character
            MOV     BYTE PTR DISPLAY2,AL               ;in each of the locations that
            MOV     BYTE PTR DISPLAY3,AL               ;are reserved for the numbers
            MOV     BYTE PTR DISPLAY4,AL               ;to be displayed in each of the
            MOV     BYTE PTR DISPLAY5,AL               ;displays.
            MOV     BYTE PTR DISPLAY6,AL               ;Once all the eight locations
            MOV     BYTE PTR DISPLAY7,AL               ;have been loaded, the display
            MOV     BYTE PTR DISPLAY8,AL               ;can be set to zeros by calling
            CALL    SCAN                               ;the digit scanning routine.
;
;---------------------------------------------------------------------------------
;                     ZERO OUT THE TIMER
;---------------------------------------------------------------------------------
            MOV     BYTE PTR HUNDS,AL                  ;Zero the hundredths counter.
            MOV     BYTE PTR SECS1,AL                  ;Zero seconds counter #1.
            MOV     BYTE PTR SECS2,AL                  ;Zero seconds counter #2.
            MOV     BYTE PTR SECS2,AL                  ;Zero seconds counter #3.
;
;---------------------------------------------------------------------------------
            STI                                        ;All done so enable interrupts.
            JMP     GO                                 ;It's SHOWTIME folks.
;
; ********************************************************************************
; *                    DIGIT MULTIPLEXING ROUTINE                               *
; ********************************************************************************
SCAN:       PUSH    AX                                 ;Save the current accumulator.
            PUSHF                                      ;Save the current flags.
            MOV     AL,DISPLAY1                        ;Get the current digit 1 value.
            OUT     DISPLED,AL                         ;Send it to the display.
            MOV     AL,DISPLAY2                        ;Get the current digit 2 value.
            ADD     AL,20h                             ;Set the high byte for digit 2.
            OUT     DISPLED,AL                         ;Send it to the display.
            MOV     AL,DISPLAY3                        ;Get the current digit 3 value.
            ADD     AL,40h                             ;Set the high byte for digit 3.
            OUT     DISPLED,AL                         ;Send it to the display.
            MOV     AL,DISPLAY4                        ;Get the current digit 4 value.
            ADD     AL,60h                             ;Set the high byte for digit 4.
            OUT     DISPLED,AL                         ;Send it to the display.
            MOV     AL,DISPLAY5                        ;Get the current digit 5 value.
            ADD     AL,80h                             ;Set the high byte for digit 5.
            OUT     DISPLED,AL                         ;Send it to the display.
            MOV     AL,DISPLAY6                        ;Get the current digit 6 value.
            ADD     AL,0A0h                            ;Set the high byte for digit 6.
            OUT     DISPLED,AL                         ;Send it to the display.
            MOV     AL,DISPLAY7                        ;Get the current digit 7 value.
            ADD     AL,0C0h                            ;Set the high byte for digit 7.
            OUT     DISPLED,AL                         ;Send it to the display.
            MOV     AL,DISPLAY8                        ;Get the current digit 8 value.
            ADD     AL,0E0h                            ;Set the high byte for digit 8.
```

Fig. 15-6. (continued)

```
                    OUT        DISPLED,AL                ;Send it to the display.
                    POPF                                 ;Restore the previous flags.
                    POP        AX                         ;Restore the previous AX.
                    RET
;
;****************************************************************************
;*                     MAIN BODY OF THE CODE                               *
;****************************************************************************
;The minimum increment for the real time display is the basic NMI rate of one
;hundredth of a second so the only location we have to look at is HUNDS since
;it's incremented at that rate.  Location SECS1 increments once a second but it
;doesn't reset to zero at a count of 60 - it's a time counter, not a clock.  In
;order to display real time the program has to increment the digits in a real
;time sequence (60 seconds = 1 minute, 60 minutes = 1 hour, 24 hours = 1 day).
;The structure of this program will be similar to the NMI routine that updates
;the timer.  The difference will be in the counting and incrementing sequence.
;----------------------------------------------------------------------------
GO:                 MOV        CL,HUNDS                   ;Get the hundredths count.
DIGIT1:             CALL       SCAN                       ;Display the current values and
                                                          ;refresh the digit display.
                    CMP        BYTE PTR HUNDS,CL          ;If the value has changed, an
                                                          ;NMI has occurred and it's time
                                                          ;to update the displayed time.
                    JZ         GO
                    MOV        AL,DISPLAY1                ;Get the current value in AL.
                    INC        AL
                    CMP        AL,0Ah                     ;Have we reached ten?
                    JZ         DIGIT2                     ;If so, bump the next digit.
                    MOV        BYTE PTR DISPLAY1,AL       ;Store it away safely.
                    JMP        GO                         ;And start again.
DIGIT2:             MOV        BYTE PTR DISPLAY1,00h      ;Put a zero in the first digit.
                    MOV        AL,DISPLAY2                ;Get the current digit 2 value.
                    INC        AL                         ;Add one to the value.
                    CMP        AL,0Ah                     ;Is it a ten?
                    JZ         DIGIT3                     ;If so, bump the next digit.
                    MOV        BYTE PTR DISPLAY2,AL       ;Store it away.
                    JMP        GO                         ;And start again.
DIGIT3:             MOV        BYTE PTR DISPLAY2,00h      ;Put a zero in digit #2.
                    MOV        AL,DISPLAY3                ;Get the current value in AL.
                    INC        AL                         ;Add one to the value in AL and
                    CMP        AL,0Ah                     ;Have we reached ten?
                    JZ         DIGIT4                     ;If so, bump the next digit.
                    MOV        BYTE PTR DISPLAY3,AL       ;Store it away safely.
                    JMP        GO                         ;And start again.
DIGIT4:             MOV        BYTE PTR DISPLAY3,00h      ;Put a zero in digit #3.
                    MOV        AL,DISPLAY4                ;Get the current digit 3 value.
                    INC        AL                         ;Add one to the value.
                    CMP        AL,06h                     ;Is it a '6'?
                    JZ         DIGIT5                     ;If so, bump the next digit.
                    MOV        BYTE PTR DISPLAY4,AL       ;Store it away
                    JMP        GO                         ;And start again.
DIGIT5:             MOV        BYTE PTR DISPLAY4,00h      ;Put a zero in the digit #4.
                    MOV        AL,DISPLAY5                ;Get the current digit 5 value.
                    INC        AL                         ;Add one to the value.
                    CMP        AL,0Ah                     ;Is it a ten?
                    JZ         DIGIT6                     ;If so, bump the next digit.
                    MOV        BYTE PTR DISPLAY5,AL       ;Store it away
                    JMP        GO                         ;And start again.
DIGIT6:             MOV        BYTE PTR DISPLAY5,00h      ;Put a zero in digit #5.
                    MOV        AL,DISPLAY6                ;Get the current value in AL.
                    INC        AL                         ;Add one to the value in AL and
                    CMP        AL,06h                     ;Have we reached '6'?
                    JZ         DIGIT7                     ;If so, bump the next digit.
```

Fig. 15-6. (continued)

```
                 MOV      BYTE PTR DISPLAY6,AL      ;Store it away safely.
                 JMP      GO                       ;And start again.
DIGIT7:          MOV      BYTE PTR DISPLAY6,00h     ;Put a zero in digit #6.
                 MOV      AL,DISPLAY7              ;Get the current digit 7 value.
                 INC      AL                       ;Add one to the value.
                 CMP      AL,0Ah                   ;Is it a ten?
                 JZ       DIGIT8                   ;If so, bump the next digit.
                 MOV      BYTE PTR DISPLAY7,AL      ;Store it away
                 JMP      GO                       ;And start again.
DIGIT8:          MOV      BYTE PTR DISPLAY7,00h     ;Put a zero in digit #7.
                 MOV      AL,DISPLAY8              ;Get the current digit 8 value.
                 INC      AL                       ;Add one to digit #8.
                 CMP      AL,0Ah                   ;Is it a ten?
                 JZ       AGAIN                    ;BLANK is too far away.
                 MOV      BYTE PTR DISPLAY8,AL      ;Store the incremented value.
                 JMP      GO                       ;And start again.
AGAIN:           CLI                               ;Disable interrupts.
                 JMP      BLANK                    ;Zero everything and restart.
;
;*********************************************************************************
;*                      THE INTERRUPT ROUTINES                                  *
;*********************************************************************************
;As noted earlier, the assembler location of 700h will be location 600h in the
;EPROM and, since the EPROM is mapped in the system from FF800h to FFFFFh, the
;8088 will see it as location FFE00h.  By using a segment of FF700h in all the
;interrupt vector table entries, the offset address for the beginning of the
;interrupt routines will be 700h, the same as the assembler location.
;-------------------------------------------------------------------------------
                 ORG      0700h                    ;Start of interrupt routines.
TEMP:            IRET                              ;Return for unwritten routines.
;  ------------------------------------------------------------------------------
;                THE KEYBOARD INTERRUPT ROUTINE
;  ------------------------------------------------------------------------------
                 ORG      0700h
GETKEY:          PUSH     AX                       ;Save the current accumulator.
                 IN       AL,KEYBOARD             ;Get the key in the accumulator
                 MOV      BYTE PTR KBDAT1,AL       ;Store the key in the buffer.
                 POP      AX                       ;Put the accumulator back.
                 IRET
;
;  ------------------------------------------------------------------------------
;                      NMI ROUTINE
;  ------------------------------------------------------------------------------
NMI:             PUSH     AX                       ;Save the accumulator.
                 PUSH     BX                       ;Save the BX register.
                 PUSH     CX                       ;Save the CX register.
                 PUSH     DX                       ;Save the DX register.
                 PUSH     DS                       ;Save the data segment.
                 MOV      AX,0000h                 ;Tell the 8088 that the data
                 MOV      DS,AX                    ;segment is now at 0000h.
NMITIME:         INC      BYTE PTR HUNDS           ;Add to the hundredths count.
                 CMP      BYTE PTR HUNDS,64h        ;Have we reached 100?
                 JNZ      ENDNMI                   ;If not, we're done.
                 MOV      BYTE PTR HUNDS,00h        ;Zero out the hundredths.
                 INC      BYTE PTR SECS1           ;Add to seconds count #1.
                 CMP      BYTE PTR SECS1,00h        ;Has it counted through 255?
                 JNZ      ENDNMI                   ;If not, we're done.
                 INC      BYTE PTR SECS2           ;Add to seconds count #2.
                 CMP      BYTE PTR SECS2,00h        ;Has it counted through 255?
                 JNZ      ENDNMI                   ;If not, we're done.
                 INC      BYTE PTR SECS3           ;Add to seconds count #3.
                 CMP      BYTE PTR SECS3,00h        ;Has it counted through 255?
                 JZ       NMITIME                  ;At the maximum so start again.
```

Fig. 15-6. (continued)

210

```
ENDNMI:         CALL    SCAN            ;Update the display.
                CALL    SCAN            ;Twice as often=twice as bright
                POP     DS              ;Restore the data segment.
                POP     DX              ;Restore the DX register.
                POP     CX              ;Restore the CX register.
                POP     BX              ;Restore the BX register.
                POP     AX              ;Restore the accumulator.
                IRET
;
;*********************************************************************************
;*                      T H E   B O O T   C O D E                               *
;*********************************************************************************
;The 8088 power up location of FFFF0h is actually 07F0h in the 2716.  The boot
;instruction has to be ORG'ed at 08F0h since the assembler wants to ORG the
;above main code at 0100.  The result is that the 2716 will have the main code
;at 0000h and the boot code at 07F0h.
;  -----------------------------------------------------------------------------
                ORG     08F0h           ;The 2716 location for the 8088
                                        ;power-up instruction allowing
                                        ;for the assembler's ORG 100
                                        ;requirement for the main code.
                JMP  START              ;Go to the main code located at
                                        ;0000h in the 2716.
                DB      00,00,00,00,00,00,00    ;Nul bytes to fill the 2716
                DB      00,00,00,00,00,00       ;with 00's after the power up
                                        ;jump described above.
;
;*********************************************************************************
;*                  THE END OF THE PROGRAM                                      *
;*********************************************************************************
BOB             ENDS                    ;Tell assembler this is the end
                                        ;of code for this segment.
                END     START           ;Tell assembler this is the end
                                        ;of the program.
```

Hex Dump of CLOCK.ASM

```
0000 - FA B0 90 E6 03 B0 17 E6 80 B0 08 E6 81 B0 0F E6
0010 - 81 B0 FE E6 81 B8 70 00 8E D0 BC F0 00 B8 00 00
0020 - 8E D8 C7 06 20 00 00 07 C7 06 22 00 70 FF C7 06
0030 - 08 00 08 07 C7 06 0A 00 70 FF C7 06 00 00 00 07
0040 - C7 06 02 00 70 FF C7 06 04 00 00 07 C7 06 06 00
0050 - 70 FF C7 06 0C 00 00 07 C7 06 0E 00 70 FF C7 06
0060 - 10 00 00 07 C7 06 12 00 70 FF B0 00 A2 80 00 A2
0070 - 81 00 A2 82 00 A2 83 00 A2 84 00 A2 85 00 A2 86
0080 - 00 A2 87 00 E8 10 00 A2 90 00 A2 91 00 A2 92 00
0090 - A2 92 00 FB EB 3C 90 50 9C A0 80 00 E6 01 A0 81
00A0 - 00 04 20 E6 01 A0 82 00 04 40 E6 01 A0 83 00 04
00B0 - 60 E6 01 A0 84 00 04 80 E6 01 A0 85 00 04 A0 E6
00C0 - 01 A0 86 00 04 C0 E6 01 A0 87 00 04 E0 E6 01 9D
00D0 - 58 C3 8A 0E 90 00 E8 BE FF 38 0E 90 00 74 F3 A0
00E0 - 80 00 FE C0 3C 0A 74 05 A2 80 00 EB E5 C6 06 80
00F0 - 00 00 A0 81 00 FE C0 3C 0A 74 05 A2 81 00 EB D2
0100 - C6 06 81 00 00 A0 82 00 FE C0 3C 0A 74 05 A2 82
0110 - 00 EB BF C6 06 82 00 00 A0 83 00 FE C0 3C 06 74
0120 - 05 A2 83 00 EB AC C6 06 83 00 00 A0 84 00 FE C0
0130 - 3C 0A 74 05 A2 84 00 EB 99 C6 06 84 00 00 A0 85
0140 - 00 FE C0 3C 06 74 05 A2 85 00 EB 86 C6 06 85 00
0150 - 00 A0 86 00 FE C0 3C 0A 74 06 A2 86 00 E9 72 FF
0160 - C6 06 86 00 00 A0 87 00 FE C0 3C 0A 74 06 A2 87
0170 - 00 E9 5E FF FA E9 F2 FE 00 00 00 00 00 00 00 00
0180 - 00 00 00 00 00 00 00 00 00 00 00 00 00 00 00 00
0190 - 00 00 00 00 00 00 00 00 00 00 00 00 00 00 00 00
```

Fig. 15-6. (continued)

```
0200 - 05DF are filled with zeros

05E0 - 00 00 00 00 00 00 00 00 00 00 00 00 00 00 00 00
05F0 - 00 00 00 00 00 00 00 00 00 00 00 00 00 00 00 00
0600 - 50 E4 00 A2 88 00 58 CF 50 53 51 52 1E B8 00 00
0610 - 8E D8 FE 06 90 00 80 3E 90 00 64 75 26 C6 06 90
0620 - 00 00 FE 06 91 00 80 3E 91 00 00 75 16 FE 06 92
0630 - 00 80 3E 92 00 00 75 0B FE 06 93 00 80 3E 93 00
0640 - 00 74 CF E8 51 FA E8 4E FA 1F 5A 59 5B 58 CF 00
0650 - 00 00 00 00 00 00 00 00 00 00 00 00 00 00 00 00
0660 - 00 00 00 00 00 00 00 00 00 00 00 00 00 00 00 00

0670 - 07CF are filled with zeros

07D0 - 00 00 00 00 00 00 00 00 00 00 00 00 00 00 00 00
07E0 - 00 00 00 00 00 00 00 00 00 00 00 00 00 00 00 00
07F0 - E9 0D F8 00 00 00 00 00 00 00 00 00 00 00 00 00
```

Fig. 15-6. (continued)

Once you've got the code in an EPROM and have the system up and running, carefully go through the assembly listing and make sure you understand how everything works. A lot of the code is similar to things we've already done so you shouldn't have any trouble following it.

Just as an aside, there are ways to cut down the byte count in the NMI routine we just developed. Rewriting it is a terrific exercise in programming and you should be able to shave a good number of bytes off the listing. I'm not going to tell you how to do it, but I'll get you started by pointing out that when you increment a byte that contains FFh it wraps around to 00h. There are two things that you should notice as you're going through the CLOCK1 listing.

The first thing is the fact that the keyboard interrupt routine has been changed. All it does now is take the value of the key that was pressed and put it in KBDAT1. You can quite easily add a routine to the listing that lets you set the time from the keyboard.

The second change is more important. Even though we've worked out the display update routine, the actual code itself isn't part of the NMI routine. It's left as a subroutine and is called twice during an NMI interval. It's also called frequently during the main portion of the code. You'd think this would be unnecessary since we've arranged for a display update to be done each and every hundredth of a second (the NMI interval). The reason for it is the way we've designed the hardware.

The displays we're using don't latch. The only time any one of the digits is actually illuminated is when we're addressing it with an OUT instruction. As soon as we move on to something else—even sending data to another digit in the display—the first digit goes dark. The 8255 latches data but our digit multiplexing routine writes new data to the port every eight microseconds.

If we limited display refresh to the NMI routine, the first seven digits would be illuminated for only eight microseconds each hundredth of a second. The last digit would stay illuminated all the time since the 8255 would latch the byte that addresses it and nothing else is sent to the 8255 until the next refresh interval.

By putting a CALL to the refresh routine in the main loop of the program, we're guaranteed to address each digit at least once every 96 microseconds—that's the amount of time it takes the 8088 to run the first conditional loop in the program. The result is that the digits are refreshed often enough for all of them to be visible at the same time. The last digit, as we've already seen, will stay illuminated longer and, consequently, will seem to be brighter.

This limitation, however, is a real restriction since the overhead for maintaining the display just takes much too much CPU time. It's a lot smarter to latch each digit in the

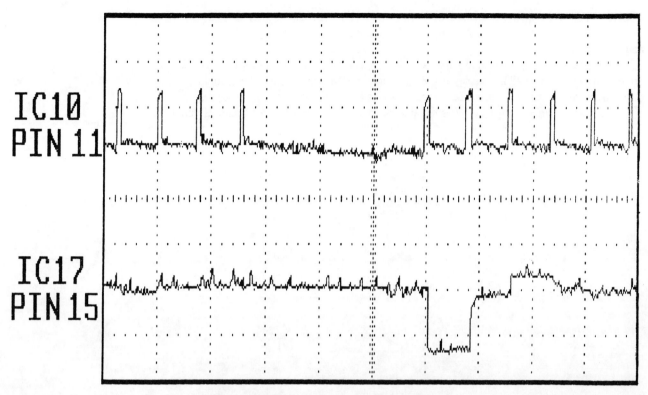

Fig. 15-7. Display latching times with the 8255.

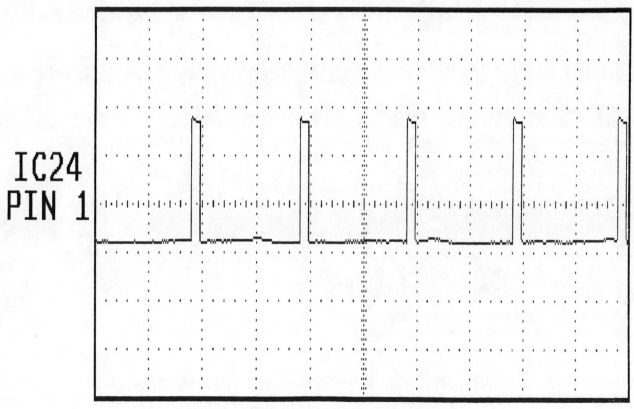

Fig. 15-8. 100 Hz NMI clock waveforms generated by IC24.

display. That will free up a wad of CPU time and even out the display brightness. Fortunately for us, it doesn't take much work to make this happen since it's an easy addition to the circuit.

Now that we've got working hardware, we have to start thinking of what can be done to make it better. This display problem is only one of a few things that should be done to make the circuit more flexible and easily adapted to a wide range of jobs.

The system we've put together is capable of doing a lot of work for you and, if you need it, the circuit can be easily expanded. The only major problem we have to work out is how to add more storage and I/O to the board. The way we're selecting RAM, ROM, and I/O is adequate for the circuit so far, but it needs a bit of work before we can make the system flexible enough to address larger memory and control almost an unlimited number of peripheral devices. That's our next step.

16

Beefing Up and Tweaking the Circuit

MAKE NO MISTAKE ABOUT IT, THE CIRCUIT WE'VE BEEN PUTTING TOGETHER IS A REAL workhorse. Just because there are things you can do to beef it up doesn't mean that what we have so far can only do wimp stuff. That would be a mistake.

We've reached the point in developing our system where the use you have for the circuit will determine what stuff you have to add to it. All the basics are there.

There are some things that we have to look into adding to the board regardless of the use you have in mind, since they'll be needed by most of the applications that the system is designed to handle. These are the "tweaking" type things. Once we get them out of the way we'll start examining the "beefing up" type additions to the board. This last group includes, using dynamic RAM, software debugging, and other things that car dealers refer to as "optional extras"—not really needed but nice to have.

Keep in mind that all of the things we'll be talking about in this chapter are really optional. Don't get the idea into your head that the circuit you have in front of you is the microprocessor equivalent of a light dimmer. Far from it. You can do really serious stuff with the board as it is. Twenty four available I/O ports, (forty eight if you plug another 8255 into the board), and 16K of memory are nothing to sneeze at. Remember, it wasn't many years ago that a system of this size and power was top secret Buck Rogers stuff. No kidding.

You've just assembled on your kitchen table something that a mere fifteen years ago would have totally blown the minds of any agency of any government. Real James Bond type stuff. It's a comment on the pace of development. And your own capabilities, of course.

LATCHING THE DISPLAY

The last piece of software we wrote for the circuit was also the first one to do real work. It wasn't very impressive since digital clocks are not exactly the last word in technology, but it did point out one problem with the design of the board if you plan on making heavy use of the display. Since the LEDs aren't latched, each digit, (with the exception of the last one), is only illuminated until the next digit in line is addressed. Since the SCAN subroutine moves from one digit to the next in eight microseconds, it's the understatement of the week to say that it's difficult to read the data. Unless you're a mutant, you'll want the data to hang around a bit longer than eight microseconds.

And that's not the only problem.

Since the only way to use the current display hardware setup is to refresh the display often enough to make it visible, a lot of valuable CPU time is being wasted. The last piece of software got the job done by putting the refresh CALL in the most frequently executed loop. As a result, the display was refreshed every 96 microseconds—the price paid for reading the numbers was too high.

In general, there are always two ways to get a job done when you're working with a microprocessor—you can build minimal hardware and let the majority of the work be done by software or you can add dedicated hardware that can be manipulated by a few words of software. There's no "right way" here because, as you can imagine, everything depends on the job you want to do.

In the case of the display, however, it makes good sense to add the parts to the board that will lift the burden of refreshing the display off the shoulders of the 8088. Putting some dedicated hardware in the circuit to drive the display will simplify the software requirements, and make it much easier for the 8088 to get on with its real job in life—running software. If you latch the display, the only time the 8088 has to think about it is, either when new data becomes available or the refresh routine is automatically run as a part of NMI routine. This is one of those cases where an hour of design work can save all kinds of software hassles and, as we've already seen:

AVOIDING HASSLES IS A GOOD THING

so let's look at what's involved in making the display self latching and completely automatic.

HARDWARE CONSIDERATIONS

Latching displays is one of the first exercises for someone who wants to get into digital design. It's such a basic necessity that several semiconductor manufacturers take the whole job of managing a seven segment display and package it in one piece of silicon. These are the standard "display-decoder-driver-latch" combinations such as the 4511, 7447, and so on. They can make system design much simpler since they can sit on the data bus and directly control the display digit.

Unfortunately, we've seen that we can't use any of them because we need a display driver that can output the segment patterns for all of the hex digits. As a result, we've been using discreet components to do each of the jobs individually. The bit patterns have been burned in IC16, a custom character generator EPROM, and IC17, a 74LS138 has been working as a combination driver—demultiplexer. The part that we're missing is obviously the latch.

You can use a small eight-bit memory for the latch but it raises unnecessary design hassles. A much easier way to do the job is to use separate latches for each of the displays—as a side benefit we'll be able to dump the necessity of multiplexing the display since IC17, the 74LS138, will be enabling the latches rather than talking directly to the display cathodes. Since each display digit will be looking at the output of it's own latch rather than time sharing the output of the character generator, there's no danger of excessive current draw. The digits can be permanently illuminated by the simple expedient of tying each of the common cathode connections to ground through the same 100 ohm resistors we've been using all along.

We'll be adding eight latches to the board since we need one for each of the digits. You can try to make room for it on the breadboard but it will be simpler to put the display and latches on a separate board and use a piece of ribbon cable with dip connectors to make the connection from one to the other.

You can see from the schematic in Fig. 16-1 that all we're doing is putting the latches between the LED digits and the rest of the circuit. You could think of each latch and digit as a single circuit element. That's not so far from the truth since Hewlett Packard and several others make a seven segment LED display with a built-in latch and decoder.

These would be terrific for our purposes but they all have two problems in common—price and availability.

Way back in the beginning of this book, we made a basic decision to build our circuit from easy to find, inexpensive parts. After all, the way to learn is to feel free to experiment—and nothing throws more of a damper on the creative urge than the possibility of having to spend a lot of bucks to replace parts. If you can't get it in onesies for less than ten bucks—you're not talking about something you can easily risk in an experiment.

BUILDING THE CIRCUIT

This addition to the circuit can either be wired onto the board or put on a separate board. Although there are advantages to both, it makes more sense to use another board because the main one is getting a bit too crowded and, if for other reason, it's nice to be able to position the display without having to move the whole circuit. In any event, I put the keyboard on a separate board and have done the same thing with the display.

PARTS
8 - 74LS373 Octal Latches
1 - 74LS240 Octal Inverting Buffer
9 - .1 μF capacitors

MINIMUM EQUIPMENT
Oscilloscope

If you're putting the display on a separate board, you'll find all the instructions you need here but if you insist on redoing the layout of the main board, you'll have to work out the details yourself. Main board real estate is too valuable to spend on what is really only a peripheral system—and one that you'll probably want to relocate in a finished system.

You may decide to put the entire circuit in a small case and, once you've arrived at a final design, that's a terrific idea. You'll find life much easier if you can put the main board at the bottom of the case and have the display elsewhere. This is true of the keyboard as well.

In any event, don't immediately dismiss the idea of reworking some of the board connections you've already made. Moving the display to a separate board is fairly simple and only involves a minimal amount of rewiring. It can save a lot of potential brain damage later on as you begin personalizing the circuit to meet your own needs. But let's get on to specifics.

THE DISPLAY BOARD

The first step in moving the display to a separate board is to turn off the power. I haven't mentioned it in a while, but I'm sure we all remember the fabulous two step procedure that absolutely protects you from the possibility of doing damage to the board. First disconnect the power leads from the supply and then turn off the supply as well. Make sure the breadboard you have for the display is large enough to accommodate the eight digits and the eight 373s. Remember that the anodes of each of the digits is going to be connected to the outputs of a 373 and the cathodes are going to be connected to ground through the current limiting resistors we're removing from the main board.

Arrange the display digits and the 373s on the separate board in a convenient arrangement—you can read that as any arrangement that lets you wire things up without having to route leads across the front of the LEDs. No sense making trouble for yourself.

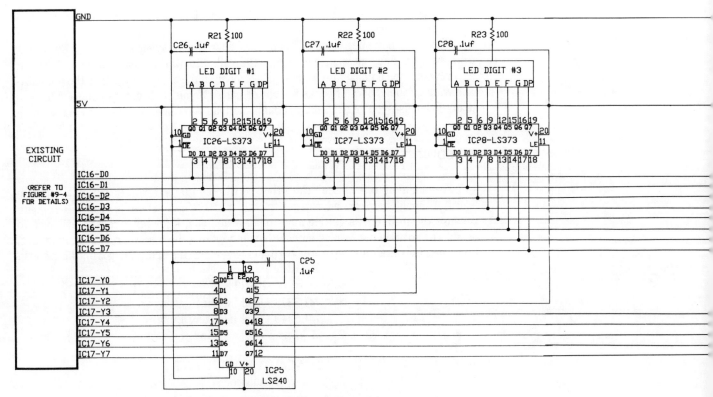

Fig. 16-1. The display latching schematic.

Wire the outputs of the 373s to the LED anodes—one 373 for each LED digit—and connect the cathodes to ground through a resistor. It would be a good idea to add the capacitors from pin #20 of each of the 373s to ground. All of the 373 inputs should be multiplexed together to a common eight-bit bus.

These eight lines, along with power, ground, and the latch enable controls, (pin #11), from each of the 373s are the lines that we have to connect to the main board. Since there are eighteen lines, they can be arranged as shown in Table 16-2 and Table 16-3, and the connection to the main board can be made with two 18-pin dip plugs and a length of ribbon cable. If you don't feel like making the cable yourself, you can easily find them in the mail order houses—and the premade cables are only a bit more expensive than the individual cost of the parts. If you're going to buy a store made cable, give some thought to getting yourself one with 24 pins. As of the moment, we only need eighteen pins, but you can never be sure what future needs you're going to have.

The character generator on the main board is going to feed all the inputs of the 373 on the main board and the outputs of IC17, the 138, (through the 240 inverting buffer), will control the individual latch enable inputs of the 373s on the display board. The wiring list for each 373 on the display board is going to be essentially the same so I'll only detail one of them. The only differences will be the number of the digit connected to the outputs and the connector position of the latch enable line. The 74LS240 is a handy package to use here since it's an inverting octal buffer. We need eight lines, (for the eight digits), and the 138 outputs have to be flipped since they're active low and the 373 latch controls are active high. If you've got some spare inverters around, you can use them in place of the 240—any inverters will do since there's nothing critical about this part of the circuit. You can easily substitute CMOS 4049s, TTL 74LS04s, or even make up some inverters from two-legged gates.

In general, you should always buffer any control and bus lines that go off the main board. Accidents will happen and it's a lot easier to replace one (or two) buffers than it is to trace through the smoking wreckage left by a disaster on the main board. In this case, we needed the buffers to invert the control lines but even if the polarity was the

218

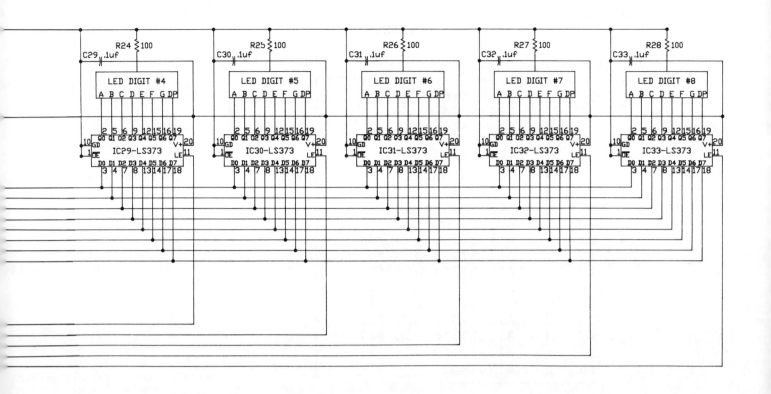

Table 16-1. Connections Made to
the 74LS373 (IC26).

CONNECTIONS TO IC26 (74LS373)	
Pin #	**Connect to**
1	Ground
2	`A' Segment Digit #1
3	Connector pin #10
4	Connector pin #11
5	`B' Segment Digit #1
6	`C' Segment Digit #1
7	Connector pin #12
8	Connector pin #13
9	`D' Segment Digit #1
10	Ground
11	Connector pin #1
12	`E' Segment Digit #1
13	Connector pin #14
14	Connector pin #15
15	`F' Segment Digit #1
16	`G' Segment Digit #1
17	Connector pin #16
18	Connector pin #17
19	DP Segment Digit #1
20	5 Volts

DISPLAY BOARD DIP CONNECTOR	
Pin #	Connect to
1	IC26 pin #11
2	IC27 pin #11
3	IC28 pin #11
4	IC29 pin #11
5	IC30 pin #11
6	IC31 pin #11
7	IC32 pin #11
8	IC33 pin #11
9	Ground
10	All 373's pin #3
11	All 373's pin #4
12	All 373's pin #7
13	All 373's pin #8
14	All 373's pin #13
15	All 373's pin #14
16	All 373's pin #17
17	All 373's pin #18
18	5 Volts

Table 16-2. Connections Made to the Display Board Dip Connector.

MAIN BOARD DIP CONNECTOR	
Pin #	Connect to
1	IC25 pin #18
2	IC25 pin #16
3	IC25 pin #14
4	IC25 pin #12
5	IC25 pin #3
6	IC25 pin #5
7	IC25 pin #7
8	IC25 pin #9
9	Ground
10	IC16 pin #9
11	IC16 pin #10
12	IC16 pin #11
13	IC16 pin #13
14	IC16 pin #14
15	IC16 pin #15
16	IC16 pin #16
17	IC16 pin #17
18	5 Volts

Table 16-3. Connections Made to the Main Board Dip Connector.

CONNECTIONS TO IC25 (74LS240)	
Pin #	Connect to
1	Ground
2	IC17 pin #15
3	Connector pin #5
4	IC17 pin #14
5	Connector pin #6
6	IC17 pin #13
7	Connector pin #7
8	IC17 pin #12
9	Connector pin #8
10	Ground
11	IC17 pin #7
12	Connector pin #4
13	IC17 pin #9
14	Connector pin #3
15	IC17 pin #10
16	Connector pin #2
17	IC17 pin #11
18	Connector pin #1
19	Ground
20	5 Volts

Table 16-4. Connections Made to the 74LS240 (IC25).

same, the protection offered by buffering is worth the time it takes to put the extra chips on the board. Remember the forty seventh Law of Life and Design:

PROTECTION SCHEMES ONLY HAVE TO WORK ONCE

and it's a small price to pay for piece of mind.

Once you have this addition to the circuit wired up and connected to the main board, you should find the circuit working exactly the same way it did before. If there are problems, they can only come from a mistake in the wiring. This hasn't exactly been a gee whiz addition to the circuit.

Disconnect the ribbon cable from the main board and turn the power back on. You can still tell if the circuit is working by watching the eight LED's hanging off IC10. They've stayed on the board for reasons exactly like this. If you have an oscilloscope, you can look at data and address lines to see if the system is working but if you don't, a flickering LED is a good poor man's substitute.

You can run any of the software we used earlier when we were first designing the I/O ports. When you're troubleshooting you want things to be as simple as possible so the best piece of software to run is the first piece of software we wrote—MATRIX.ASM in Chapter 7. If the program works, disconnect the power, plug the display board back on the main board, and run the program again. If it still works, you've either miswired one of the control lines or you haven't connected the digit cathodes to ground through the current limiting resistors.

If the program doesn't run, you've made a mistake in one of the two power lines—5 volts and ground. In any event, it's still a wiring error and the only way you'll be able to find it is to carefully check each connection against the wiring lists. And you have removed all the old leads from the main board, haven't you?

MAPPING AND DECODING

There's no end of things you can do with the circuit we've built—the only restrictions are the limits of your own imagination. You've got enough potential muscle on the board to handle any application that comes to your mind. While you have to write the software and add any special purpose hardware, the basic circuit we've assembled packs a real wallop in terms of raw power—it's up to you to tell it what to do.

Most single board controllers are based around eight-bit CPUs like the 6502, 6809, 8085, Z-80, and so on. While all of these are perfect for most applications, they just don't have the varied repertoire that you'll find in the 8088 instruction set. The 8088 might not be the "state of the art" as far as microprocessors go, but there's no doubt that it's a perfect choice for our controller.

No matter what you plan on doing with the circuit, it's a good bet that you'll want to add to the basic design. More memory, more I/O, reserved addresses, and other similar things are just about the first things you'll be adding to the board when you start working on your own applications. It's important to understand the methodology you should employ when you've decided to add to the main board. It's not a trivial thing. We went through all the details each time we added memory and I/O but it's important enough to go through it again with an eye to increasing the amount of memory and I/O on the board. Now that we've got a working circuit in front of us and the experience of building it behind us, we can take an educated look at how we've been developing the system map.

THE MEMORY MAP

For no particular reason other than an appreciation of symmetry, I've divided the 8088's 1 meg address space into two halves—the bottom is for RAM and the top is for ROM. We've been building the RAM up from 00000h and the ROM down from FFFFFh. Since we only have 2K of each in the system, our RAM ends at 007FFh and the ROM starts at FF800h.

The simplicity of the circuit so far has made it really easy for us to select either ROM or RAM in software and hardware. All we had to do is watch the state of A19, the high address bit. A high on the line meant a ROM address and a low meant a RAM address. This is great for a limited system but it presents problems whenever the system gets expanded.

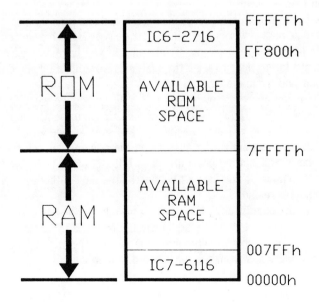

Fig. 16-2. The complete system memory map.

222

To see what I mean, let's take a look at what we're doing when the system is first turned on.

The 8088 looks for its first instruction at FFFF0h and, considering how we've mapped in the 2716, that translates to an absolute address of 007F0 in the EPROM. Everything seems fine like that but it leaves a bit to be desired as far as rigorous system mapping is concerned. A look at the address lines will show you exactly why.

The 2716, and everything else in our system, is paying no attention whatsoever to address lines A11 to A18. For ROM addressing that means that FFFF0h is the same as FF7FFh, E07FFh, or any address that has the high bit set in the high byte and 7FFh as the lower three hex digits. The same analysis is possible with RAM. The first address, 00000h, is the same as 88800h, 6F000h, or any address that has the high bit clear in the high byte and 000h as the lower three hex digits. If this is unclear, write the bytes out in binary and remember that the state of the eight address lines, A11 through A18, have no meaning.

This is no particular problem as long as we keep it in mind when we're developing software, but it can lead to an incredible amount of brain damage if you forget it when you're adding memory to the board. The way to avoid problems is to develop your software as if the system had a full compliment of memory. I agree that it would be unusual, to say the least, to write a program that goes about storing variables in nonexistent memory but if you get sloppy about addressing, you'll have to rewrite your software every time you add memory to the board. If you look through the software we've written so far, you'll notice that addresses are always specified as complete sixteen or twenty-bit hex numbers.

This is a simple practice that can eliminate complex debugging when errors start to show up.

THE I/O MAP

The discussion we just had about memory addressing applies to the I/O map as well. The 8088 can address 65,536 different ports but there's an instruction set restriction in addressing them. The OUT port#, AL (or AX) instruction can only be used for ports 00 through FFh. If you want to address a port numbered between 0100h through FFFFh, you have to use the OUT DX, AL (or AX) instruction.

We've been using the lower 255 (FFh) ports and have divided them in half by using address line A7 as a toggle. Both IC14 and IC22 control the enabling of I/O ports. The first one turns on the 8255 while the second one turns on the 8259.

This enabling scheme, (using A7), is a simple one that's perfectly adequate for the system we have working at the moment, but it can lead to the same sort of addressing ambiguities we saw when we were talking about the memory map. And reading a nonexistent port is as silly an exercise as writing to a nonexistent memory location.

Adding I/O ports to the system presents you, the designer, with the same sort of problems as adding memory. Putting chips on the board is a waste of time unless you first work out how they'll be mapped in the system and, more importantly, how they'll be selected. The reason you have to address a port by a specific number is that the 8088 expects only one port to be living at that address. This isn't as silly as it sounds since the 8088 expects you to have made sure that when a unique port is addressed, only that port is enabled.

In microprocessorland, two is not better than one.

SELECTION AND DECODING

The 8088 uses the address and data lines for operations involving both I/O and memory and it tells the system what it's doing by putting the appropriate level on the IO/MEM

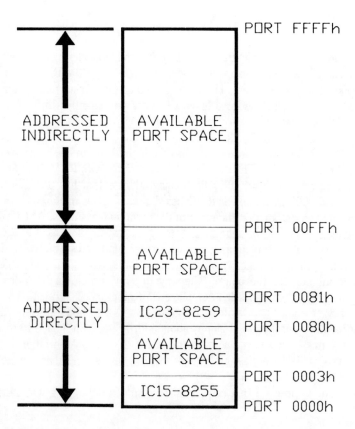

PORT FFFFh

ADDRESSED INDIRECTLY — AVAILABLE PORT SPACE

PORT 00FFh

AVAILABLE PORT SPACE

PORT 0081h

ADDRESSED DIRECTLY — IC23-8259

PORT 0080h

AVAILABLE PORT SPACE

PORT 0003h

IC15-8255

PORT 0000h

Fig. 16-3. The complete system I/O map.

line, pin #28. Unfortunately, as you undoubtedly know by now, it takes a lot more than the state of pin #28 to have the circuit uniquely enable only one memory location or I/O port—it takes a lot of low level silicon glue to decode the address and enable one and only one location or port. Admittedly, it's a bit easier for memory than I/O since a lot of bits can be packed in one memory package while I/O controllers can only address a handful of ports. In our system, we only have to enable one memory chip to talk to any address in a 2K range, while the 8255 can only handle a maximum of four ports.

There are even further complications. It's often necessary to use a small range of memory as so called ''reserved addresses''. This can happen when you want to have some devices mapped directly into the 8088's address space. The simplest example of this would be to add a bell or buzzer to the circuit. You could set it up as an I/O port but these are usually much too valuable to waste on something like this. It's a better idea to build a simple gated oscillator and use a memory location to enable it with the instruction of your choice. It doesn't matter what instruction you use since the enabling circuitry for the bell watches the address lines and is turned on any time it sees the address on the bus.

The basic idea behind all these things—adding ports, memory, and creating special locations—is to design decoding circuitry that can react whenever the correct combination of bits appears on the address bus. This sounds fairly straightforward—and it is in theory—but the practicalities can turn out to be mind boggling design problems. There are twenty address lines in the 8088's address bus and being able to pick one unique address means that you need circuitry that can decode twenty lines.

If you go back through the complications we went through to set up the simple mapping techniques in our circuit, you can imagine what the problem would be like to design a series of decoders that pick one and only one address from more than a million possible addresses. Mind blowing—but there's a way to handle it.

MAPPING ROMs

The basic problem in address line decoding is the fact that there are twenty lines to monitor. In the worst of all possible worlds you can tackle the problem with a series of TTL or CMOS selectors such as the 4051 or 74LS138—chips we've already put to use. The 138 is a usual candidate for this type of operation because, with its three enable inputs and three address inputs, it can be wired up to watch up to six address lines. By using the output of that 138 as enable inputs for other 138s, you could slowly zero in on the one address you need and the result would be a single control line that became active whenever a particular address showed up on the bus.

You could do things this way, (many designers have), and you would wind up with perfectly serviceable decoding circuitry. Of course, the 138s wouldn't be all you'd need. Chances are you'd find it necessary to sprinkle the circuit liberally with inverters, NAND gates, and all the other logical glue that holds the whole subsystem together.

A much better approach to the problem is to use a mapping ROM. In actual fact, we've already used one on the circuit but we didn't refer to it as that—we called it a ''character generator''. All a mapping ROM does is watch a bunch of input lines and put unique data out in response to unique data in. That's exactly the job being done by our character generator—it's translating hex data into bit patterns for the seven segment displays.

A mapping ROM, or ''state machine'' can be put anywhere in a circuit to monitor as many lines as you want. The best way to understand this is to see how it would be used in our circuit.

Boy, can it save you design time.

The last program we wrote for the system used six I/O ports—four of them (0000h - 0003h) were in the 8255 and the remaining two (0080h and 0081h) were the command ports for the 8259. We've got circuitry on the board to select a second 8255 mapped in as ports 0004h - 0007h but I haven't put the parts on the board yet. In order to decode the I/O addresses for these ten ports we used two decoders and a slew of inverters and other gates. Everything works okay but if you examine the circuit, you'll see that we have to add more circuitry to select more ports on the bottom (0008h to 007Fh). Let's suppose that we're going to run an application that needs a lot more ports. I leave it to your imagination to figure out what kind of design problems would have to be overcome if we were to limit ourselves to the standard decoder—selector approach.

The 2716 EPROMs we've been using have eleven address lines and two chip select lines. If we think of the EPROM as a data selector, all these lines can be considered as address inputs. Since the RAM has a byte wide output bus, we're looking at a decoder with thirteen inputs and eight outputs. It's really much more versatile than that because a standard decoder would have eight mutually exclusive outputs while we can program the ROM to put out any byte we want in response to a given set of bits on the address inputs.

In the simplest case, we could use a properly programmed EPROM to replace the circuitry now being used to enable both the 8259 and the 8255. In this case, we only have to look at eight address lines since the ports we're using are between 0000h and 00FFh. Since the EPROM has eleven address lines, we can use the extra three lines to monitor the next three 8088 address lines. This doesn't do anything for us at the moment since we're only interested in decoding eight-bit addresses but remember we get the last three lines for free and, in any event, a future application may use some of the higher I/O ports (those with an address above 00FFh) and the simple act of connecting the three high bit EPROM address lines to the 8088 address bus gives us the ability to decode ports 0000h to 07FFh. Not bad.

Since this ROM is going to be an I/O port decoder, we'll tie its Output Enable control (pin #20) to an inverted version of the IO/$\overline{\text{MEM}}$ line from the 8088 and that will be the toggle that turns the ROM's outputs on and off. The Chip Enable line (pin #18) will be left tied to ground to permanently enable the chip. The reason for this is that while a

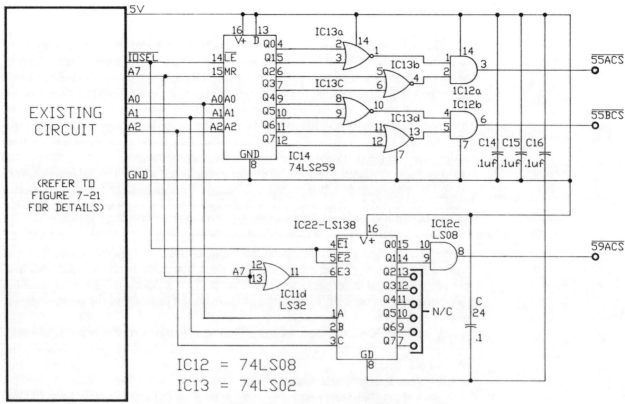

Fig. 16-4. The current I/O decoding circuit.

slow EPROM has an access time of 450 nanoseconds, this can be cut by more than 150 nanoseconds by keeping the chip enabled. It cost you a bit in terms of power but hey, remember the fifty ninth Law of Life and Design:

EVEN NOTHING COSTS SOMETHING

but chopping that much off the access time means that even the slowest EPROM can be used in a 5 MHz 8088 system.

We'll connect the EPROM address lines to the bottom eleven lines of the 8088's address bus and all that's left to do is see how it has to be programmed to match the I/O map we decided to use and the ports we currently have working in the system.

The most straightforward way to build the table in the EPROM is to think of its outputs as mutually exclusive. That's not the way they really are, of course, but since we're only talking about controlling the enabling of three chips (two 8255s and an 8259) it's possible to assign an EPROM output to each one of them.

If you were surprised at how much EPROM space we wasted when the character generator was being programmed, you'll be astounded at the amount of unused space we'll wind up with in the I/O decoder. Since we have, at this point at least, only ten I/O ports, we'll only be using ten locations in the EPROM.

In more complex applications where there are lots of ports and even some reserved addresses you'd want to decode, the mapping ROM would serve as the brute force selector that watches the bus and does the initial work of decoding the 8088's lower eleven address lines and providing you with eight encoded outputs.

The amount of power and flexibility this scheme gives you is really extraordinary if for no reason other than that EPROMs can be easily erased and rewritten. That means that a particular encoding scheme can be changed by simply burning another EPROM. There would have to be some hardware modifications as well but that's what jumper blocks and dip switches are for. A bit of slick circuit design would let you make hardware changes by simply moving jumpers around instead of doing some cut and paste operations on the PC board.

Before we can start laying out the program for our circuit, we have to be clear about what the EPROM outputs have to control. In this case it's not very difficult since they'll only be connected to three chips and all of them have active low chip enable lines. This means that every bit in the EPROM that isn't going to specifically enable either the 8259 or one of the 8255's has to be set high.

In order to put the mapping ROM to work in the circuit we've built so far, we'll assign the EPROM D0 output as the controlling line for the first 8255, the D1 output as the controlling line for the second 8255, and D2 output as the controlling output for the 8259. Since we have so much empty space in the ROM, we can even assign IC10, the 373 used for the first port we put on the board, as I/O port 0008h and put it on the ROM's D3 output. Being able to address a port containing eight LEDs can come in really handy as a status indicator. Let's just keep in mind that the 373's latch enable input is an active high, not an active low, and that will have to be taken into account when the EPROM is programmed.

So now the stage is all set. The EPROM is going to be mapped into the 8088's I/O space from 0000h through 07FFh, it will be permanently enabled to cut down the access time, and its outputs will be enabled by an inverted version of the IO/MEM line. All that's left to do is work out the coding of the EPROM.

In a more complex system, the EPROM would reduce the eleven 8088 address lines to eight outputs and those outputs would then be further decoded to enable various reserved addresses and I/O ports. How much logic you'd have to hang on the EPROM outputs would depend entirely on how many ports and addresses you wanted to decode. In our system we can keep things very simple and assign each enable line to one of the EPROM's output lines since we only have to control four enable inputs and there's no

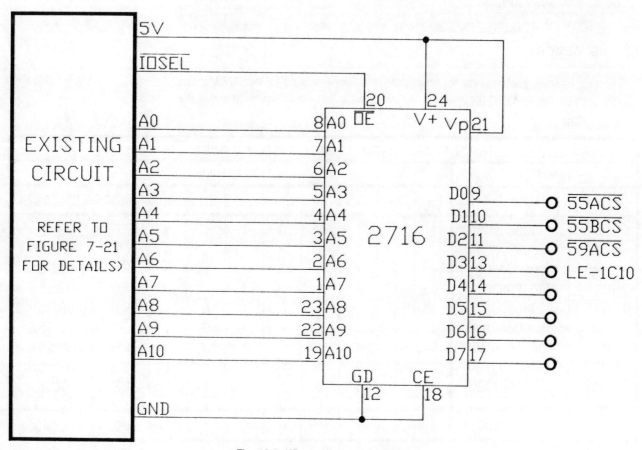

Fig. 16-5. I/O mapping eprom schematic.

sense making things more complicated than necessary. When there are lots of enable pins to control, two or even more EPROM output lines would have to be decoded to generate the needed enabling signals.

The byte table for the EPROM shows you exactly how much room we're leaving empty. Seems like a real waste but remember that this should only be the beginning. As you develop the circuit to meet your own needs you'll be adding to the chart and as long as you have less than nine I/O devices to control, you'll be able to assign each one to a separate EPROM output. When things go beyond this, however, you'll have to rethink the encoding scheme because you'll have to use various combinations of EPROM output signals to enable the I/O devices. This can be done with simple gating or with dedicated decoders such as the 4051, 74LS138, or others we've already used on the board. You can even use the EPROM outputs to enable other EPROMs in a daisy chained fashion. This is the most painless way to handle large numbers of devices that are enabled or toggled by putting a unique address on the 8088's data bus.

The only difficulty a circuit solution like this can lead to has to do with the characteristics of EPROMs, not the basic idea. Even the fastest EPROMs aren't going to be able to access data reliably in much under 100 nanoseconds and this can turn into a real problem as you up the system speed. If you're using a 10 MHz 8088-1, a 100 nanosecond EPROM is going to be operating right on the edge. In this case, you'd be better off doing your development work on a slower system and then transferring the code in the EPROM to a bipolar PROM, since they can be found with access times of well under 50 nanoseconds.

Even in a system as small as ours, the mapping ROM will replace a lot of logic and decoders. If you add the EPROM to the circuit, both IC14 and IC22 become history and several gates will be freed up. One other big advantage is that it will become easy to add more ports to the circuit because selecting them will be a simple matter of changing the bit pattern in the EPROM.

ADDING MEMORY

Sooner or later you're going to need more memory—either ROM or RAM. The 4K we have on the board at the moment is more than adequate for learning about the

I/O MAPPING EPROM TRUTH TABLE											
INPUTS		OUTPUTS									
PORT	BINARY DATA	D7	D6	D5	D4	D3	D2	D1	D0	HEX	ENABLE
00	00000000000	1	1	1	1	0	1	1	0	F6	8255A
01	00000000001	1	1	1	1	0	1	1	0	F6	8255A
02	00000000010	1	1	1	1	0	1	1	0	F6	8255A
03	00000000011	1	1	1	1	0	1	1	0	F6	8255A
04	00000000100	1	1	1	1	0	1	0	1	F5	8255B
05	00000000101	1	1	1	1	0	1	0	1	F5	8255B
06	00000000110	1	1	1	1	0	1	0	1	F5	8255B
07	00000000111	1	1	1	1	0	1	0	1	F5	8255B
08	00000001000	1	1	1	1	1	1	1	1	FF	IC10
80	00010000000	1	1	1	1	0	0	1	1	F3	8259
81	00010000001	1	1	1	1	0	0	1	1	F3	8259

Fig. 16-6. The anatomy of the I/O mapping eprom.

system and getting programming experience but it's more than likely that you'll want to add to that as you begin to work on real world applications. Besides, the eighty sixth Law of Life and Design correctly points out that:

YOU CAN NEVER HAVE TOO MUCH MEMORY

and, whether or not it's ever used, it's comforting to know that extra memory is on the board.

One of the great truths of microprocessor-based design is that you want to keep things as simple as possible. Unfortunately, that truth is often thrown out the window when it comes to adding memory—more specifically, when it comes to adding RAM.

As everyone knows, RAM comes in two basic flavors—static RAM and dynamic RAM—and while it's true that the latter packs more bits in a single package, it's also true that using it can lead to a first class ticket to the rubber room. The design hassles can be unbelievable.

DYNAMIC RAM

Using dynamic RAM in a single board system like ours is, in words of two syllables, a mistake. The amount of brain time that has to be devoted to designing the support circuitry is enormous and setting out to do it can get so complex that it's easy to forget what the whole subsystem was to be used for in the first place. Since this book is aimed at dissecting the whole process of microprocessor-based circuit design, it would be incomplete without a discussion of dynamic RAM. I know that most computers use dynamic RAM but the complications caused by its use are worthy of a separate book.

The basic hassle with dynamic RAM stems directly from the fact that its fundamental storage cell is nothing more than a capacitor, and a really small one at that. Whenever you store a "1" in a dynamic RAM cell, all you're doing is putting a charge on a capacitor and as we all know, that's far from being permanent. The instant you store the data, it starts to leak away. Not very reassuring, is it?

The way RAM designers get around this problem is to read the value of the cell while the data is still there and then write it back in again. This process of reading and

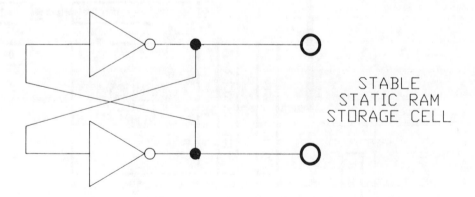

STABLE
STATIC RAM
STORAGE CELL

Fig. 16-7. Typical ram storage cell.

UNSTABLE
DYNAMIC RAM
STORAGE CELL

229

rewriting data is euphemistically referred to as *"refreshing"* the cell. Most dynamic RAM's require that a refresh of *each* cell be done at least every 2 milliseconds although the newer, larger dynamic RAMs (256k and above) only need a refresh every 4 milliseconds. A bit of simple arithmetic will show you that refreshing even a small system can take a long time—as a matter of fact, it could well turn out to be impossible.

Let's say we had a full 512K X 8 bits of dynamic RAM in our circuit and we were designing refresh circuitry. Since this operation is time critical, the first thing to do would be work out the minimum amount of time each refresh operation would take. Assuming the memory was composed of sixteen 256K X 1 dynamic RAM chips, we would have to do 524,288 refresh cycles in 4 milliseconds. That translates into a time of some 7.6 nanoseconds per refresh cycle. You'll remember that our 4.77 MHz clock means that the most basic time division in our system is 200 nanoseconds, so a refresh of all the RAM in the system is, in no uncertain terms, a clear impossibility. So what's the deal?

RAM makers can do arithmetic as well as any of us so, recognizing this difficulty, they designed the RAM's internal circuitry so that a read done of one cell will refresh all the cells in the row. Remember that when you get down to the substrate level, all RAM has two basic parts—the control circuit and the matrix of memory cells. The RAM matrix has the storage cells organized in rows and columns so that each cell can be accessed by specifying a unique X and Y, or row and column address.

The amount of refresh cycles that have to be performed, therefore, depends on the number of rows, not the number of bits. This goes a long way toward making re-

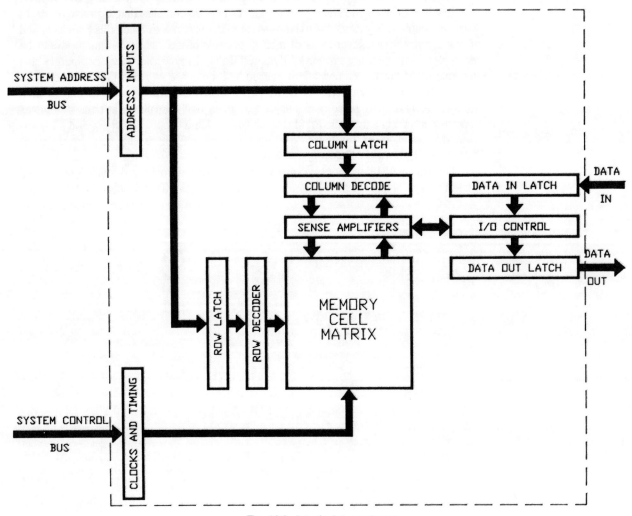

Fig. 16-8. A typical dynamic ram.

fresh a more realistic operation. Since most 256K X 1 RAM's have a matrix organized as 256 rows by 1024 columns, we can cut the minimum refresh time considerably. Instead of having to do 524,288 refresh cycles every 4 milliseconds, we only have to do a read of 512 row addresses in the same time. This works out to be about 8 microseconds per refresh cycle. Things are looking better. But, not that much better.

Even at 8 microseconds per refresh cycle, we still have problems to work out. Let's suppose that we write a refresh subroutine that will be called often enough to properly refresh all the RAM in the system. Put on your thinking caps people, it's arithmetic time.

We'll make things easy for ourselves by assuming that we've somehow arranged our circuit so that all 512 row addresses are located in the same segment. We'll also assume that we can find an 8088 instruction that meets the following criteria:

1. It can access a memory location in one machine cycle.
2. It doesn't change the value in the location.

We'll make the further assumption that, in addition to having all 512 row addresses in the same segment, they're also successive addresses. Given all these assumptions, (and remember that not all of them are even possible), let's see just how much time we're going to need for our refresh operation.

The memory refresh subroutine would take the form of a loop that runs through the memory addresses—an instruction that executes 512 times. This means that the whole operation would take 800 nanoseconds (one machine cycle takes four clocks) times 512 addresses, or about 400 microseconds—not considering the time needed for getting to the subroutine or any other instructions that would be needed.

What all this hypothetical head scratching tells us is that every 4 milliseconds of CPU time we're going to lose at least 400 microseconds to do a refresh operation. That's ten percent, people!

In the best of all possible worlds, with instructions that probably don't exist and ignoring normal subroutine overhead, the best we can expect is a ten percent loss in processing time.

That's a pretty steep price to pay—especially when you consider that a more realistic estimate (based on real instructions) would more than likely be twice that.

Microprocessors like the Z-80 make using dynamic RAM a bit easier because they have a built in autoincrementing counter that's put on the address bus while the Z-80 is busy decoding instructions and the bus is free. This means you can add minimal circuitry to the board to decode these addresses and use them to cycle through the dynamic RAM's row addresses.

That sort of convenience isn't part of the 8088 since it's parallel fetch and execution architecture and multiplexed address and data bus scheme don't leave the bus free for any great period of time. Most of the systems that use dynamic RAM with an 8088 use a different, non-CPU technique for dynamic RAM housekeeping—*Direct Memory Access*.

Chips such as the 8237 are DMA controllers that can handle memory transfers without bothering the CPU. They're programmed in much the same manner as the 8255 and 8259 that we're already familiar with. We drew up an impossible wish list when we were working out the refresh overhead for a system with 512K of dynamic RAM and found out that even if we used nonexistent type 8088 instructions, it would take some 400 microseconds do a refresh.

Well, if we delegate the job to a DMA controller, we can get the job done in that time. The 8237 would be programmed by the CPU to do a memory read of each row address in the system at least once every 4 milliseconds. The mechanics of the operation would require a clock that would activate the 8237 at least every 4 milliseconds. Once it's activated, the 8237 puts the 8088 on hold to remove it from the bus and then does a read of the row addresses. By running the 8237 with the system's 4.77 MHz clock, each refresh read can be accomplished in 4 clock cycles. The microprocessor isn't involved in the refresh and, since it's on hold throughout, it isn't even aware of what's happening on the bus. But don't get the idea that this technique gives you something for nothing. The ninety second Law of Life and Design is:

TIME MARCHES ON REGARDLESS

and while the 8088 might be blissfully unaware of memory refresh, the clock keeps ticking. The overhead for memory refresh still exists in real time—the ten percent loss in time is still there.

It used to be true that the larger the memory system, the more the benefit that could be gotten from using dynamic RAM. Some of that had to do with memory chip density—how many bits you could squeeze in a single package—and some of it had to do with the cost per bit.

Once upon a time, dynamic memory was cheap. When you could buy a 41256 for three bucks, it became attractive to go through the brain damage necessary to design the support circuitry. After all, a half a meg of RAM would only cost you 24 dollars. But milk used to cost twenty five cents a quart as well. And I don't know where you can even find a Meloroll anymore.

A small board system like ours can certainly support dynamic RAM but it makes a lot more sense to save brain cells and stick with using static RAM. Right at this moment, taking the numbers from a typical mail order catalog, there's an eight dollar savings in store for you by building a 64K system with dynamic RAM rather than static RAM. And that savings will get wiped out by the price of the 8237 and whatever other logic you have to put on the board to handle dynamic RAM. But wait, there's more.

The static RAM I'm pricing is 32K X 8 bit chips. That means you can get 64K by just adding two chips to the board. And there's no additional circuitry required—just plug the chips onto the board in the same way we added the 6116. There are some more address lines to connect but that's about the only difference. The equivalent memory in dynamic RAM takes eight packages. That's a lot more wiring and, if you plan on producing a PC board, a lot more traces.

There's even a further advantage. The static RAM is CMOS low power stuff so you get hassle free circuits, noise immunity, battery powered data retention, and other good stuff—and you get it all for free!

Adding static RAM to the board is probably the easiest exercise in design you can imagine. All the address and data lines on the new RAM are put in parallel with the old RAM. The only difference in wiring is in the chip select inputs and even that's simple.

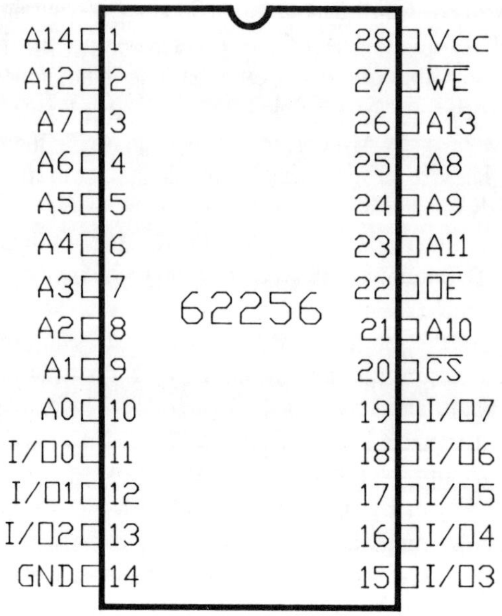

```
         A14 ┌1        28┐ Vcc
         A12 ┌2        27┐ WE
          A7 ┌3        26┐ A13
          A6 ┌4        25┐ A8
          A5 ┌5        24┐ A9
          A4 ┌6        23┐ A11
          A3 ┌7        22┐ OE
          A2 ┌8  62256 21┐ A10
          A1 ┌9        20┐ CS
          A0 ┌10       19┐ I/O7
        I/O0 ┌11       18┐ I/O6
        I/O1 ┌12       17┐ I/O5
        I/O2 ┌13       16┐ I/O4
         GND ┌14       15┐ I/O3
```

Fig. 16-9. Pinouts of the 62256.

Let's say you wanted to replace our lone 6116 with two pieces of 62256 32K X 8 static RAM. At the moment we're enabling the 6116, IC7, by using a gated combination of the IO/$\overline{\text{MEM}}$ and A19 address lines. The same sort of idea can be used to control the chip select pins of these two new memories but, obviously, we need more than the single A19 line to get the job done.

We can still use the RAMSEL signal but we have to add some gating to be able to automatically select one RAM chip or the other. Each of the 62256's is going to be mapped in our system to cover a 32K address space. The first one will live from 0000h to 7FFFh and the second one will live just above that from 8000h to FFFFh.

Just looking at the addresses should give you a clue as to what we have to add to our circuit. The 62256's have 15 address lines, (A0 to A14), since they're able to store 32K bytes. The difference between addressing one chip and the other shows up on the 8088's A15 line. A low on that line means we're accessing an address from 0000h to 7FFFh and a high means we're looking at an address in the next 32K block, or 8000h to FFFFh. The 8088's A15 line, therefore, becomes the toggle we need to choose a particular 62256.

We have to create a new control signal called RAM1 that's produced by gating $\overline{\text{RAMSEL}}$ and the 8088's A15 line. As with all gating problems there are lots of ways to get the job done. One way would be to use a dedicated controller like the 74LS138 or, to set things up for future RAM expansion, a mapping ROM. You should really go this route if you plan on expanding memory beyond these two chips.

If, on the other hand, you decide that all you'll ever put on the board is two RAM chips (of any size), you can do the chip selecting by using one inverter. Let $\overline{\text{RAMSEL}}$ continue controlling the output enable pins of both memory ICs and make RAM1 identical to the A15 line of the 8088. Just tie RAM1 to the chip enable input of the low order RAM and, through the inverter, to the chip enable pin of the high order RAM as well.

This scheme will result in one of the memories being enable all of the time but since the outputs are still controlled by $\overline{\text{RAMSEL}}$, bus contention won't be a problem. Remember that unless $\overline{\text{RAMSEL}}$ and RAMRW are both low, the data in the RAM will be unchanged. Even though one RAM chip will always be on the bus it's outputs won't be enabled unless $\overline{\text{RAMSEL}}$ is active. Since the data pins of these memories serve as both input and output, they won't put any stored data on the bus unless the output enable pin is low and that only happens when $\overline{\text{RAMSEL}}$ is low.

There's nothing wrong with this circuit solution from the point of view of getting the job done, but it's a rather short sighted method of decoding RAM since there's no easy way to add more to the circuit. It's your circuit and you're the one shelling out the bucks to buy the parts, so it's your decision. As for me, I've opted to use a mapping ROM. It lets me add memory more easily, reserve particular addresses as hardware toggles, and change the entire circuit configuration by the simple expedient of reprogramming the ROM.

TROUBLESHOOTING

The more experience you get in electronics, the more you realize that nothing ever works the first time around. No matter how hard you try to watch every single detail, it's a foregone conclusion that there's something you're overlooking. And it's usually something that meets the fabulous three "S" test. I absolutely guarantee that when, after an agonizing number of hours plowing through wiring, reading through notes, or tracing through listings, you finally find the problem, it will be Small, Stupid, and Sneaky.

The secret to maximizing the circuit and minimizing brain damage at the same time is to keep everything modular. Hardware is easier to design and software is easier to debug if you can break the overall problem down into small, manageable, human sized pieces. It's hard to work the kinks out of software on a prototype system like ours but the 8088 gives you two powerful tools, interrupt 1 and interrupt 3.

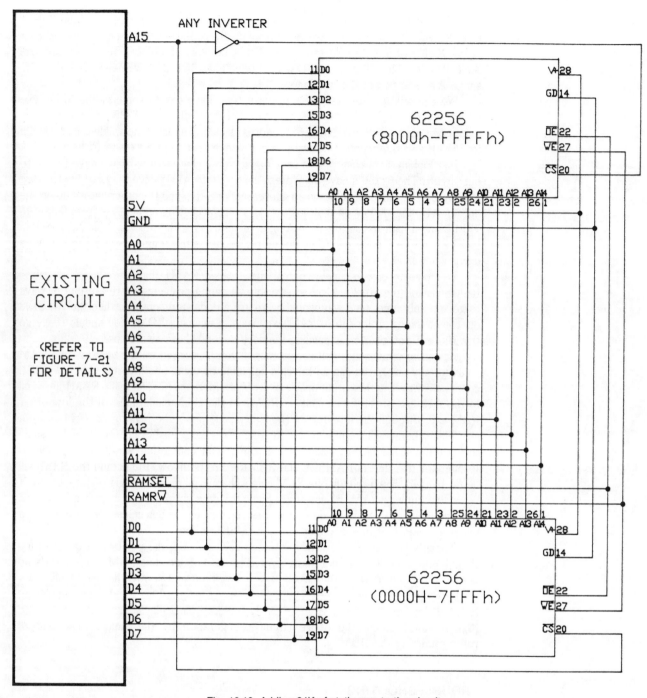

Fig. 16-10. Adding 64K of static ram to the circuit.

When you issue an INT1 instruction, the 8088 will automatically generate an INT1 after executing each instruction. This Single Step Interrupt is an invaluable debugging aid since the interrupt routine it runs is entirely up to you. You can have it dump a memory location to the display, light a combination of LEDs, or anything else that will help you keep track of what your program is doing.

If you're pretty confident that you know where the problem is, you can replace any instruction with an INT instruction. Since this is only one byte long, it can replace any one of the 8088 instructions. This will let you run your diagnostic routine at any point in your program. It takes some work and EPROM programming to systematically work your way through suspect parts of your code but hey, no-one ever said it would be easy. If you think that's difficult, try the same thing with another microprocessor!

The same debugging techniques apply to hardware. We added elements to our circuit in tiny increments to make sure each one of them would be working correctly. Not only that, but we thoroughly tested each subsection before we gave it our official okie-dokie and treated it as bug free. This can sometimes be done with hardware alone or, as is usually the case, with a couple of words of software.

Any software that you write to test a new hardware addition to the circuit should be as simple as possible. A few MOVs, CMPs, JNZs, and some OUTs should be the extent of the instruction repertoire. A good example of this sort of thing was the way we went about adding the I/O ports to the board. You should use this as a model for your own circuit diagnostics.

But of course, the more experienced you get, the more difference there'll be between what you do and what I do. Circuit design is, in the final analysis, a creative activity and the more complex the job, the more ways there are of doing it. Final designs aren't good or bad since the bottom line is whether or not they work. Any design can be made more elegant—it's just a matter of putting in the time. But no design is elegant, or anything else for that matter, unless it works. That's the absolute test.

The circuit you have in front of you is a serious piece of design capable of doing anything you might ask of any microprocessor-based circuit. Now that you've taken it this far, you have all the things you need to take it further. You know exactly how it works and you understand why each design decision was made. You've got all of the understanding necessary to add, modify, or entirely rework the basic circuit.

All you have to do is come up with an idea, apply the same type of reasoning and analysis we've gone through together and work out the solution. And take my word for it, if you've come this far, there's absolutely nothing stopping you from going further on your own. You really can. Believe it.

17

So Now What?

Good question. If you've made it this far and are currently staring at the world's most tediously made digital clock, you deserve a couple of pats on the back. Understanding the basic ins and outs of microprocessor-based circuits isn't hard, but it's not as easy as . . . say, opening a pack of gum, for instance.

If nobody's around to pat you on the back, you've got my official okie-dokie to do it yourself and consider it as coming from me.

But this isn't really the end of things—quite the contrary. By going through the system development in this book, you should have no trouble taking it any further. As a matter of fact, by far the most important lesson you should have learned from these pages is that the basic approach to designing around microprocessors isn't really much different than any other kind of electronics.

In a real sense, once you've got the basics of the design worked out and running, (like the schematic shown in Fig. 7-21), most of your bench time is going to be devoted to designing the circuitry needed to connect the microprocessor circuit to the real world. And that should be much more familiar territory.

There's no reason whatsoever why you can't go out, pick any other microprocessor on the market, sit down, and work out a basic circuit to bring it to life. The steps involved are exactly the same ones we went through together as we worked our way through the book. Remember that CPUs might differ in detail and capabilities, but when you get right down to it, the basics of the design are always the same. You need memory, control, and I/O.

The only stumbling block you might find, and the one place where most people have trouble, is in writing software. But even that's not too big a deal. You probably realize by now that I've only taken advantage of a small part of the 8088 instruction in writing the software for this book. If you're used to assembler programming, you probably found a lot of the code to be overly simple. I couldn't agree with you more since there are much more efficient ways of designing a digital clock, counting, and implementing a keyboard interrupt routine. But, there's a reason for it.

When you're developing a system around a microprocessor, you want to keep the software as simple as possible to make troubleshooting as simple as possible. Sending one byte out a simple port may not be the last word in software elegance, but it's a terrific tool for debugging hardware. There are alternatives, and big companies spend zillions of dollars on equipment to make those alternatives possible.

If you've got that kind of cash you can do the same thing, but most people have a much more modest collection of test equipment. The one thing you'll find that will be absolutely indispensable is an oscilloscope—not only can it make diagnostics a lot easier, but it's really the only tool that lets certain tests be performed. Scopes aren't cheap but by forgetting about delayed sweep, being willing to accept a 20 MHz bandwidth, and hunting out closeouts, you can get by with spending less than four hundred bucks.

Software skills, unfortunately, can be bought. The best approach is to get an introductory book on machine language programming for the microprocessor you're using. One nice thing about the 8088 is that it works in lots of PCs and, as a result, lots of people are writing the kind of books you need. One book you might want to look at is "IBM Assembly Language Simplified" by Dr. Ruth Wessler (TAB #2939). It starts off at ground level and does a good job of introducing a large part of the 8088 instruction set.

Designing with the 8088 also means there's no shortage of software tools such as debuggers, assemblers, and so on. You can't imagine how much of an advantage this is until you start hand coding bytes. You can do things this way but it's much too tedious and a real waste of your undoubtedly valuable time. I know it's a waste of mine.

So, once again we turn to the question of quo vadis? as my friend Larry says. What kind of stuff do you design for the circuit now? You got me—it depends on what you want to do.

There's lots of available I/O on the board and the system maps are flexible enough to accommodate a varied amount of ROM and RAM. You're the only one who knows what you have in mind. Things like a system controller or EPROM burner come to mind but that's up to you. A couple of pieces of advice, however.

It would be a bad idea to design a PC board for the circuit, since you'll undoubtedly want to change it as you work out applications of your own. You might consider putting together a wire wrapped version of the circuit but, unless you want to find out about wire wrapping, I don't see much point in doing it.

Keeping the circuit on solderless breadboards will make it nice and easy to play around with changing it—and don't forget about keeping notes . . . good notes.

If you come up with some interesting stuff, drop me a note either through TAB or Radio Electronics Magazine and let me know about it. And if you're having trouble, let me know what it is and I'll see what I can do about helping you out. If you have a computer and modem, you can call 212-666-5015 and leave me a message on the bulletin board. I check it fairly frequently and I'll leave you an answer.

But we've finally come to the end. There's lots more that can be said but there's nothing more to say. The rest is up to you. So get to work. Don't forget to stay in touch.

Appendix A

My Bench

ALL THE DEVELOPMENT WORK THAT PRODUCED THE CIRCUITRY AND SOFTWARE IN THIS book was done with a fairly minimal amount of tools. You can overburden yourself with equipment and wind up spending more time wiring up test stuff than actually developing the circuit.

I laid out the circuit exactly as shown in the placement diagrams in each chapter and used the same kind of solderless breadboards you probably have on your bench. A lot of people don't like them because they're so prone to noise and capacitance problems, but it's easier to deal with these problems than it is to change a wirewrapped board.

In any event, here's the setup I used.

1. QT59S and QT59B solderless breadboards.
2. A 100 MHz oscilloscope.
3. A 50 MHz digital storage scope.
4. A standard multimeter.
5. A homemade logic probe.
6. An IBM compatible computer.
7. A pure ASCII producing word processor.
8. Several different 8088 assemblers.

It should be noted that the storage scope was only used to produce the drawings of actual waveforms and didn't play any real part in the work of developing the circuit.

Appendix B

The 8088 Instruction Set

M OST OF THE EMPHASIS IN THIS BOOK HAS BEEN ON THE HARDWARE ASPECTS OF THE
8088. We've spent a lot of time putting together the pieces necessary to breathe
life into the 8088, but haven't devoted a lot of energy to the ins and outs of programming. Software is a big subject.

All the programs used to test and exercise the circuitry has been written using only
a small part of the 8088's instruction set. I did this intentionally because I wanted it to
be as easy to follow as possible. There's no doubt that an experienced programmer would
be able to get the same jobs done with much smaller listings. Chances are, however,
that the code would be more difficult to follow.

There's nothing wrong with writing code in what seems to you to be an intuitive
manner. Just as with hardware, the important thing is to first get something that works—
elegance comes later.

There's no getting around the fact that you've got to come to grips with software
in order to use the 8088—or any other microprocessor for that matter—but that's not
the job of this book.

To help get you started, however, and to make it easier for you to understand the
listings we used in developing the circuit, here's a real down and dirty summary of the
whole instruction set. Each page deals with one instruction and there are explanations
and examples to show how the instruction is used and what it does.

This is not a substitute for a good book on programming since we all know that there's
a world of difference between knowing what an instruction is and understanding how
to put them together.

The syntax for instructions that operate on two bytes or words is:

Instruction Destination, Source

and unless otherwise noted, both the destination and source may be any combination
of registers, memory locations, or immediate data.

AAA—ASCII Adjust for Addition

This instruction converts the contents of the AL register into a valid unpacked decimal number. If you're not sure about this, refer to the discussion of packed and unpacked
decimal numbers in Chapter 4.

It's most often used when you're adding two ASCII characters and want the result
stored as an ASCII character. If the AX register contained 0733h and you executed the
following instruction:

you would wind up with 076ch in AL. If you then executed an AAA, the result would be converted to an unpacked decimal and the whole number would be stored in AX. In this case, 33h and 39h are an ASCII 3 and 9 respectively and, added together as decimals give you 12. The 07 in the high nibble of AL would be changed to a zero and the low nibble would become a 2. The carry would be transferred to AH to convert the byte there from an 07h to an 08h. The final outcome of issuing the AAA would be to store 0802h in the AX register. The AAA instruction affects the Carry Flag and the Auxiliary Carry Flag.

AAD—ASCII for Division

In order to use this instruction, both AH and AL have to contain valid unpacked decimal numbers and you want to use the value there as the numerator in a division operation. When you issue an AAD the 8088 will convert the contents of AX to hex and input the result in AL.

If you had stored 0802h in the AX register and issued an AAD, the 8088 would assume that the 02h in the AL register was the units digit and the 08h in AX was the tens digit. The result of the instruction would be to convert the 82 to a hex number so after the AAD had been executed, the AX register would contain a 0052h (the hex equivalent to a decimal 82). The AAD instruction affects the Sign Flag, Parity Flag, and Zero Flag.

AAM—ASCII Adjust for Multiplication

This instruction is similar to AAD but is used after multiplication to convert the hex number in AL to two unpacked decimal numbers in AX. It assumes that the two numbers you've just multiplied together are valid unpacked decimal numbers.

If the result of a multiplication leaves 27h in AL, issuing an AAM will cause 0309h to be stored in AX. The AAM instruction affects the Sign Flag, Parity Flag, and Zero Flag.

AAS—ASCII Adjust for Subtraction

This is similar to the AAA instruction but is used after subtraction. It also assumes that the subtraction operation involved two valid unpacked decimal numbers. The result of the subtraction in the AX register will be converted to two unpacked decimal numbers.

If the result of a subtraction leaves 063Ah, issuing an AAS will cause an 0504h to be stored in AX. The AAS instruction affects the Carry and Auxiliary Carry Flag.

ADC—Add With Carry

There are several variations to this instruction since the source and destination can be registers, memory locations, or immediate data. In general, the use of ADC is:

ADC destination, source

The destination and source values are added together and the result of the addition is stored in the destination. This instruction checks the current state of the Carry Flag as well. If the Carry Flag is set, ADC adds one to the result of the addition and updates the Carry Flag. The ADC instruction affects the Auxiliary Carry Flag, Carry Flag, Overflow Flag, Parity Flag, Sign Flag, and Zero Flag.

ADD—Addition

This is similar to the ADC instruction but it doesn't check the state of the Carry Flag during execution. The use of ADD is:

ADD destination, source

The destination and source can be several combinations of registers, memory locations, and immediate data. The ADD instruction affects the Auxiliary Carry Flag, Carry Flag, Overflow Flag, Parity Flag, Sign Flag, and Zero Flag.

AND—Logical AND

This instruction performs a logical AND operation on any one of several operands. The syntax for this instruction is:

AND destination, source

The result of the operation is stored in the destination. The AND instruction affects the Carry Flag, Overflow Flag, Parity Flag, Sign Flag, and Zero Flag.

CALL—CALL Subroutine

This is similar to a GOSUB instruction in BASIC. When you issue a CALL instruction, the 8088 saves the Instruction Pointer and current Code Segment, and Flags on the stack. Once this is done, it begins executing the instructions at the specified destination.

When it finds a RETurn instruction it pops the original Instruction Pointer, Code Segment, and Flags from the stack and resumes operation just past the CALL instruction.

The location of the subroutine can be specified several different ways depending on whether the subroutine is located in the current segment. The CALL instruction has no affect on any flags.

CBW—Convert a Byte to a Word

The CBW instruction carries the sign of the AL register into the AH register to convert the single AL byte to a 16-bit value.

If the high order bit of AL is a one, issuing a CBW will cause an FFh to be stored in AH. If the high order bit of AL is a zero, issuing a CBW will cause a 00h to be stored in AH. The CBW instruction has no affect on the flags.

CLC—Clear the Carry Flag

The CLC instruction clears the Carry Flag. Issuing a CLC causes a zero to be stored in the Carry Flag. The CLC instruction only affects the Carry Flag.

CLD—Clear the Direction Flag

The CLD instruction will cause a zero to be stored in the Direction Flag. This will result in having all of the the string instructions auto-increment the SI and DI registers. The CLD instruction only affects the Direction Flag.

CLI—Clear Interrupt Enable Flag

The CLI instruction stores a zero on the Interrupt Enable Flag. This causes the 8088 to ignore any interrupt requests that show up on the INTR line. NMI requests, of course, are not disabled. The CLI instruction only affects the Interrupt Enable Flag.

CMC—Complement the Carry Flag

The CMC instruction causes the Carry Flag to change state. If it's set, a CMC will clear it. Conversely, if it's clear, a CMC will set it. The CMC instruction only affects the Carry Flag.

CMP—Compare

The CMP instruction will compare two values and store the result of that comparison in several flags. The two operands may be any of a variety of memory locations, registers, or immediate data.

When a CMP is issued, the source is subtracted from the destination and the results are transferred to the flags. No change is made on the operands being compared. The CMP instruction affects the Carry Flag, Auxiliary Carry Flag, Overflow Flag, Parity Flag, Sign Flag, and Zero Flag.

CMPS—Compare String

The CMPS instruction compares the bytes or words whose locations are stored in the SI and DI registers and transfers the result of the comparison to the flags.

The comparison is done by subtracting the destination from the source but neither of these two bytes or words are changed. The CMPS instruction affects the Carry Flag, Auxiliary Carry Flag, Overflow Flag, Parity Flag, Sign Flag, and Zero Flag.

CWD—Convert Word to Doubleword

The CWD instruction is similar to the CBW instruction. It extends the sign of the AX register into the DX register. If the high order bit of the AX register is a one, issuing a CWD will cause FFFFh to be stored in the DX register. If the high order bit of the

AX register is a zero, issuing a CWD will cause 0000h to be stored in the DX register. The CWD instruction has no affect on the flags.

DAA—Decimal Adjust for Addition

The DAA instruction will convert the contents of the AL register into two packed decimal (BCD) numbers. A DAA should only be used after you've added two packed decimal numbers.

If you're not clear about the difference between packed and unpacked decimal numbers, refer to the discussion on this subject in Chapter 4. If the AL register contains 15h as a packed decimal and you add 26h to it, issuing a DAA instruction will convert the result in AL from a 3Bh to a 41h. The DAA instruction affects the Carry Flag, Auxiliary Carry Flag, Parity Flag, Sign Flag, and Zero Flag.

DAS—Decimal Adjust for Subtraction

The DAS instruction converts the value in AL to packed decimal (BCD) numbers. It assumes that the value in AL is the result of the subtraction of two valid packed decimal numbers.

If the value that gets stored in AL is a 6Eh. After issuing a DAS, the value in AL will be converted to 68h. The DAS instruction affects the Carry Flag, Auxiliary Carry Flag, Parity Flag, Sign Flag, and Zero Flag.

DEC—Decrement

The DEC instruction subtracts one from the destination and stores the result in the destination. A DEC instruction may operate on a memory location or register. The DEC instruction affects the Overflow Flag, Auxiliary Carry Flag, Parity Flag, Sign Flag, and Zero Flag.

DIV—Divide

The DIV instruction will do an unsigned division of two 8- or 16-bit quantities. If 8-bit division is done, the quotient will be in AL and the remainder will be in AH. If 16-bit division is done, the quotient will be in AX and the remainder will be in DX. The DIV instruction affects the Carry Flag, Auxiliary Carry Flag, Overflow Flag, Parity Flag, Sign Flag, and Zero Flag.

ESC—Escape

The ESC instruction has no affect on the 8088 and is treated exactly the same as a NOP except that it will cause the data at the addressed location to be put on the bus.

The ESC is used as the means for coprocessors to identify their instructions when they appear on the data bus in much the same fashion as Escape sequences are sent to printers to control formatting. The ESC instruction has no affect on any flags.

HLT—Halt

The HLT instruction causes the 8088 to enter an idle state and keep on effectively executing a series of NOPs. The 8088 will leave the idle state if the reset line is activated, an NMI is received, or, (if interrupts are enabled), an interrupt request on the INTR line. The HLT instruction has no affect on any flags.

IDIV—Integer Divide

The IDIV instruction will do a signed division of two 8- or 16-bit quantities. The dividend may be a register or value stored in a memory location. If 8-bit division is done, the quotient will be in AL and the remainder will be in AH. If 16-bit division is done, the quotient will be in AX and the remainder will be in DX. The DIV instruction affects the Carry Flag, Auxiliary Carry Flag, Overflow Flag, Parity Flag, Sign Flag, and Zero Flag.

IMUL—Integer Multiply

The IMUL instruction will do a signed multiplication of two 8- or 16-bit quantities. The multiplicand may be a register or value stored in a memory location. If an 8-bit source is used, it's multiplied by AL and the result is put in AH and AL. If a 16-bit source is used, it's multiplied by AX and the result is put in AX and DX. The IMUL instruction affects the Carry Flag and Overflow Flag.

IN—Input a Byte or Word

The IN instruction reads a value from an I/O port and puts it in the accumulator. Ports 0 through 255 may be specified directly but higher numbered ports must be addressed indirectly through the DX register. The IN instruction has no affect on any flags.

INC—Increment

The INC instruction adds one to the destination and stores the result in the destination. An INC instruction may operate on a memory location or register. The INC instruction affects the Overflow Flag, Auxiliary Carry Flag, Parity Flag, Sign Flag, and Zero Flag.

INT—Interrupt

The INT instruction causes the 8088 to execute the interrupt routine whose address has been stored in the interrupt vector table.

The interrupt routine is identified by the following syntax:

INT type number

If you're not clear about interrupts, refer to the discussions in Chapter 13. The INT instruction affects the Interrupt Flag and the Trap Flag.

INTO—Interrupt on Overflow

The INTO instruction will cause a type 4 interrupt to be generated if the Interrupt Flag has been set. If the Interrupt Flag is clear, the INTO instruction will be ignored. This is one of the predefined interrupts and is functionally the same as an INT 4 instruction. The INTO instruction has no affect on any flags.

IRET—Return From Interrupt

The IRET instruction is used at the end of interrupt routines. When the 8088 executes this instruction it expects the previous Instruction Pointer, Code Segment, and Flags to be available on the stack. The IRET instruction has no affect on any flags.

JA/JNBE—Jump if Above / Jump if Not Below or Equal

The JA instruction causes a program branch to be taken if both the Zero Flag and Carry Flag are zero. The JA/JNBE instruction has no affect on any flags.

JB/JNAE—Jump if Below / Jump if Not Above or Equal

The JB instruction causes a program branch to be taken if the Carry Flag is one. The JB/JNAE instruction has no affect on any flags.

JBE/JNA—Jump on Below or Equal / Jump on Not Above

The JBE instruction causes a program branch to be taken if either the Carry Flag or Zero Flag are one. The JBE instruction has no affect on any flags.

JC—Jump on Carry

The JC instruction causes a program branch to be taken if the Carry Flag is one. The JC instruction has no affect on any flags.

JCXZ—Jump if CX Register is Zero

The JCXZ instruction causes a program branch to be taken if the CX register is zero. The JCXZ instruction has no affect on any flags.

JE/JZ—Jump if Equal / Jump if Zero

The JE instruction causes a program branch to be taken if the Zero Flag equals one. The JE instruction has no affect on any flags.

JG/JNLE—Jump if Greater / Jump if Not Less or Equal

The JG instruction causes a program branch to be taken if the Zero Flag is zero and the Sign Flag equals the Overflow Flag. The JG instruction has no affect on any flags.

JGE/JNL—Jump if Greater or Equal / Jump if Not less

The JGE instruction causes a program branch to be taken if the Sign Flag equals the Overflow Flag. The JGE instruction has no affect on any flags.

JL/JNGE—Jump if Less / Jump if Not Greater or Equal

The JL instruction causes a program branch to be taken if the Sign Flag is not equal to the Overflow Flag. The JL instruction has no affect on any flags.

JLE/JNG—Jump if Less or Equal / Jump if Not Greater

The JLE instruction causes a program branch to be taken if the Zero Flag is one or the Sign Flag is not equal to the Overflow Flag. The JLE instruction has no affect on any flags.

JMP—Jump

The JMP instruction causes a program branch to be taken. It can be a jump to a new Code Segment and offset or just a new offset in the current segment. The new location can be specified by using register values, memory locations, or immediate data. The JMP instruction has no affect on any flags.

JNC—Jump on Not Carry

The JNC instruction causes a program branch to be taken if the Carry Flag is zero. The JNC instruction has no affect on any flags.

JNE/JNZ—Jump if Not Equal / Jump if Not Zero

The JNE instruction causes a program branch to be taken if the Zero Flag equals zero. The JNE instruction has no affect on any flags.

JNO—Jump on Not Overflow

The JNO instruction causes a program branch to be taken if the Overflow Flag is zero. The JNO instruction has no affect on any flags.

JNS—Jump on Not Sign

The JNS instruction causes a program branch to be taken if the Sign Flag is zero. The JNS instruction has no affect on any flags.

JNP/JPO—Jump on Not Parity / Jump on Parity Odd

The JNP instruction causes a program branch to be taken if the Parity Flag is zero. The JNP instruction has no affect on any flags.

JO—Jump on Overflow

The JO instruction causes a program branch to be taken if the Overflow Flag is one. The JO instruction has no affect on any flags.

JP/JPE—Jump on Parity / Jump on Parity Equal

The JP instruction causes a program branch to be taken if the Parity Flag is one. The JP instruction has no affect on any flags.

JS—Jump on Sign

The JS instruction causes a program branch to be taken if the Sign Flag is one. The JS instruction has no affect on any flags.

LAHF—Load Register AH from the Flags Register

The LAHF instruction copies some of the flags into the corresponding bit positions in the accumulator. The remaining bits are unaffected.

Issuing a LAHF instruction transfers the Sign Flag to bit 7 of the accumulator, the Zero Flag to bit 6, the Auxiliary Carry Flag to bit 4, the Parity Flag to bit 2, and the Carry Flag to bit 0. The LAHF instruction has no affect on any flags.

LDS—Load a Pointer using Register DS

The LDS instruction causes the contents of a memory location to be loaded into a register and the contents of the next memory location to be loaded into the DS register. Issuing this instruction will cause four bytes (two words) to be transferred from memory locations to registers. The syntax for this instruction is:

LDS register, memory location

where the register is the named register to be loaded and the memory location is the location of the first two bytes to be transferred. The LDS instruction has no affect on any flags.

LEA—Load Register with Offset Address

The LEA instruction transfers the memory address to a register rather than transferring the value stored at that address. The LEA instruction is typically used in string handling routines since it can be used to load the location of a lookup or translate table to an index register. The LEA instruction has no affect on any flags.

LES—Load Pointer Using Register ES

The LES instruction is similar to the LDS instruction except that the contents of the second memory word is to be transferred to register ES.

The LES instruction has no affect on any flags.

LOCK—Issue the Bus Lock Signal

The $\overline{LOCK}$ instruction is a maximum mode instruction that causes the 8088 to activate the $\overline{LOCK}$ pin. This is a prefix instruction that causes the $\overline{LOCK}$ pin to be active during the execution of the following instruction. The $\overline{LOCK}$ instruction has no affect on any flags.

LODS—Load a String

The LODS instruction is used in string processing. It transfers the value pointed to by the SI register to the accumulator. A LODS can operate on either a byte or word. Byte transfers are made to AL and word transfers are made to AX. Once the transfer is completed, the SI register is automatically updated in the direction indicated by the setting of the Direction Flag. The LODS instruction has no affect on any flags.

LOOP—Loop

The LOOP instruction is a prefix that uses the CX register as a counter to determine how many times to execute a particular routine. Each time the LOOP instruction is executed, it decrements the CX register. If the register has reached zero, the program will go on to the next instruction. If not, the routine indicated by LOOP will be executed again. The LOOP instruction is very similar to a JMP except that it uses the CX register to see whether the JMP should be taken. The LOOP instruction has no affect on any flag.

LOOPZ/LOOPE—Loop While Equal / Loop While Zero

The LOOPE instruction is similar to the LOOP instruction except that along with the check of the CX register, the LOOPE instruction will continue to execute the specified routine if the CX register is not zero and the Zero Flag is one. The LOOPE instruction has no affect on any flags.

LOOPNZ/LOOPNE—Loop While Not Zero / Loop While Not Equal

The LOOPNZ instruction is similar to the LOOPE instruction except that it continues to execute the specified routine if the CX register is not equal to zero and the Zero Flag is zero. The LOOPNE instruction has no affect on any flags.

MOV—Move

The MOV instruction is one of the most used members of the 8088's instruction set. It can operate on various combinations of memory locations, registers, and immediate in either byte or word size operands. The MOV instruction has no affect on any flags.

MOVS—Move String

The MOVS instruction transfers the byte of data pointed to by the SI register to the location pointed to by the DI register. Once the transfer is completed, it updates both the SI and DI registers.

By using this instruction with the REP prefix, or with some sort of conditional test, large blocks of memory can be moved. The MOVS instruction has no affect on any flags.

MUL—Multiply

The MUL instruction does an unsigned multiplication operation on the value in the accumulator and the indicated source. This may be an immediate value or a number stored in a register or memory location.

If the source is a byte, AL should contain the operator and the result will be stored in AH and AL. If the source is a word, AX should contain the operator and the result will be stored in DX and AX. The MUL instruction affects the Carry Flag and Overflow Flag.

NEG—Negate

The NEG instruction will subtract the value at the destination from zero and replace the original value with the result of the operation.

The NEG instruction affects the Auxiliary Carry Flag, Carry Flag, Overflow Flag, Parity Flag, Sign Flag, and Zero Flag.

NOP—No Operation

The NOP instruction causes the CPU to do absolutely nothing for the next instruction cycle. The NOP instruction has no affect on any flags.

NOT

The NOT instruction complements all the bits of the specified byte or word located in the indicated memory location or register. The NOT instruction has no affect on any flags.

OR—Logical Or

The OR instruction performs a logical OR operation on the specified bytes or words located in the indicated memory locations or registers and stores the result in the destination. The OR instruction affects the Carry Flag, Overflow Flag, Parity Flag, Sign Flag, and Zero Flag.

OUT—Output

The OUT instruction transfers the byte or word from the accumulator to the specified I/O port. Ports 0 through 255 may be specified directly but higher numbered ports must be addressed indirectly through the DX register. The OUT instruction has no affect on any flags.

POP—Pop from the Stack

The POP instruction transfers the word pointed to by the Stack Pointer to the destination indicated in the instruction. Once the operation is finished, the Stack Pointer is incremented by two. The POP instruction has no affect on any flags.

POPF—Pop the Flags

The POPF instruction transfers the word pointed to by the Stack Pointer to the Flags Register. Once the operation is finished, the Stack Pointer is incremented by two. It should be noted that this is the only way to change some of the flags, (the Trap Flag, etc.) The POPF instruction affects all the flags.

PUSH—Push

The PUSH instruction transfers the word at the indicated destination to the top of the stack and then decrements the Stack Pointer by two to point to the new top of the stack. The PUSH instruction has no affect on any flag.

PUSHF—Push the Flags

The PUSHF instruction transfers the current flags register to the top of the stack and then decrements the Stack Pointer by two to point to the new top of the stack. The PUSHF instruction has no affect on any flags.

RCL—Rotate through Carry Left

The RCL instruction rotates the bits at the specified location to the left by the number indicated in the instruction. The Carry Flag is included in the operation. If AL contains 23h, the Carry Flag is one, and the specified count contained in the CL register is 4h, the following will happen when an RCL AL, CL is executed:

```
Start              1    0 0 1 0   0 0 1 1        23h
          RCL 1    0    0 1 0 0   0 1 1 1        47h
          RCL 2    0    1 0 0 0   1 1 1 0        8Eh
          RCL 3    1    0 0 0 1   1 1 0 0        1Ch
Finish    RCL 4    0    0 0 1 1   1 0 0 1        39Ah
```

The RCL instruction affects the Carry Flag and the Overflow Flag.

RCR—Rotate through Carry Right

The RCR instruction is identical to the RCL instruction except for the direction. The RCR instruction affects the Carry Flag and the Overflow Flag.

REP—Repeat

The REP instruction is a prefix that will cause the following string instructions to continue until the CX register has been decremented to zero. Each time the instruction is executed, the CX register is decremented by one. When the CX register equals zero, the program will fall through to the following instruction. The REP instruction has no affect on any flags.

246

REPE/REPZ—Repeat While Equal / Repeat While Zero

The REPE instruction is similar to the REP instruction but it also checks the value of the Zero Flag. REPE will continue execution of the string instruction as long as the Zero Flag is one. The REPE instruction has no affect on any flag.

REPNE/REPNZ—Repeat While Not Equal / Repeat While Not Zero

The REPNE instruction is similar to the REP instruction but it also checks the value of the Zero Flag. REPNE will continue execution of the string instruction as long as the Zero Flag is zero. The REPNE instruction has no affect on any flag.

RET—Return

The RET instruction is used to indicate the end of a subroutine or procedure branched to by a CALL instruction. When this instruction is executed, an appropriate number of bytes are popped off the stack to return program execution to the location immediately following the CALL. The RET instruction has no affect on any flag.

ROL—Rotate Left

The ROL instruction is very similar to the RCL instruction except that the Carry Flag is not used. The number of rotations to make is either one or the number specified in the CL register. The ROL instruction affects the Carry Flag and the Overflow Flag.

ROR—Rotate Right

The ROR instruction is identical to the ROL instruction with the exception of the direction of movement. The ROR instruction affects the Carry Flag and the Overflow Flag.

SAHF—Store AH Register in the Flag Register

The SAHF instruction transfers bits 7, 6, 4, 2, and 0 from register AH to the corresponding bits in the Flags Register. The SAHF instruction affects the Auxiliary Carry Flag, Carry Flag, Parity Flag, Sign Flag, and Zero Flag.

SAL/SHL—Shift Arithmetic Left/Shift Logical Left

The SAL instruction performs a shift to the right and the number of shifts is either one or the number contained in the CL register. If AL contains 64h, and the specified count contained in the CL register is 3h, the following will happen when an SAL AL, CL is executed:

Start			0	1	1 0	0 1	0 0		64h
	SAL 1		1	1	0 0	1 0	0 0		C8h
	SAL 2		1	0	0 1	0 0	0 0		90h
Finish	SAL 3		0	0	1 0	0 0	0 0		20Ah

The SAL instruction affects the Carry Flag, Overflow Flag, Parity Flag, Sign Flag, and Zero Flag.

SAR—Shift Arithmetic Right

The SAR instruction is identical to the SAL instruction except for the direction of movement. When an SAR is issued, the bits shift to the right and zeros are inserted at the left (into the high bit). The Sign bit (bit 8) is unaffected. The SAR instruction affects the Carry Flag, Overflow Flag, Parity Flag, Sign Flag, and Zero Flag.

SBB—Subtract with Borrow

The SBB instruction subtracts the source from the destination and can do either byte or word operations. If the Carry Flag is a one, one is subtracted from the result of the subtraction in the destination. The SBB instruction affects the Auxiliary Carry Flag, Carry Flag, Overflow Flag, Parity Flag, Sign Flag, and Zero Flag.

SCAS—Scan String

The SCAS instruction compares the data at a memory location pointed to by the Destination Index with the contents of the accumulator. The operation may be on either a byte or word. The comparison is made by subtracting the data from the accumulator but neither of these bytes are changed. The result of the comparison is indicated by changes in the Flags Register and DI is updated in accordance with the setting of the Direction Flag. By combining this instruction with the REP prefix, rapid searches may be made through tables of data. The SCAS instruction affects the Auxiliary Carry Flag, Carry Flag, Overflow Flag, Parity Flag, Sign Flag, and Zero Flag.

SEG—Override Segment Register

The SEG prefix causes the next instruction to use the segment in the SEG instruction to calculate to the absolute address of the data. The SEG instruction has no affect on any flags.

SHR—Shift Logical Right

The SHR instruction is similar to the SAR instruction except that all eight bits are affected by the shift as opposed to seven bits in the SAR instruction. The SHR instruction affects the Carry Flag, Overflow Flag, Parity Flag, Sign Flag, and Zero Flag.

STC—Set the Carry Flag

The STC instruction causes a one to be stored in the Carry Flag. The STC instruction affects only the Carry Flag.

STD—Set the Direction Flag

The STD instruction causes a one to be stored in the Direction Flag. This means that string instructions will auto-decrement the Source Index and Destination Index Registers. The STD instruction affects only the Direction Flag.

STI—Set the Interrupt Enable Flag

The STI instruction will store a one on the Interrupt Enable Flag. This means that the 8088 will recognize all interrupts on the INTR line. The STI instruction only affects the Interrupt Enable Flag.

STOS—Store String

The STOS instruction will transfer a byte or word from the accumulator to the destination addressed by the Destination Index Register. Once the transfer is completed, DI will be updated in accordance with the setting of the Direction Flag. The STOS instruction has no affect on any flags.

SUB—Subtract

The SUB instruction will subtract the source from the destination and place the result in the destination. Both the destination and source may be specified as either memory locations or registers. The source may additionally be specified to be immediate data. The SUB instruction affects the Auxiliary Carry Flag, Carry Flag, Overflow Flag, Parity Flag, Sign Flag, and Zero Flag.

TEST—Test

The TEST instruction will perform a logical AND of the destination and the source. The result of the operation will be reflected in the Flag Register but both the destination and source will remain unchanged.

If a test instruction is followed by a JNZ, the jump will be made if both the destination and source have ones in corresponding bit positions. The TEST instruction can be used with either byte or words and may incorporate either memory locations, registers, or immediate data. The TEST instruction affects the Carry Flag, Overflow Flag, Parity Flag, Sign Flag, and Zero Flag.

WAIT—Wait

The WAIT instruction causes the 8088 to enter an idle state and remain there while the TEST line remains active (low). This is a convenient way for external devices to place the 8088 on hold until they have completed their operation. The TEST line is also a useful device when new hardware is being debugged since the 8088 can be halted temporarily at specific points to examine the state of the bus. The TEST instruction has no affect on any flags.

XCHG—Exchange

The XCHG instruction will cause the destination and source to swap their contents. The contents may be a byte or word and either the source or destination (or both) may be a register. The XCHG instruction has no affect on any flags.

XLAT—Translate

The XLAT instruction lets the 8088 perform a table lookup operation by replacing the byte in the accumulator with a byte from a table whose starting location is pointed to by the BX register. The table may be a maximum of 256 bytes long. The initial value in AL is used as the offset into the table and is ultimately replaced by the byte located at the offset. The XLAT instruction has no affect on any flags.

XOR—Exclusive OR

The XOR instruction performs a logical exclusive OR of the source and destination and stores the result in the destination. Both the source and destination may be any needed combination of registers or memory locations. The source may also be immediate data. The XOR instruction affects the Carry Flag, Overflow Flag, Parity Flag, Sign Flag, and Zero Flag.

Index

Parts List

Other Bestsellers From TAB

☐ **THE DIGITAL IC HANDBOOK—Michael S. Morley**

This book will make it easier for you to determine which digital ICs are currently available, how they work, and in what instances they will function most effectively. The author examines ICs from many major manufacturers and compares them not only by technology and key specification but by package and price as well. If you've ever been overwhelmed by the number of choices, this book will help you sort through the hundreds of circuits and evaluate your options. 624 pp., 273 illus.

Hard $49.50   **Book No. 3002**

☐ **50 CMOS IC PROJECTS—Delton T. Horn**

Provides practical projects designed to use the popular CMOS family of integrated circuits. Horn presents a general introduction to CMOS ICs and technology . . . provides full schematics including working diagrams and parts lists . . . offers construction hints as well as suggestions for project variations and combinations. This book discusses: the basics of digital electronics, safe handling of CMOS devices, breadboarding, tips on experimenting with circuits, and more. You'll find signal generator and music-making projects, time-keeping circuits, game circuits, and a host of other miscellaneous circuits. 224 pp., 226 illus.

Paper $20.95   **Hard $26.95**
Book No. 2995

☐ **MASTER HANDBOOK OF 1001 PRACTICAL ELECTRONICS CIRCUITS SOLID-STATE EDITION— Edited by Kendall Webster Sessions**

Tested and proven circuits that you can put to immediate use in a full range of practical applications! You'll find circuits ranging from battery chargers to burglar alarms, from test equipment to voltage multipliers, from power supplies to audio amplifiers, from repeater circuits to transceivers, transmitters, and logic circuits. Whatever your interest or electronics specialty, the circuits you need are here, ready to be put to immediate use. 420 pp., 1001 illus.

Paper $21.95   **Hard $28.95**
Book No. 2980

☐ **ELECTRONIC DATABOOK—4th Edition—Rudolf F. Graf**

If it's electronic, it's here—current, detailed, and comprehensive! Use this book to broaden your electronics information base. Revised and expanded to include all up-to-date information, the fourth edition of *Electronic Data-book* will make any electronic job easier and less time-consuming. This edition includes information that will aid in the design of local area networks, computer interfacing structure, and more! 528 pp., 131 illus.

Paper $25.95   **Hard $34.95**
Book No. 2958

☐ **ALARMS: 55 ELECTRONIC PROJECTS AND CIRCUITS—Charles D. Rakes**

Make your home or business a safer place to live and work—for a price you can afford. Almost anything can be monitored by an electronic alarm circuit—from detecting overheating equipment to low fluid levels, from smoke in a room to an intruder at the window. This book is designed to show you the great variety of alarms that are available. There are step-by-step instructions, work-in-progress diagrams, and troubleshooting tips and advice for building each project. 160 pp., 150 illus.

Paper $15.95   **Hard $19.95**
Book No. 2996

☐ **FIBEROPTICS AND LASER HANDBOOK—2nd Ed.—Edward L. Safford, Jr. and John A. McCann**

Explore the dramatic impact that lasers and fiberoptics have on our daily lives—PLUS, exciting ideas for your own experiments! Now, with the help of experts Safford and McCann, you'll discover the most current concepts, practices, and applications of fiberoptics, lasers, and electromagnetic radiation technology. Included are terms and definitions, discussions of the types and operations of current systems, and amazingly simple experiments you can conduct! 240 pp., 108 illus.

Paper $19.95   **Hard $24.95**
Book No. 2981

☐ **HOW TO DESIGN SOLID-STATE CIRCUITS—2nd Edition—Mannie Horowitz and Delton T. Horn**

Design and build useful electronic circuits from scratch! The authors provide the exact data you need on every aspect of semiconductor design . . . performance characteristics . . . applications potential . . . operating reliability . . . and more! Four major categories of semiconductors are examined: Diodes . . . Transistors . . . Integrated Circuits . . . Thyristors. This second edition is filled with procedures, advice, techniques, and background information. All the hands-on direction you need to understand and use semiconductors in all kinds of electronic devices is provided. Ranging from simple temperature-sensitive resistors to integrated circuit units composed of multiple microcircuits, this new edition describes a host of the latest in solid-state devices. 380 pp., 297 illus.

Paper $19.95   **Hard $24.95**
Book No. 2975

☐ **20 INNOVATIVE ELECTRONICS PROJECTS FOR YOUR HOME—Joseph O'Connell**

O'Connell carefully guides the budding inventory and enhances the ability of the experienced designer. This book is a no-nonsense approach to building unusual yet practical electronic devices. More than just a collection of 20 projects, this book provides helpful hints and sound advice for the experimenter and home hobbyist. Particular emphasis is placed on unique yet truly useful devices that are justifiably time- and cost-efficient. Projects include a protected outlet box (for your computer system) . . . a variable ac power controller . . . a remote volume control . . . a fluorescent bike light . . . and a pair of active minispeakers with built-in amplifiers. 256 pp., 130 illus.

Paper $15.95   **Hard $21.95**
Book No. 2947

Other Bestsellers From TAB

Building the 8088 Circuit

If you're interested in building the circuits described in this book but don't want to type in the programs yourself, you can order a disk with all the software listed in the book. This disk contains the source code and object code as well as hex dumps of all the programs.

Having the code on a disk eliminates the possibility of typing or assembly errors and the included object code is ready to be burned in an EPROM

If you don't want to burn EPROMs yourself, you can order any of the preprogrammed EPROMs described below.

The disks and EPROMS are guaranteed to be free of any manufacturing defects and will be replaced at no charge within 30 days of purchase.

The software listings are available on 3.5 or 5.25 inch disks for either IBM compatible computers (PC/XT/AT,PS/2) or the Apple II series of computers.

Please send $19.95 for each 5 1/4 inch disk, $24.95 for each 3 1/2 inch disk, and $19.95 for each EPROM, plus $1.50 shipping and handling.

I'm interested. Send me:

The disk in the following format:
Apple 3.5 _____   Apple 5.25 _____   IBM 3.5 _____   IBM 5.25 _____

The following preprogrammed EPROMs:
_____ MATRIX.BIN (Figure #7-18)   _____ 8255.BIN (Figure #8-7)
_____ COUNT.BIN (Figure #9-7)   _____ KBTEST1.BIN (Figure #11-5)
_____ KEYBOARD.BIN (Figure #14-3)   _____ CLOCK.BIN (Figure #15-6)
_____ CHARGEN.BIN (The character generator for the display)

_____ TAB BOOKS catalog ($1.00) (with a coupon worth $1.00 on your next TAB purchase)

Check/Money Order enclosed for $_____ plus $1.50 shipping and handling for each order.
☐ VISA   ☐ MasterCard   ☐ American Express
Account No. _____ Expires _____

Name _____

Address _____

City _____ State _____ Zip _____

Signature _____

Mail To: **TAB BOOKS Inc.**
          Blue Ridge Summit, PA 17294-0850

OR CALL TOLL-FREE TODAY: **1-800-822-8158**

IN PENNSYLVANIA AND ALASKA CALL: **717-794-2191**

(In PA, NY, and ME add applicable sales tax. Orders subject to credit approval. Orders outside U.S. must be prepaid with international money orders in U.S. dollars.)
*Prices subject to change without notice.

TAB 3171